MOTION AND TIME STUDY

MOTION AND TIME STUDY

An Introduction to Methods, Time Study, and Wage Payment

BY BENJAMIN W. NIEBEL

Head of Department and Professor of Industrial Engineering

The Pennsylvania State University

REVISED EDITION

1958

RICHARD D. IRWIN, INC.

HOMEWOOD, ILLINOIS

REVISED EDITION

First printing, April, 1958
Second printing, January, 1960

Library of Congress Catalogue Card No. 58–8653

PRINTED IN THE UNITED STATES OF AMERICA

Preface to Revised Edition

THE INCREASING TENDENCY IN recent years for industry to automate both its direct labor and its office operations has greatly increased the percentage of indirect labor employees. In order to establish standards on indirect operations that do not have regular cyclic occurrence, the analyst must rely on means of developing standards that will give valid results in the least time. More emphasis is being placed in industry on work sampling, standard data, and fundamental motion times, as a means for establishing standards on indirect labor operations in preference to stop watch study. The principal purpose of this revision of *Motion and Time Study* is to discuss more fully these phases of motion and time study.

In particular, the revised edition includes more material on work sampling, indirect labor standards, curve plotting, and maintenance of standards. In addition, sections have been added on creative thinking, decision-making techniques, human dimensions, using process charts, sound control, visual requirements of work place, memomotion study, cycle graphic and chronocycle graphic study, motion time analysis, and dimensional motion times. Also, new material is included on leveling operator performance. The new edition contains many new line drawings and illustrations to assist the reader in the more technical explanations. To give this edition a broader application in methods work, several examples have been introduced that are characteristic of process-type industries.

The suggestions of the many colleges and universities that have adopted the text have materially helped in shaping the revised edition. This edition has the same purpose as the first, that is, to provide a practical up-to-date college text in the area of methods, time study, and wage payment; and to give practicing analysts from both labor and management an authentic source of reference material.

The author wishes to acknowledge in particular, the Procter & Gamble Company, the Armstrong Cork Company, and Mr. H. A. Knappenberger who have given valuable suggestions.

B. W. NIEBEL

UNIVERSITY PARK, PENNSYLVANIA
March, 1958

Preface to First Edition

THIS BOOK HAS BEEN DESIGNED as a college text to provide training in the areas of methods, time study, and wage payment so that, upon graduation, young engineers, businessmen, and labor leaders may make their respective organizations as productive and efficient as possible. Throughout the text, fundamental principles, with many practical examples, have been emphasized, so that the student will have an appreciation of, and insight into, the techniques used by industry in its motion study, micromotion study, time study, and wage payment plans.

Industry, business, and government agencies recognize the necessity for continually improving methods which will assure profitable operation. This means there must be creative thinking. There must be teamwork between management and labor assuring high performance of both parties. Only so can this country maintain its leading position in production. Because of the increasing competition from foreign markets as well as the unparalleled industrial expansion in this country, only the most progressive businesses can expect to continue profitable operation.

This text describes the procedures used in conducting proved methods programs that will result in substantial savings in labor and material in any type of business. In order to assure full realization of method improvements, it is fundamental that output must be accurately determined. This book presents accepted and proved techniques of work measurement and outlines the many helpful controls made possible once fair time standards have been developed. When properly pursued, even greater gains can be achieved through the installation of sound wage incentive plans. In this text, the requirements and methods of installation of successful wage payment plans are discussed in detail.

In addition to being a suitable college text for students interested in the area of Industrial Engineering, Business Management, Labor Relations, Industrial Psychology, and other areas concerned with productivity and human relations, this book will be of particular interest and benefit to business executives, industrialists, and government agency representatives.

The shop foreman should find the book helpful in establishing a systematic approach for improving methods within his department. The many diversified examples and case histories should provide the necessary spark to begin improvement in some area of every enterprise.

Union officials should find this text helpful in explaining the techniques, principles, philosophies, and economic necessity of method changes and work measurement. It is hoped through intelligent use of the book that a more closely knit team of management and labor can be evolved.

The author wishes to express his appreciation for the many concerns that co-operated extensively in the supplying of examples and illustrations used throughout this text. Particular appreciation is extended to the Westinghouse Electric Company which provided the background and many of the illustrations for the chapters on operation analysis. Also the A.C. Spark Plug Division, the General Electric Company, The Eastman Kodak Company, Meylan Watch Company, Lafayette Instrument Co., the Warner and Swasey Company, National Industrial Conference Board, J. D. Woods & Gordon Limited, M.T.M. Association, the Work-Factor Company, the National Safety Council, the International Association of Machinists, the United States Steel Co., the Sylvania Electric Products Company, the Industrial Management Society, the Material Handling Institute, the Methods Engineering Council, the Brown & Sharpe Mfg. Co., Black and Webster, Inc., provided helpful and valuable information.

Especial appreciation is expressed to Dr. C. A. Anderson who offered many helpful suggestions in the preparation of the manuscript. Acknowledgement is also made to Professors D. C. Ekey and G. L. Thuering for their assistance in editing portions of the manuscript and to Mrs. W. P. Henszey and Mrs. Gus Steinmetz who carefully and thoroughly assisted in the proof reading. Acknowledgement is also made to Mrs. B. W. Niebel who typed the manuscript and provided the incentive that led to its completion.

B. W. NIEBEL

UNIVERSITY PARK, PENNSYLVANIA
April, 1955

Contents

ix

6. Man and Machine, Gang, and Operator Process Charts . .   113

    Man and machine process charts. Construction of the man and machine
    process chart. Using the man and machine process chart. Gang process
    charts. Construction of the gang process chart. Using the gang process
    chart. Operator process chart. Construction of the operator process chart.
    Using the operator process chart. Summary: man and machine, gang,
    and operator process charts.

7. Motion Study   129

    The fundamental motions. Definitions of basic divisions of accomplish-
    ment. Principles of motion economy. Explanation of Laws of Mo-
    tion Economy. Practical Use of Motion Study in the Planning
    Stage: Motion analysis as applied in planning.

8. Micromotion Study   162

    Preparing for the micromotion study. Micromotion study as a training
    aid. Micromotion equipment. The motion-picture camera. The lens. The
    shutter. Black-and-white versus color film. Light meter. Tripod. Flood-
    lights. Projection equipment. Microchronometer. Splicer and viewer. Op-
    tical screen. Storage of films. Summary.

9. Taking Motion Pictures for Micromotion Study and Film
    Analysis   178

    Taking the moving pictures. Analyzing the film. Create an improved
    method. Teach and standardize the new method. Other motion study
    techniques involving photographic methods.

10. Synthetic Basic Motion Times   193

    Definition of synthetic basic motion times. Necessity of synthetic basic
    motion times. Work-Factor. Methods-Time Measurement. Comparison
    of Work-Factor and Methods-Time Measurement. Basic Motion Time-
    study. Basic Motions. Variable factors. Turns. Simultaneous arm motion.
    Application technique. Motion-Time Analysis. Dimensional Motion
    Times. Applying synthetic basic motion times. Summary.

11. Determination of Factory Cost   215

    Job analysis. Job evaluation. Selection of factors. Determination of labor
    standards. Conclusion.

12. Time Study Requirements   224

    A fair day's work. Time study requirements. Responsibilities of the time
    study man. Foreman's responsibility. The union's responsibility. Oper-
    ator's responsibility. Conclusion.

13. Time Study Equipment   232

    The stop watch. Time-recording machines. Motion-picture camera. Time
    study board. Time study forms. Auxiliary equipment.

14. Elements of Time Study   245

    Choosing the operator. Approach to the operator. Analysis of materials
    and methods. Recording the significant information. Observer's position.
    Dividing the operation into elements. Taking the study. Snapback

CHAPTER 1

Methods, Time Study, and Wage Payment Today

The Production Function

Early writers have thought of the industrial engineer and the production manager as being responsible for directing the efforts of those engaged in the location, construction, equipping, maintenance, and operation of modern industrial enterprises.[1] However, since the termination of World War II, the activities of the production group have been for the most part centered in the operation of industry. The areas of opportunity existing in the field of production for students enrolled in engineering, industrial management, business administration, industrial psychology, and labor-management relations are: (1) methods, (2) time study and wage payment, (3) production control, and (4) tool design. Other positions, such as personnel or industrial relations, cost, and budgeting, are closely related to, and dependent on, the production group.

These opportunities are not confined to manufacturing industries. They exist and are equally important in such enterprises and businesses as department stores, hotels, hospitals, educational institutions, and any other area where the combined effects of men, materials, and facilities are used to fulfill an objective. However, it is in the production of goods and services that the greatest demand has been made for personnel who

---

[1] D. S. Kimball and D. S. Kimball, Jr., *Principles of Industrial Organization* (6th ed.; New York: McGraw-Hill Book Co., Inc., 1947); W. R. Spriegel and R. H. Lansburgh, *Industrial Management* (4th ed.; New York: John Wiley & Sons, Inc., 1947).

have received training in the area of methods, time study, and wage payment.

The production section of an industry may well be called the heart of that industry, and once the activity of this section is interrupted, the whole industry ceases to be productive. The production department includes the methods engineering, time study, and wage payment activity, which offers the young technical graduate one of the most satisfying fields of endeavor.

It is in the production department that material to produce is requisitioned and controlled; sequence of operations and methods determined; tools ordered; time values assigned; work scheduled, dispatched, and followed up; and customers kept satisfied. Training in this field demonstrates how production is accomplished, where it is done, when it is performed, and how long it takes to do it. A background including

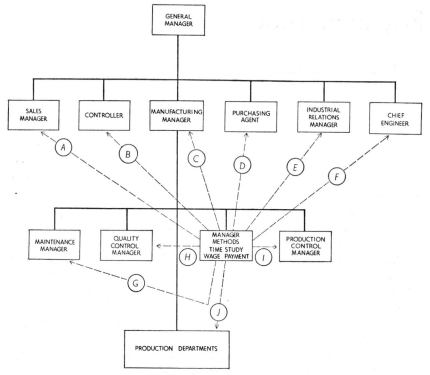

A - Selling price largely determined by manufacturing methods.
B - Time standards are the bases of standard costs.
C - Standards (direct and indirect) provide the bases for measuring performance of production departments.
D - Time is a common denominator for comparing competitive equipment and supplies.
E - Good labor relations maintained with equitable standards and fair base rates.
F - Methods and processes strongly influence product designs.
G - Standards provide the bases for preventative maintenance.
H - Standards enforce quality.
I - Scheduling is based on time standards.
J - Methods and standards provide how the work is to be done and how long it will take.

FIG. 1–1. Typical organization chart showing the influence of methods, time study, and wage payment on the operation of the enterprise.

such training will prove invaluable, whether one's ultimate objective is in the field of sales, production, or cost.

If the production department be considered the heart of an industrial enterprise, it may be said that the *methods, time study, and wage payment* activity is the center of the production group. Here, more than any other place, is determined whether a product is going to be produced on a competitive basis. Here is where initiative and ingenuity can introduce great manufacturing savings through improved methods and tooling. It is in this department that good labor relations are maintained through establishment of fair labor standards, or may be impeded by setting one inequitable rate.

The work of methods, time study, and wage payment offers a real challenge. Industries having competent engineers, business administrators, industrial relations personnel, specially trained supervisors and psychologists who are carrying out methods, time study, and wage payment techniques are inevitably better able to meet competition and better equipped to operate profitably. (See Figure 1–1.)

Scope of Methods Engineering and Time Study

The field of methods engineering, time study, and wage payment includes designing, creating, and selecting the best manufacturing methods, processes, tools, equipment, and skills to manufacture a product after working drawings have been released by the product engineering section. Also included is the responsibility of determining the time required to produce the product and then following through to see that predetermined time standards are met.

This procedure includes defining the problem related to expected cost, breaking the job down into operations, analyzing each operation so as to determine most economical manufacturing procedures for quantity involved, applying proper time values, and then following through to assure that the prescribed method is put into operation.

Methods Engineering

The terms "operation analysis," "work simplification," and "methods engineering" are frequently used synonymously. In most cases the person is referring to a technique for increasing the production per unit of time and, consequently, reducing the unit cost. Experience has shown that to achieve the maximum returns from a methods engineering program, a systematic procedure should be followed. The Westinghouse Electric Corporation, in its Operation Analysis program, advocates the following steps for assurance of most favorable results:

1. Make a preliminary survey.
2. Determine extent of analysis justified.
3. Develop process charts.
4. Investigate the approaches to operation analysis.

5. Make motion study when justified.
6. Compare the old and the new method.
7. Present the new method.
8. Check installation of the new method.
9. Correct time values.
10. Follow up the new method.

Actually, methods engineering includes the procedures of all of these ten steps.

Methods engineering can be defined as the systematic procedure for subjecting all direct and indirect operations to close scrutiny so as to introduce improvements that will result in making the work easier to perform and will allow the work to be done in less time and with less investment per unit.

Time Study

A close association exists in the function of the time study man and the methods engineer. Although their respective objectives differ, a good time study man is a good methods engineer, as he will include methods engineering as a basic component of his position. Time study is the technique of establishing an allowed time standard to perform a given task, based upon measurement of work content of the prescribed method, with due allowance for fatigue and personal and unavoidable delays.

In order to be assured that the prescribed method is the best method, the time study engineer frequently finds himself in the role of a methods engineer. In small industries these two activities are often handled by the same individual.

Wage Payment

The wage payment function, similarly, is closely associated with the time study and methods sections of the production activity. In general, the wage payment section is responsible for releasing standards of production to the factory and maintaining the incentive plans or plan so that they function smoothly and efficiently. Because of the nature of an enterprise, it may be necessary to have two entirely different wage payment plans in effect, or even three (daywork, piecework, group incentives), and the administration of these falls on the wage payment group.

The function of job evaluation, which is a technique for equitably determining the relative worth of the different work assignments within an organization, is usually a responsibility of the wage payment section.

At this point it might be well to emphasize that production control, plant layout, purchasing, cost accounting and control, and process and product design are additional areas that are closely related both to the methods and the standards functions. All of these provinces depend on data, facts, and procedures of operation from the methods and standards department in order to operate effectively. These relationships are briefly discussed in Chapter 22.

TEXT QUESTIONS

1. What job opportunities exist in the general field of production?
2. What is the scope of methods engineering?
3. What activities are considered the key links to the production group within a manufacturing enterprise?
4. What is meant by the terms "operation analysis," "work simplification," and "methods engineering"?
5. What steps have the Westinghouse Electric Corporation advocated in order to assure real savings during a method improvement program?
6. What is the function of the time study department?
7. Is it possible for one enterprise to have more than one type of wage payment plan? Explain.

GENERAL QUESTIONS

1. How do well-organized methods, time study, and wage payment procedures benefit the company?
2. Show the relationship between time study and methods engineering. Explain each fully.
3. Discuss the reasoning behind the statement, "A good time study man is a good methods engineer."
4. Comment on the general responsibility of the wage payment group.
5. Why does the purchasing department need data and information from the methods, time study, and wage payment department? Give several examples.

CHAPTER 2

Development of Motion and Time Study

The Work of Taylor

FREDERICK W. TAYLOR IS GENerally conceded to be the father of modern time study in this country. However, time studies were conducted in Europe many years before the time of Taylor. In 1760, a Frenchman, Perronet, made extensive time studies on the manufacture of No. 6 common pins, and arrived at a standard of 494 per hour. Sixty years later an English economist, Charles Babbage, made time studies on No. 11 common pins, and as a result of these studies determined that one pound (5,546 pins) should be produced in 7.6892 hours.[1]

Taylor began his time study work in 1881 while associated with the Midvale Steel Company in Philadelphia. After twelve years' work, he evolved a system which is based upon the "task" idea. Here Taylor proposed that the work of each employee be planned out by the management at least one day in advance, and that each man receive complete written instructions describing his task in detail and noting the means to be used in accomplishing it. Each job was to have a standard time which was to be fixed after time studies had been made by experts. This time was to be based upon the work possibilities of a first-rate man, who, after being instructed, was able to do the work regularly. In the timing process Mr. Taylor advocated the breaking of the work assignment into small divisions of effort known as "elements." These were

---

[1] Charles Babbage, *On the Economy of Manufactures*, 1832.

6

timed individually, and their collective values were used to determine the allowed time of the task.

In June, 1895, Taylor presented his findings and recommendations at a Detroit meeting of the American Society of Mechanical Engineers. His paper was received without enthusiasm because many of the engineers present interpreted his findings to be a new piece rate system rather than a technique for analyzing work and improving methods.

The distaste that prevailed in the minds of many of the engineers of the time relative to piecework can well be appreciated. Standards were established by estimates made by supervisors, and, at best, these were far from being accurate or consistent. Both management and employees were rightfully skeptical of piece rates based on the foreman's guess. Management looked upon the rates with doubt, in view of the possibility of the foreman making a conservative estimate so as to protect the performance of his department. The worker, because of unfortunate past experiences, was concerned over any rate established merely by judgment and guess, since the rate vitally affected his earnings.

Then in June, 1903, Taylor presented his famous paper, "Shop Management," at the Saratoga meeting of the A.S.M.E. in which he gave the elements of the mechanism of scientific management as follows:

Time-study, with the implements and methods for properly making it.

Functional, or divided, foremanship, with its superiority to the old-fashioned single foreman.

The standardization of all tools and implements used in the plants, and also of the acts or movements of workmen for each class of work.

The desirability of a planning room or department.

The "exception principle" in management.

The use of slide-rules and similar time-saving implements.

Instruction cards for the workman.

The task idea in management, accompanied by a large bonus for the successful performance of the task.

The "differential rate."

Mnemonic systems for classifying manufactured products as well as implements used in manufacturing.

A routing system.

Modern cost system.

Taylor's "Shop Management" technique was well received by many factory managers, and with modifications had many satisfactory installations.[2]

At this time many men without the qualifications of Taylor, Barth,

---

[2] C. Bertrand Thompson in 1917 reported on the record of 113 plants which had installed "scientific management." Of these, 59 were considered to have completely successful installations, 20 had partly successful installations, and 34 plants considered their installation failures. C. Bertrand Thompson, *The Taylor System of Scientific Management* (Chicago: A. W. Shaw Co.).

Merrick, and other early pioneers, but eager to make a name for themselves in this new field, established themselves as "Efficiency Experts" and endeavored to install scientific management programs in industry. Here they encountered a natural resistance to change from employees, and since they were not equipped to handle problems of human relations, they met with great difficulty. Anxious to make a good showing and equipped with only a pseudoscientific knowledge, they generally established rates that were too difficult to meet. The situation would become so acute that management would be obliged to discontinue the whole program in order to continue operation.

In other instances, factory managers would allow the establishment of time standards by the foreman, and, as has been pointed out, this seldom was satisfactory.

Then, too, once standards were established, many factory managers of that time, interested primarily in the reduction of labor costs, would unscrupulously cut rates once some employee made what the employer felt was too much money. The result was harder work at the same take-home pay and sometimes less take-home pay; naturally, violent worker reaction resulted.

These developments spread in spite of the many favorable installations started by Taylor. At the Watertown Arsenal, labor objected to the new time study system to such an extent that in 1910 the Interstate Commerce Commission started an investigation of time study. Several derogatory reports on the subject influenced Congress in 1913 to add a rider to the government appropriation bill, stipulating that no part of the appropriation should be made available for the pay of any person engaged in time study work. This restriction applied to the government-operated plants where government funds were used to pay the employees.

The Military Establishment Appropriation Act, 1947 (Public Law 515 79th Congress) and the Navy Department Appropriation Act, 1947 (Public Law 492, 79th Congress) provide as follows:

Sec. 2. No part of the appropriation made in this Act shall be available for the salary or pay of any officer, manager, superintendent, foreman or other person having charge of the work of any employee of the United States Government while making or causing to be made with a stopwatch, or other time-measuring device, a time study of any job of any such employee between the starting and completion thereof, or of the movements of any such employee while engaged upon such work; nor shall any part of the appropriation made in this Act be available to pay any premiums or bonus or cash reward to any employee in addition to his regular wages, except as may be otherwise authorized in this Act.

Finally, in July, 1947, the House of Representatives passed a bill which allows the War Department to use time study, and in 1949, the prohibition against the use of stop watches was dropped from appropriation language, and to this date no restriction of time study practice prevails.

Motion Study

Frank B. Gilbreth was the founder of the modern motion study technique which may be defined as the study of body motions used in performing an operation, with thought toward improving the operation by eliminating the unnecessary motions, simplifying the necessary motions, and then establishing the most favorable sequence of motions, so that maximum efficiency is realized.

Frank Gilbreth, with assistance from his wife, Lillian Gilbreth, also developed the moving picture technique for studying motions, which has carried through many walks of life today. In industry, this technique is known as micromotion study, but the study of movements through the aid of the slow motion moving picture is by no means confined to industrial application. The world of sports finds it invaluable as a training tool to show development of form and skill. Mrs. Gilbreth still continues in motion study work today, and has made in recent years many contributions to work simplification as applied to the home. Her ideas have received considerable attention in the design of kitchen ranges, refrigerators, sinks, washing machines, and other household appliances.

Early Contemporaries

Carl G. Barth, an associate of F. W. Taylor, developed a production slide rule for determining the most efficient combination of speeds and feeds for cutting metals of various hardness, giving due consideration to depth of cut, size of tool, and life of tool.

Barth is also noted for the work he did relative to determination of allowances. He made an investigation of the number of foot-pounds of work which a man could do in a day. He then developed a rule that for a certain push or pull on a man's arms it is possible for him to be under load for a certain percentage of the day.

Harrington Emerson applied scientific methods to work on the Santa Fe Railroad and wrote a book, *Twelve Principles of Efficiency,* in which he made an effort to inform management as to procedures for efficient operation. Emerson is widely known for his Emerson Efficiency Gain Sharing Wage Payment Plan. His work in the field of wage payment is discussed in a later chapter of this text.

Morris L. Cooke, former director of the Department of Public Works in Philadelphia, made an effort to bring the principles of scientific management into city governments. In 1940, Cooke and Philip Murray, past president of the CIO, published a manuscript, "Organized Labor and Production," in which they brought out the fact that both labor and management have as their goal "Optimum Productivity." This they defined as "the highest possible balanced output of goods and services that management and labor skills can produce, equitably shared and consistent with a rational conservation of human and physical resources."

After Taylor retired, Dwight V. Merrick started a study of unit times, and these were published in the *American Machinist* edited by L. P. Alford. Merrick, with the assistance of Carl Barth, developed a technique for determining allowances on a rational basis. Merrick is also known for his multiple piece rate wage payment plan in which he recommends three graded piece rates.

Organizations

From 1911 to the present writing there has been an organized effort to keep industry abreast of the latest developments started by Taylor and Gilbreth. Technical organizations have contributed much toward bringing the science of time study, motion study, work simplification, and methods engineering up to present-day standards.

In 1911 the Conference of Scientific Management, under the leadership of Morris L. Cooke and Harlow S. Persons, was started at Amos Tuck School of Dartmouth College.

In 1912 the Society to Promote the Science of Management was organized and operated until 1915, when it was renamed the Taylor Society.

The Society of Industrial Engineers was organized in 1917 by men interested in production methods.

The American Management Association was formed in 1922 by groups interested in training personnel through so-called "Corporation Training Schools." Today its main purpose is "to advance the understanding of the principles, policies, practices, and purposes of modern management and of the method of creating and maintaining satisfactory relations in commerce and industry; to work toward the practical solution of current business problems and the development of the science of management." Annually the A.M.A. presents the Gantt Memorial Medal for the most distinguished contribution to industrial management as a service to the community.

The Society for the Advancement of Management (S.A.M.) was organized in 1936 by the merging of the Society of Industrial Engineers and the Taylor Society. This organization has continued the emphasis on the importance of time study and methods and wage payment up to the present time. Annually, it offers the "Taylor" key for the outstanding contribution to the advancement of the art and science of management as conceived by Frederick W. Taylor. Also, the "Gilbreth" medal is awarded annually for noteworthy achievement in the field of motion, skill, and fatigue study.

In 1946 the Industrial Incentive award was instituted by S.A.M. The desire of the donors is to recognize accomplishment, and to stimulate further endeavor in the field of financial and nonfinancial incentives.

The American Institute of Industrial Engineers has had a rapid growth since its founding at Columbus, Ohio on September 9, 1948. It is a national technical society of Industrial Engineers. The purpose of the A.I.I.E. is to maintain the practice of industrial engineering on a professional level; to foster a high degree of integrity among the members of the industrial engineering profession; to encourage and assist education and research in areas of interest to the industrial engineer; to promote the interchange of ideas and information among members of the industrial engineering profession; to serve in the public interest by the identification of men qualified to practice as industrial engineers; to promote professional registration of industrial engineers.

Present Trends

Time and motion study has steadily improved since the 1920's until today it is recognized as a necessary tool for the effective operation of business or industry. The practitioner of the art and science of time and motion study has come to realize the necessity of taking into consideration the "human element" in his work. No longer is the "cut and dried" procedure so characteristic of the "efficiency expert" acceptable. Today, consideration, through employee testing and training, is given to the fact that individuals differ in their performance potential. Such factors as sex, age, health and well-being, physical size and strength, aptitude, training, attitudes, and response to motivation have a direct bearing on output. Furthermore, the analyst of today recognizes that workers object, and rightfully so, to being treated as machines. Workers tend to dislike and fear a purely scientific approach to methods, work measurement, and wage incentives. They inherently dislike any change from their present way of operation. This psychological reaction is not characteristic of factory workers only but is the normal reaction of all people. Management frequently will reject worthwhile methods' innovations because of their reluctance to change. In fact, in the experience of the writer, management has been harder to sell on new ideas than any other group within the plant. After all, they are responsible for the existing method or procedure, and they frequently will defend it regardless of the potential savings through change.

Workers tend to fear methods and time study, for they see that this will result in an increase in productivity. To them, this means but one thing—less work and consequently less pay. They must be sold on the fact that they, as consumers, benefit from lower costs, and that with lower costs, broader markets result which means more work for more men for more weeks of the year.

Some fear of time study today is without a doubt due to the unpleasant experiences occurring in the days of the efficiency expert. To many workers, motion and time study is synonymous with the "speed up" or the "stretch out." These terms denote the use of incentives to spur employees to higher levels of output, followed by the establishing of the new levels as normal production, thus forcing the workers to still greater exertions to maintain even their previous earning power. In years past, undoubtedly some short-sighted and unscrupulous managements did resort to this practice.

The practitioner of motion and time study today must use the "humane" approach. He must be well versed in the study of human behavior and be accomplished in the art of communications. He must be a good listener at all times, indicating he respects the ideas and thinking of others, particularly the man on the bench. He must give credit where credit is due. In fact, he should get in the habit of always giving the "other fellow" credit, even if there is some question as to the other fellow deserving it.

Regardless of one's technical knowledge and ability, he will have little success in motion and time study work unless he is competent in dealing with the human element.

Motion and time study received added stimulus during World War II when Franklin D. Roosevelt, through the Department of Labor, advocated establishment of standards, from which increases in production resulted. On November 11, 1945, Regional War Labor Board III (for Pennsylvania, southern New Jersey, Maryland, Delaware, and the District of Columbia) issued a memorandum stating the policy of the War Labor Board on incentive proposals. Sections I, II and IV are reproduced since they contain matter pertinent to standards and wage incentives.

I—*General Considerations Applicable to All Incentive Proposals*

1. The expected effect of an incentive plan should be an increase in the present production per man-hour without increasing the unit labor cost in the plant, department, or job affected.

2. The proposal should not be in effect merely a means of giving a general increase in wages, nor should it result in wage decreases.

3. The plan should offer more pay only for more output.

4. If a union has bargaining rights for workers affected, the plan in all of its details should be collectively bargained.

5. No incentive wage plan should be proposed as a substitute for carrying out the responsibilities of both the management and employees.

6. No incentive plan should be put into operation, even if the money is held rather than advanced to the workers, until the approval of the War Labor Board has been secured.

II—*Establishing Incentive Rates for a Specific Production Operation*

When incentive rates are proposed for a specific production job or job classification the following principles apply:

1. Where feasible the operation should be *time studied* carefully to set the production standard. Results of this time study in as much detail as possible should appear in the application. If a time study is impracticable, the application should show why.

2. If a time study is impracticable, the production standard may be based

upon *records of past production* provided: (*a*) The records for an appropriate production period are submitted with the application; (*b*) The applicant establishes that the period is representative and that the present product, methods, prospective volume of work, and work force are comparable to those existing during the particular period of past production; (*c*) Exceptionally high or low production figures for short periods are satisfactorily explained in the application.

3. The production standard should be a quantity of output *higher than has been attained previously* by the average worker, or at least, higher than has been attained customarily. If the production standard is below an amount previously attained at some one or more times, the application should explain fully the reasons therefor.

IV—*Plant-wide Incentive Plans*

Because plant-wide incentive plans are comparatively new to American industry and because the effects of such plans on worker efficiency and production are difficult to predict, the Regional Board is not adopting a position on them at this time, but will consider each case on its individual merits. The general considerations set forth in I above are applicable here.

A great number of colleges and universities in their industrial engineering curricula are teaching the principles, techniques, and philosophies of this field. Some labor unions are training their representatives in the results and uses of the science. Management of both small and large industries are embarking on mass training programs, realizing the potentialities of a well-formulated program utilizing this tool.

Since World War II an annual national Time Study and Methods Conference has been conducted jointly by S.A.M. and A.S.M.E. to keep industry abreast of this field and to continue the progress which has been so apparent during the past ten years.

The Industrial Management Society annually presents a Time and Motion Study and Management Clinic. Here leaders of government, labor, and industry, along with engineers, gather to discuss common problems and to increase their knowledge of what is being done in the area of methods, standards, and wage payment.

TEXT QUESTIONS

1. Where were time studies originally made and who conducted them?
2. Explain Frederick W. Taylor's principle of functional foremanship.
3. What effect has Congress had on time study?
4. What is meant by motion study and who is generally conceded to be the founder of the motion study technique?
5. What is Carl G. Barth primarily noted for in the production end of industry?
6. Which organizations are concerned with advancing the ideas of Taylor and the Gilbreths?
7. Was the skepticism exhibited by management and labor in regard to rates established by "efficiency experts" understandable? Why?

8. What psychological reaction is characteristic of workers when method changes are suggested?

9. Explain the importance of the humanistic approach in methods and time study work.

GENERAL QUESTIONS

1. How is time and motion study used in industry today?

2. Why are labor unions training their representatives in the time and motion study technique?

3. Who have been the latest recipients of the Industrial Incentive award? What contributions have these people made to warrant the award presentation?

4. Explain the function of the A.M.A. as compared to the A.I.I.E.

5. Why was the government restriction on the use of stop watches carried through the World War II years?

6. Interview a group of five industrial workers and obtain their opinions as to the necessity of motion and time study.

CHAPTER 3

The Operation and Flow Process Chart

EVERY CRAFTSMAN HAS HIS tools which facilitate his performance. Just as the machinist has his micrometers and calipers and the patternmaker his chisels and plane, so does the methods analyst have at his disposal tools which enable him to do a better job in a shorter period of time. One of the most important tools of the methods engineer is the process chart. A process chart is defined as a graphic presentation of any manufacturing process. In methods work, one usually uses five different types of process charts, each of which has its specific application. These are:

1. Operation process chart.
2. Flow process chart.
3. Man and machine process chart.
4. Gang process chart.
5. Operator process chart.

The operation and flow process charts are used principally to present the problem. A problem cannot be solved unless it is properly presented. Consequently, these charts will be discussed at this time in preparation for the discussion of the problem solving approach of "operation analysis" (Chapters 4 and 5). Man and machine, gang, and operator process charts are presented in Chapter 6.

Frank Gilbreth is generally credited with being the original designer of process charts, although superintendents, methods engineers, and general foremen have always used this tool in one form or another, but not under the name "process chart." Process charts have wide application in improving a method; however, they must be used with caution because considerable time can be consumed in their construction.

The methods analyst must exercise judgment as to the amount of detail he attempts to include on any job. He, more than any one else in the factory, must be governed by the law that we never introduce any change, adjustment, or modification unless it is going to pay for itself within a reasonable time. Thus, the methods analyst must know when it is economically wise to construct a process chart or charts, and be fully cognizant as to the type he should use. The methods analyst must avoid getting the reputation of being "chart happy." If he spends all of his time in the construction of charts, he will have no time for creative thinking that leads to actual methods improvement.

Operation Process Chart

The operation process chart shows all operations, inspections, time allowances, and materials used in a manufacturing process. It clearly shows the sequence of events in chronological order from the raw material to the packaging of the finished product. It points out the entrance of all components and subassemblies to the main assembly. Just as a blueprint gives design details such as fits, tolerances, and specifications at a glance, so does an operation process chart give manufacturing details at a glance.

The A.S.M.E. standard definition of an operation process chart is as follows:

An operation process chart is a graphic representation of the points at which materials are introduced into the process, and of the sequence of inspections and all operations except those involved in material handling. It includes information considered desirable for analysis such as time required and location.[1]

Before we can improve a design, we must first get a blueprint of the product as it is presently designed. Likewise, before we can improve a manufacturing process, it is well to construct an operation process chart so that we understand the problem fully and will be able to determine what areas afford most possibilities of attack with the thought toward improvement. The operation process chart effectively states the problem, and if a problem cannot be stated, it usually cannot be solved.

Construction of the Operation Process Chart

In the construction of the operation process chart, two symbols are used: a small circle usually $\frac{3}{8}$ inch in diameter, denotes an operation, and a small square, $\frac{3}{8}$ inch on a side, denotes an inspection.

---

[1] Extracted from *ASME Operation and Flow Process Chart Standard, 1947*, with permission of the publisher, The American Society of Mechanical Engineers, 29 West 39th Street, New York, N.Y.

An operation takes place when the part being studied is intentionally transformed or when it is being studied or planned prior to performing productive work on it.

An inspection takes place when the part being studied is being examined to determine its conformance to standard.

Before beginning the actual construction of the operation process chart, the analyst should identify it with the title placed at the top of the paper. Usually, the identifying information, which would include part number, drawing number, process description, present or proposed method, date, and name of person doing the charting, would be headed with the words "Operation Process Chart." Sometimes additional information may be added so as to identify completely the subject being charted. This may include such items as chart number, plant, building, and department.

Vertical lines are used to indicate the general flow of the process as work is being accomplished, while horizontal lines feeding into the vertical flow lines are used to introduce material, either purchased or upon which work has been performed during the process. In general, the operation process chart should be so constructed that vertical flow lines and horizontal material lines do not cross. If for some reason it has become necessary to cross a vertical and a horizontal line, conventional practice, to show that no juncture occurs, is to draw a small semicircle in the horizontal line at the point where the vertical flow line crosses (see Figure 3–1).

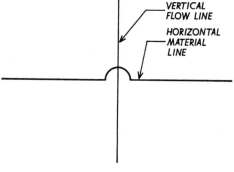

VERTICAL FLOW LINE

HORIZONTAL MATERIAL LINE

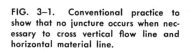

FIG. 3–1. Conventional practice to show that no juncture occurs when necessary to cross vertical flow line and horizontal material line.

When starting the actual construction of the operation process chart, the analyst first selects the major item of the assembly for charting. This usually would be the component on which the greatest number of operations will be performed. If no disassembly operations occur in the process, then the analyst should begin his chart in the upper right-hand corner of the paper. In the event disassembly operations compose part of the process, it is well to start plotting the major item more to the left and closer to the center of the paper. This will allow room for portraying disassembly operations which are shown as other operations, but material is represented as flowing from the process by a horizontal material line drawn to the right from the vertical flow line. Material introduced to the main component of assembly is portrayed by horizontal lines entering the vertical flow lines from the left.

Once the component that is to be first charted has been selected, it should be identified, as well as the material from which it is produced. This is done by drawing a horizontal material line. Above this line should be a brief description of the material, with an indication of the quantity required. If a drawing number or specification number applies, it should be included. In order to identify the part itself, the name of the part and its drawing number are shown in capital letters directly above the material description (see Figure 3–2).

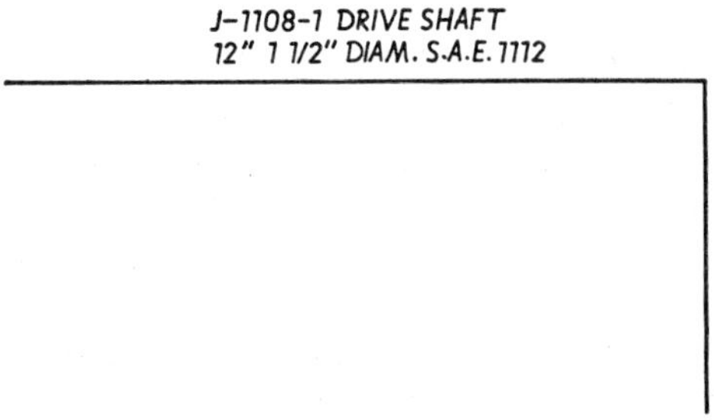

J–1108–1 DRIVE SHAFT
12" 1 1/2" DIAM. S.A.E. 1112

FIG. 3–2. Identification of part in the construction of the operation process chart.

Next, a vertical flow line is drawn in a downward direction from the right-hand end of the horizontal material line. The vertical flow line is extended a short distance (about ¼ inch), and then the symbol for the first operation or inspection, as the case may be, is drawn. To the right of the symbol is placed a brief but specific description of the event, such as "Drill, Ream, and Chamfer" or "Check O.D. and I.D." Immediately under the operation or inspection is recorded the facility on which the event is performed, as "#3 W. & S." or "Single End Plug Gage." To the left of the symbol is shown the time required to perform the work on one piece. After this information has been recorded, the vertical flow line is extended from the bottom of the symbol, and the next event is recorded. This charting procedure is continued until a second component joins the first. A horizontal material line is drawn to indicate the point at which the second component enters the process (see Figure 3–3).

Purchased items that subsequently enter the process are introduced by a horizontal line, the same as manufactured items. The purchased material or component is identified by part name, drawing number, and the source of supply (see Figure 3–4).

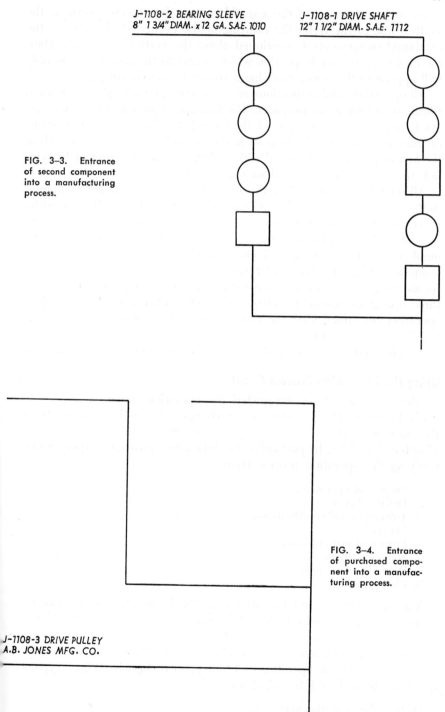

J–1108-2 BEARING SLEEVE
8" 1 3/4" DIAM. x 12 GA. S.A.E. 1010

J–1108-1 DRIVE SHAFT
12" 1 1/2" DIAM. S.A.E. 1112

FIG. 3–3. Entrance of second component into a manufacturing process.

FIG. 3–4. Entrance of purchased component into a manufacturing process.

J–1108-3 DRIVE PULLEY
A.B. JONES MFG. CO.

As each component of the assembly enters the process shown on the vertical line to the right, the charting of the events which occur to the combined components is continued along the vertical flow line. Thus, the final operation or inspection which occurs to the complete assembly will appear in the lower right-hand corner of the charting paper.

All operations and inspections are numbered chronologically for identification and reference purposes. The first operation is identified with an "O–1" in the center of its symbol, the second "O–2" and so on. Inspections are numbered in a similar manner in their own independent series. Thus, the first inspection is identified with an "INS–1" in the center of its symbol, the second "INS–2" and so on.

All operations taking place on the various components are numbered in the same series. Likewise, all inspections appearing on the operation process chart are numbered in one series. For example, if the first component on the chart had six operations performed upon it, they would be numbered O–1, O–2, O–3, O–4, O–5, and O–6. If, at this point, a second component joins the first, and three operations were performed on the second component prior to its assembly to the first component, then these three operations would be identified as O–7, O–8, and O–9. The first operation performed after the first and second components are brought together would be O–10.

A typical completed operation process chart appears in Figure 3–5.

Using the Operation Process Chart

After the analyst has completed the operation process chart, he is ready to use it. He should review each operation and inspection from the standpoint of the primary approaches to operation analysis (see Chapters 4 and 5). In particular, the following approaches apply when studying the operation process chart:

1. Purpose of operation.
2. Design of part.
3. Tolerances and specifications.
4. Materials.
5. Process of manufacture.
6. Setup and tools.
7. Working conditions.
8. Plant layout.

The procedure is for the analyst to adopt the questioning attitude on each of the above criteria that influence the cost and output of the product under study.

The most important question that the analyst should ask when studying the events on the operation and flow process chart is "Why." Typical questions that should be asked are:

"Why is this operation necessary?"
"Why is this operation performed in this manner?"

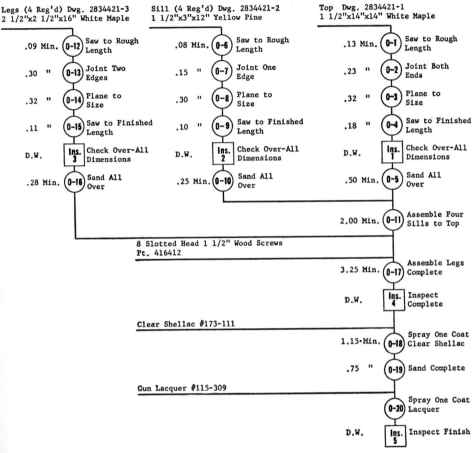

OPERATION PROCESS CHART

Manufacturing Type 2834421 Telephone Stands--Present Method
Part 2834421 Dwg. No. SK2834421
Charted By B.W.N. 4-12-

FIG. 3–5. Operation process chart illustrating manufacture of telephone stands.

"Why are these tolerances this close?"
"Why has this material been specified?"
"Why has this class of operator been assigned to do the work?"

The analyst should take nothing for granted; he should ask these and other pertinent questions about all phases of the process and then proceed to gather the information to answer the questions, so that a better way of doing the work may be introduced.

The question "Why" immediately suggests other questions including What, How, Who, Where, and When. For example, the analyst should ask:

1. *"What* is the purpose of the operation?"
2. *"How* can the operation be better performed?"
3. *"Who* can best perform the operation?"
4. *"Where* could the operation be performed at a lower cost?"
5. *"When* should the operation be performed so as to give the least amount of material handling?"

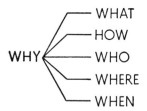

For example, in the operation process chart shown in Figure 3–5, the analyst might ask the following questions to determine the practicability of the method improvements indicated:

Question	*Method Improvement*
1. Can fixed lengths of 1½″ x 14″ white maple be purchased at no extra square footage cost?	Eliminate waste ends from lengths that are not multiples of 14″.
2. Can purchased maple boards be secured with edges smooth and parallel?	Eliminate jointing of ends (operation 2).
3. Can boards be purchased to thickness size and have at least one side planed smooth? If so how much extra will this cost?	Eliminate planing to size.
4. Why cannot two boards be stacked and sawed into 14″ sections simultaneously?	Reduce time of .18 (operation 4).
5. What percentage of rejects do we have at the first inspection station?	If the percentage is low, perhaps this inspection can be eliminated.
6. Why should the top of the table be sanded all over?	Eliminate sanding one side of top and reduce time (operation 5).
7. Can fixed lengths of 1½″ x 3″ yellow pine be purchased at no extra square footage cost?	Eliminate waste ends from lengths that are not multiples of 12″.
8. Can purchased yellow pine boards be secured with edges smooth and parellel?	Eliminate jointing of one edge.

9. Can sill boards be purchased to thickness size and have one side planed smooth? If so, how much extra will this cost? — Eliminate planing to size.

10. Why cannot two or more boards be stacked and sawed into 14″ sections simultaneously? — Reduce time of .10 (operation 9).

11. What percentage of rejects do we have at the first inspection of the sills? — If the percentage is low, perhaps this inspection can be eliminated.

12. Why is it necessary to sand the sills all over? — Eliminate some sanding and reduce time (operation 10).

13. Can fixed lengths of 2½″ x 2½″ white maple be purchased at no extra square footage cost? — Eliminate waste ends from lengths that are not multiples of 16″.

14. Can a smaller size than 2½″ x 2½″ be used? — Reduce material cost.

15. Can purchased white maple boards be secured with edges smooth and parallel? — Eliminate jointing of edges.

16. Can leg boards be purchased to thickness size and have sides planed smooth? If so, how much extra will this cost? — Eliminate planing to size.

17. Why cannot two or more boards be stacked and sawed into 14″ sections simultaneously? — Reduce time (operation 15).

18. What percentage of rejects do we have at the first inspection of the legs? — If the percentage is low, perhaps this inspection can be eliminated.

19. Why is it necessary to sand the legs all over? — Eliminate some sanding and reduce time (operation 16).

20. Could a fixture facilitate assembly of sills to top? — Reduce assembly time (operation 11).

21. Can sampling inspection be used on first inspection of assembly? — Reduce inspection time (operation 4).

22. Is it necessary to sand after one coat of shellac? — Eliminate operation 19.

By answering these questions, the analyst will be aware of other questions that may lead to improvement. Ideas seem to generate ideas, and the experienced analyst will always arrive at several possibilities for improvement. He must keep an open mind and not let previous disappointments discourage the trial of new ideas.

The completed operation process chart helps visualize the present method with all of its details, so that new and better procedures may be devised. It shows the analyst what effect a change on a given operation will have on preceding and subsequent operations. The mere construction of the operation chart will inevitably suggest possibilities for improvement to the alert analyst.

This process chart indicates the general flow of all components entering into a product, and since each step is shown in its proper chronological sequence, the operation process chart is in itself an ideal plant layout. Consequently, methods' analysts, plant layout engineers, and those in related fields will find this tool extremely helpful in making new layouts and in improving existing ones.

The operation process chart is an aid in promoting and explaining a proposed method. Since it gives so much information so clearly, it provides an ideal comparison between two competing solutions.

Flow Process Chart

By A.S.M.E. standard definition, a flow process chart is a "graphic representation of all operations, transportations, inspections, delays, and storages occurring during a process or procedure, and includes information considered desirable for analysis such as time required and distance moved."[2]

In general, the flow process chart contains considerably more detail than the operation process chart. Consequently, it is not adapted to complicated assemblies as a whole. It is used primarily on one component of an assembly at a time in order to effect maximum savings in the manufacture of that particular component. The flow chart is especially valuable in recording hidden costs, such as distances traveled, delays, and temporary storages. Once these nonproductive periods are highlighted, the analyst can take steps for improvement.

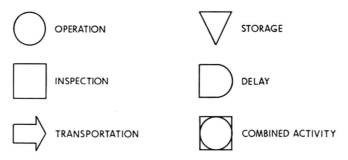

FIG. 3-6. Standard flow process chart symbols.

[2] *Ibid.*

The flow process chart, in addition to recording operations and inspections, shows all the moves and delays in storage encountered by an item as it goes through the plant. In addition to the operation and inspection symbols used in the construction of operation process charts, several other symbols are used. A small arrow signifies a transportation, which can be defined as the moving of an object from one place to another, except when the movement takes place during the normal course of an operation or an inspection. A large capital "D" indicates a delay. A delay occurs when a part is not permitted to be immediately processed at the next work station. An equilateral triangle standing on its vertex signifies a storage, which occurs when a part is held and protected against unauthorized removal. When it becomes necessary to show a combined activity, such as one operator performing an operation and an inspection at a work station, then a square, ⅜ inch on a side with a small circle ⅜ inch in diameter inscribed within the square, is used as the identifying symbol.

Construction of the Flow Process Chart

As in the case of the operation process chart, the flow process chart should be properly identified with a title appearing at the top. It is customary practice to head the identifying information with the words "Flow Process Chart." The identifying information usually shown includes part number, drawing number, process description, present or proposed method, date, and the name of the person doing the charting.

Sometimes additional data is valuable in order to identify completely the job being charted. This may include the plant, building or department, chart number, quantity, and cost information.

Since the flow chart represents but one item rather than an assembly, a neat-appearing chart can be constructed by starting on the top central section of the paper. First, a horizontal material line is drawn, over which is shown the part number and description as well as the material from which the part is processed. A short vertical flow line (about ¼ inch) is then drawn to the first event symbol, which may be an arrow indicating a transportation from the storeroom. Just to the right of the transportation symbol is recorded a brief description of the move, such as "moved to cut-off saw by material handler." Immediately under this is shown the type of material handling equipment (if any) used. For example, "hand two-wheeled truck" or "gasoline-powered fork truck" would identify the equipment employed. To the left of the symbol is shown the time required to perform the event, and about 1 inch still further to the left, the distance in feet moved is recorded (see Figure 3–7).

This charting procedure is continued by recording all operations, inspections, moves, delays, permanent storages, and temporary storages that occur during the processing of the part. All events are numbered chronologically for reference purpose, using a separate series for each event class.

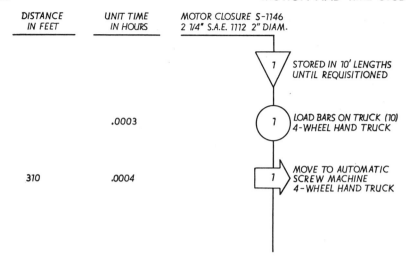

DISTANCE IN FEET	UNIT TIME IN HOURS	MOTOR CLOSURE S-1146 2 1/4" S.A.E. 1112 2" DIAM.
		1 — STORED IN 10' LENGTHS UNTIL REQUISITIONED
	.0003	1 — LOAD BARS ON TRUCK (10) 4-WHEEL HAND TRUCK
310	.0004	1 — MOVE TO AUTOMATIC SCREW MACHINE 4-WHEEL HAND TRUCK

FIG. 3–7.   Distance, unit time, and element description as shown on flow process chart.

The transportation symbol is used to indicate the direction of the flow. Thus, when straight-line flow is taking place, the symbol is plotted with the arrow pointing to the right side of the paper. When the process reverses or backtracks, the change of direction is illustrated by plotting the arrow so that it points to the left. If a multifloor building is housing the process, the arrow pointing upward indicates that the process is moving upward, and a downward direction of the arrow shows the flow of work to be descending.

To determine the distances moved, it is not necessary to measure accurately each move with a tape or six-foot rule. Usually, a sufficiently correct figure will result by counting the number of columns that the material is moved past and then multiplying this number, less one, by the span. Moves of five feet or less are usually not recorded; however, they may be if the analyst feels that it will materially effect the over-all cost of the method being plotted.

It is important that all delay and storage times be included on the chart. It is not sufficient just to indicate that a delay or storage takes place. Since the longer a part stays in storage or is delayed, the more cost it accumulates, it is therefore important to know the length of time it spends at each delay and at each storage.

The most economical method of determining the duration of delays and storages is to mark several parts with chalk indicating the exact time that they went into a storage or were delayed. Then periodically check the section to see when the parts marked are brought back into production. By taking a number of cases and recording the elapsed time, and then averaging the results, the analyst will obtain sufficiently accurate time values.

O = Op ▽ - Storage
□ - insp D - Delay
⇨ - Trans ⊡ - combined activity

Using the Flow Process Chart

The flow process chart, like the operation process chart, is not an end in itself, but merely a means to an end. It is used as a tool of analysis for eliminating the hidden costs of a component. Since the flow chart clearly shows all transportations, delays, and storages, it is helpful in reducing either the quantity or duration of these elements.

FLOW PROCESS CHART

SUBJECT CHARTED Shower head face CHART NO. 1128
DRAWING NO. BA-14782 PART NO. B-14782-2 CHART OF METHOD Present
CHART BEGINS Bar stock storage CHARTED BY E. Dunnick
CHART ENDS Assembly Department Storeroom DATE 9-7-54 SHEET 1 OF 2

DIST. IN FEET	UNIT TIME IN MIN.	CHART SYMBOLS	PROCESS DESCRIPTION	DIST. IN FEET	UNIT TIME IN MIN.	CHART SYMBOLS	PROCESS DESCRIPTION
		▽ 1	Stored in bar stock storage until requisitioned		60	D 6	Delayed waiting press operator
20	.02	○ 1	Bars loaded on truck upon receipt of requisition.	100		⇨ 5	Move to Bliss 74½ press #16 by operator.
600	.05	⇨ 1	Move extruded rod to air saw # 72.		.075	○ 7	Pierce 6 holes
15	.02	○ 2	Bars removed from truck and stored on rack near machine.		120	D 7	Delayed waiting drill press operator.
	120	D 1	Delayed waiting for operation to begin.	50		⇨ 6	Move to drill press by operator.
	.077	○ 3	Saw slug on air saw.		.334	○ 8	Rough ream + chamfer L.+G. drill press # 19
	30	D 2	Delayed waiting for move — man.		30	D 8	Delayed waiting drill press operator.
70	.03	⇨ 2	Move slugs to Nat. Maxi-press # 8	20		⇨ 7	Move to Avey drill press # 21 by operator.
	15	D 3	Delayed awaiting forging operation.		.152	○ 9	Drill three 13/64" holes Avey press # 21.
	.234	○ 4	Forge (3-man operation)		20	D 9	Delayed awaiting turret lathe operator.
	10	D 4	Delayed waiting for press operator	60		⇨ 8	Move to turret lathe section by operator
30		⇨ 3	Move to press by operator.		.522	○ 10	Turn stem + face # 3 W. + S.
		○ 5	Trim Flash Bliss 74½ press # 16.		60	D 10	Delayed awaiting turret lathe operator.
	30	D 5	Delayed waiting for pickling operator.	30		⇨ 9	Move to adjacent turret lathe operator.
100		⇨ 4	Move to pickling tanks by operator.		.648	○ 11	Form outside diameter and face back.
	007	○ 6	Pickle (HCL tank)		15	D 11	Delayed waiting press operator.

FIG. 3–8. Flow process chart.

FLOW PROCESS CHART

SUBJECT CHARTED _Shower head face_ _____ CHART NO. _1128_

DRAWING NO. _BA-14782_ PART NO. _B-14782-2_ ___ CHART OF METHOD _Present_

CHART BEGINS _Bar stock storage_ _____ CHARTED BY _E. Dunnick_

CHART ENDS _Assembly Department Storeroom_ _ DATE _9-7-_ SHEET _2_ OF _2_

DIST. IN FEET	UNIT TIME IN MIN.	CHART SYMBOLS	PROCESS DESCRIPTION	DIST. IN FEET	UNIT TIME IN MIN.	CHART SYMBOLS	PROCESS DESCRIPTION
60		⑩⟩	Move to Bliss 20 B press by operator				
	.097	⑫	Stamp identification Bliss 20 B press #21				
	15	⑫	Delayed waiting next press operator				
	.167	⑬	Broach six holes to size Bliss 20 B press #22				
	60	⑬	Delayed waiting for move-man				
350	.012	⑪⟩	Move to inspection by move-man				
	20	⑭	Delay waiting for inspector				
	.05	①	Inspect complete (10% spot check)				
15		⑫⟩	Move to storeroom by inspector				
		▽2	Stored until requisitioned				

SUMMARY

EVENT	NUMBER	TIME	DISTANCE
OPERATIONS	13	2.393 min.	
INSPECTIONS	1	.05 "	
TRANSPORTATIONS	12		1545 ft.
STORAGES	2	undetermined	
DELAYS	14	605 min.	

FIG. 3-8   (continued)

Once the analyst has constructed the flow process chart, he uses the questioning approach based on the considerations primary to operation analysis. With the flow process chart, special consideration will be given to:

1. Material handling.
2. Plant layout.
3. Delay time.
4. Storage time.

In all probability, the analyst has already constructed and analyzed an operation process chart of the assembly of which the part under study in the flow chart is a component. The flow chart was constructed of the components of the particular assembly where it was thought further study of the hidden costs would be practical. If the operations and inspections performed on the component have already been studied, then the analyst would not spend a great deal of time in restudying them when analyzing the flow chart. He would be more concerned in studying the distance parts must be moved from operation to operation, and what delays occur. Of course, if the flow chart was constructed initially, then all of the primary approaches to operation analysis should be used for study of the events shown on the flow process chart. These are:

1. Time for each operation, inspection, move, delay, and storage.
2. Distance in feet each time the item being plotted is transported.

In order to eliminate or minimize delay and storage time so as to improve deliveries to customers, as well as reduce cost, the analyst should consider these check questions in studying the job:

1. How often is the full amount of material not delivered to the operation?
2. What can be done to schedule materials to come in more even quantities?
3. What is the most efficient batch or lot size, or manufacturing quantity?
4. How can schedules be rearranged to provide longer runs?
5. What is the best sequence for scheduling orders to allow for type of operation, tools required, colors, etc.?
6. What can be done to group similar operations to be performed at the same time?
7. How much can down time and overtime be reduced by improved scheduling?
8. What is the cause of emergency maintenance and rush orders?
9. How much delay and storage time can be saved by making schedules more regular by running certain products on certain days?
10. What alternate schedules can be developed to use materials most efficiently?
11. Would it be worthwhile to accumulate pickups, deliveries, and shipments?
12. What is the proper department to do the job so it will be done with the same class of work and save a move, delay, or storage?

13. How much would be saved by doing the job on another shift? At another plant?
14. What is the best and most economical time to run tests and experiments?
15. What information is lacking on orders issued to the factory that may cause a delay or storage?
16. How much time is lost by shifts changing at different hours in related departments?
17. What are the frequent interruptions to the job, and how should they be eliminated?
18. How much time does the employee lose waiting for or by not receiving the proper instructions, blueprints, and specifications?
19. How many holdups are caused by congested aisles?
20. What improvements can be made in the location of doorways and aisles and the making of aisles which will reduce delays?

Specific check questions, to shorten distances traveled and reduce material handling time, that should be used by the analyst include:

1. Can a facility be economically relocated in order to reduce distances travelled?
2. What can be done to reduce the handling of materials?
3. What is the correct equipment for handling the materials?
4. How much time is lost in getting materials to and from the work station?
5. Should product grouping be considered rather than process grouping?
6. What can be done to increase the size of the unit of material handled to reduce handling, scrap, and down time?
7. How can elevator service be improved?
8. What can be done about runways and roadways to speed up transportation?
9. What is the proper position in which to place material to reduce the amount of handling required by the operator?
10. What use can be made of gravity delivery?

A study of the completed flow chart (Figure 3–8) will familiarize the analyst with all pertinent details related to the direct and indirect costs of a manufacturing process so that they can be analyzed for improvement. Unless all the facts relating to a method are known, it is difficult to improve that method. Casual inspection of an operation will not provide the information needed to do a thorough job of method improvement. Since distances are recorded on the flow process chart, it is exceptionally valuable in showing how the layout of a plant can be improved. Intelligent use of the flow process chart will result in improvements.

The Flow Diagram

Although the flow process chart gives most of the pertinent information relative to a manufacturing process, it does not show a pictorial plan of the flow of work. Sometimes this added information is helpful in developing a new method. For example, before a transportation can be shortened, it is necessary to see or visualize where room can be provided to add a facility so that the transportation distance can be diminished. Likewise, it is helpful to visualize potential temporary and permanent storage areas, inspection stations, and work points. The best way to provide this information is to take an existing drawing of the plant layout of the areas involved, and sketch in the flow lines indicating the movement of the material from one activity to the next. Such a pictorial presentation of the layout of floors and of buildings which shows the location of all activities appearing on the flow process chart is known as a flow diagram.

When constructing a flow diagram, the analyst should identify each activity by symbol and number corresponding to those appearing on the flow process chart. The direction of movement is indicated by placing small arrows periodically along the flow lines. These arrows will point the direction of flow.

If it is desirable to show the flow of more than one item, a different color can be used to show the flow of each part.

Figure 3–9 illustrates a flow diagram made in conjunction with a flow process chart to improve the production of the Garand (M1) rifle at Springfield Armory. This pictorial presentation together with the flow process chart resulted in savings that increased production from 500 rifle barrels per shift to 3600—with no more employees. Figure 3–10 illustrates the flow diagram of the revised layout.

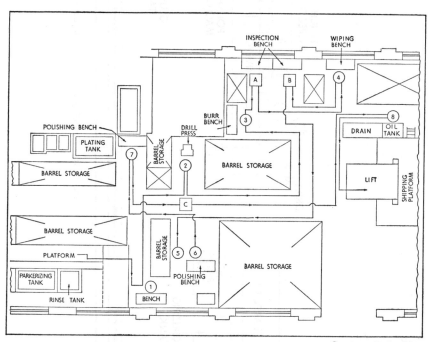

Courtesy: R. A. Olsen

FIG. 3–9. Flow diagram of old layout of group of operations on the Garand rifle.

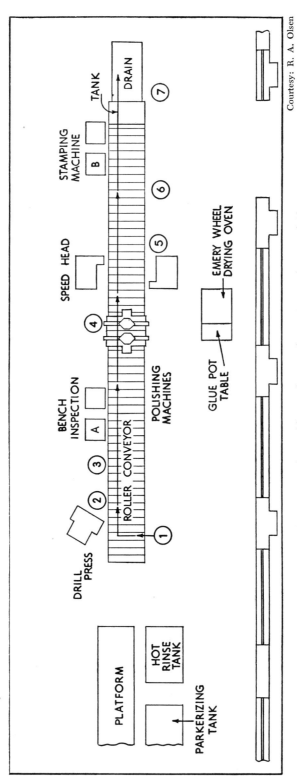

FIG. 3–10. Flow diagram of revised layout of group of operations on the Garand rifle.

Courtesy: R. A. Olsen

It can be seen that the flow diagram is a helpful supplement to the flow process chart wherever relocation of work and storage stations takes place. The flow diagram shows up backtracking and areas of possible traffic congestion, and facilitates the making of an ideal plant layout.

Summary: Operation and Flow Process Charts

The methods analyst should become familiar with the operation and flow process charts and the flow diagram so that he will be able to use these valuable tools in the solution of problems. Just as there are several types of tools available for a particular job, so several designs of charts can be utilized in assisting in the solution of an engineering problem. However, in determining a specific solution, one chart usually has advantages over another. The analyst should know the specific functions of each of the process charts and only resort to those that he needs to help solve his specific problems. In summary, their functions are:

1. *Operation Process Chart*—Used to analyze relations between operations. Good for studying operations and inspections on assemblies involving several components. Helpful for plan layout work.
2. *Flow Process Chart*—Used to analyze hidden or indirect costs, such as delay time, storage cost, and material handling costs. Best chart for complete analysis of the manufacture of one component part.
3. *Flow Diagram*—Used as a supplement to the flow chart, especially where considerable floor space is involved in the process. Shows up backtracking and traffic congestion. Necessary tool in making revised plant layouts.

Both the operation and flow process chart and the flow diagram have their place in developing improvements. Their correct use will aid in presenting the problem, solving the problem, selling the solution, and installing the solution.

TEXT QUESTIONS

1. Who uses process charts?
2. Who is credited as being the original designer of process charts?
3. What does the operation process chart show?
4. What symbols are used in the construction of the operation process chart?
5. How are materials introduced into the general flow when constructing the operation?
6. How does the flow process chart differ from the operation process chart?
7. What is the principal purpose of the flow process chart?
8. What symbols are used in the construction of the flow process chart?
9. When would you advocate the use of the flow diagram?
10. How can the flow of several different products be shown on the flow diagram?
11. Why are the operation and flow process charts merely a means to an end?

GENERAL QUESTIONS

1. What are the limitations of the operation and flow process charts, and the flow diagram?
2. What relation is there between the flow chart and material handling? Between the flow diagram and plant bottlenecks? Between the operation process chart and material specifications?
3. What is the connection between effective plant layout and the operation process chart?

CHAPTER 4

Operation Analysis

Operation analysis is a procedure used by the methods engineer to analyze all productive and nonproductive elements of an operation with the thought of improvement. Methods engineering in itself is concerned with devising methods that increase production per unit of time and reduce unit costs. Operation analysis is in reality a technique for accomplishing the goal of methods engineering.

In the post–World War II era, with competition becoming increasingly keen, the subject of operation analysis has become increasingly important. It is a procedure that can never be regarded as being completed. Competition usually necessitates continuing study of a given product so that the manufacturing processes can be improved and a part of the gains can be passed on to the consumer in the form of a better product at a reduced selling price. Once this is done by a given producer, competitors invariably introduce similar improvement programs, and it is only a matter of time until they have produced a more salable product at a reduced price. This starts a new cycle in which the given producer again reviews his operations, improves his manufacturing processes, and again necessitates improvements in competitive plants. Conditions in industry cannot be static; otherwise, bankruptcy would result. Progress is the only key to continued profitable operation.

Another basic economic law, that of supply and demand, must be considered when savings are effected. The volume of goods consumed is inversely proportional to the selling price. As we develop improvements that inaugurate real savings, we broaden the market through lower selling price. This procedure has been proven time and time again. This was done with electric lighting, refrigerators, radios, automobiles, and many other products. As progress allowed reduction in cost, more people could afford to purchase. The increased volume permitted further economies, which again resulted in lower prices, and lower prices further increased the volume. Each time the selling price of any commodity is reduced as little as 5 per cent, the product is immediately brought within reach of more people's pocketbooks.

Experience has proved that practically all operations can be improved if sufficient study is given to them. Since the procedure of systematic analysis is equally effective in large and small industries, job shop and mass production, we can safely conclude that the subject of operation analysis is applicable in all areas of manufacturing, business, and government establishments.

Approach to Operation Analysis

Probably one of the most common attitudes of industrialists is that their problems are unique. Consequently, they feel that any new method will be impractical for them. Actually all work, whether it be clerical, machine, assembly, or general labor, is much the same. The Gilbreths concluded that any work, whether productive or nonproductive, was done by using combinations of seventeen basic movements which they call "Therbligs." Regardless of what the operation is, when considered in the light of its basic divisions, it will be found to be quite similar to others. For example, the elements of work in driving a car are much like those required to operate a turret lathe; the basic motions employed in dealing a bridge hand are almost identical with certain manual inspection and machine loading elements. The fact that all work is similar in many respects verifies the principle that if methods can be improved in one plant, opportunities exist for methods improvement in all plants.

Anyone who is engaged in methods work is well aware of the natural inherent resistance to change that prevails in all men's minds, regardless of their level in the organization. Overcoming this resistance to change is one of the major obstacles in the path of an improvement program. Managers will continually make statements to the effect that, "It might have worked at the —— plant, but our operation is quite different." Supervisors will say, "It can't work here," and even the operator will bluntly declare, "It won't work." Selling the whole organization on "It will work here" is a never ending job for the methods engineer. One who is successful in this type of work never accepts anything as being right just because it exists today or has been done this way for years. Instead, he questions, probes, investigates, and finally, after all angles are considered, he makes his decision for the moment. Always he is conscious that this method may be satisfactory today, but it will not be tomorrow, as there is always a better way.

Operation Analysis Procedure

The use of a systematic procedure is invaluable if real savings are to be realized. The first step is to get all information related to the anticipated volume of the work. It is necessary to determine the expected volume, the chance of repeat business, the life of the job, the chance for design changes, and the labor content of the job, so it can be determined how much time and effort should be devoted toward improving the present method or planning the new job. If the job promises to be quite active, a more detailed study will be justified than if the volume appears to be low.

Once an estimate is made as to quantity, life of job, and labor content, then all factual manufacturing information should be collected. This information would include all operations, facilities used to perform the operations, and operational times; all moves or transportations, facilities used for transportation, and transportation distances; all inspections, inspection facilities, and inspection times; all storages, storage facilities, and time spent in storage; all vendor operations together with their prices; and all drawings and design specifications. After all this information which affects cost is gathered, it must be presented in a form suitable for study. One of the most effective ways of doing this is through the Flow Process Chart (see Chapter 3). This chart graphically presents all manufacturing information, much as a blueprint shows all design information.

Upon completion of the flow process chart, the analyst reviews the problem with thought toward improvement. Up to this point, he has merely stated the problem, which is a necessary procedure in order to solve it. One of the most common techniques used by methods men is to prepare a check sheet for asking questions on every activity shown on the flow chart. Typical questions are: "Is this operation necessary? Can the operation be better performed another way? Can it be combined with some other operation? Are tolerances closer than necessary? Can a more economical material be used? Can better material handling be incorporated?"

A typical check list of pertinent questions developed by the Methods Engineering Council of Pittsburgh, Pennsylvania is shown in Figure 4–1. This figure also illustrates how this form was used to make a cost reduction study on an electric blanket control knob shaft. By redesigning the shaft so it could be economically produced as a die casting rather than a screw machine part, the cost was reduced from $68.75 per thousand pieces to $17.19 per thousand pieces.

The analyst asks and answers all related questions on the check sheet

Date ____9/15____ Dept. ____11____ Dwg. ____18-4612____ Sub. ____2____

Mould _____ Die _____ Style _____ Item ____2____

Pattern _____ Ins. Spec. ____C____ L. Spec. _____ Sub. _____

Part Description ____Blanket control knob shaft____

Operation ____Turn, groove, drill, tap, knurl, thread, cut-off____ Operator ____Blazer____

DETERMINE AND DESCRIBE

1. PURPOSE OF OPERATION

To form contours of 3/8" S.A.E. 1112 rod on automatic screw machine to achieve drawing specifications.

2. COMPLETE LIST OF ALL OPERATIONS PERFORMED ON PART

No.	Description	Work Sta.	Dept.
1.	Turn, groove, drill, tap, knurl, thread, cut-off	B. & S.	11
2.	Burr	Bench	12
3.	Inspect 1%	Bench	18
4.			
5.			
6.			
7.			
8.			
9.			
10.			

3. INSPECTION REQUIREMENTS

a—Of previous oprn.

b—Of this oprn. Yes. Perhaps S.Q.C. will reduce amount of inspection.

DETAILS OF ANALYSIS

Can purpose be accomplished better otherwise? *Yes - by die casting*

Can oprn. being analyzed be eliminated? *No*

be combined with another? *No*

be performed during idle period of another? *Yes, by machine coupling*

Is sequence of oprns. best possible? *Yes*

Should oprn. be done in another dept. to save cost or handling? *Perhaps can be purchased outside at a savings.*

Are tolerance, allowance, finish and other requirements necessary?

suitable to purpose?

4. MATERIAL   Zinc base die cast metal would be less expensive.

Consider size, suitability, straightness, and condition.

Can cheaper material be substituted?

Cutting compounds and other supply materials

5. MATERIAL HANDLING

a—Brought by 4 wheel truck to automatics

b—Removed by hand 2 wheel trucks

c—Handled at work station by

Should crane, gravity conveyors, totepans, or special trucks be used?

Consider layout with respect to distance moved. *Perhaps gravity to burring station.*

6. SET-UP (Accompany description with sketches if necessary)

This is satisfactory as being done.

How are dwgs. and tools secured?

Can set-up be improved?

Trial pieces.

Machine Adjustments.

Tools

Suitable?
Provided?
Ratchet Tools
Power Tools
Spl. Purpose Tools
Jigs, Vises
Special Clamps
Fixtures
  Multiple
  Duplicate

a—Tool Equipment

Present

Suggestions   Redesign part to be made as zinc base die casting rather than S.A.E. 1112 screw machine part.

7. CONSIDER THE FOLLOWING POSSIBILITIES.

1. Install gravity delivery chutes.
2. Use drop delivery
3. Compare methods if more than one operator is working on same job.
4. Provide correct chair for operator.
5. Improve jigs or fixtures by providing ejectors, quick-acting clamps, etc.
6. Use foot operated mechanisms.
7. Arrange for two handed operation.
8. Arrange tools and parts within normal working area.
9. Change layout to eliminate back tracking and to permit coupling of machines.
10. Utilize all improvements developed for other jobs.

8. WORKING CONDITIONS.

Generally satisfactory.

a—Other Conditions

9. METHOD (Accompany with sketches or Process Charts if necessary.)

a—Before Analysis and Motion Study.

RECOMMENDED ACTION

yes, to accumulate
for tumbling.

Light o.k.
Heat o.k.
Ventilation, Fumes o.k.
Drinking Fountains o.k.
Wash Rooms o.k.
Safety Aspects o.k.
Design of Part o.k.
Clerical Work Required (to fill
out time cards, etc.) o.k.
Probability of Delays o.k.
Probable Mfg. Quantities o.k.

Arrangement of Work Area

Placement of

Tools.

Materials.

Control knob shaft designed as screw machine part.

b—After Analysis and Motion Study

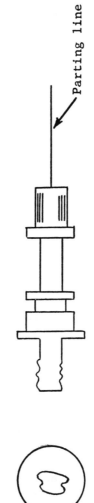

Parting line

Control knob redesigned as die cast part. Threads on left-hand
extension cover only 50 per cent of periphery; likewise knurl on
right end extension on half of periphery thus allowing piece to
be easily removed from die.

See Supplementary Report
Entitled *Die Cast*
Control shaft.

Date

OBSERVER ____ R. Guild ____   APPROVED BY ____ R. Hussey ____

FIG. 4-1 (continued)

for all steps appearing on the flow chart. This procedure invariably evolves efficient ways of performing the work. As these ideas develop, it is well to record them immediately so that they will not be forgotten. It is also wise to include sketches at this time. Usually, the analyst is surprised at the numerous inefficiencies that prevail and will have little trouble in compiling many improvement possibilities. One improvement usually leads to another. The analyst must have an open mind and creative ability if he is to be a real success in this type of work. The check sheet is also useful in giving methods training to factory foremen and superintendents. Thought-provoking questions, when intelligently used, help factory supervisors to develop constructive ideas. The check sheet serves as an outline which can be referred to by the discussion leader who is handling the methods training.

The Ten Primary Approaches to Operation Analysis

The Westinghouse Electric Corporation has developed an operation analysis program in which it gives emphasis to using the "10 Primary Approaches to Operation Analysis" when studying the flow chart of the prevailing method.

These approaches include:

1. Purpose of Operation
2. Design of Part
3. Tolerances and Specifications
4. Materials
5. Process of Manufacture
6. Setup and Tools
7. Working Conditions
8. Material Handling
9. Plant Layout
10. Principles of Motion Economy

These points of analysis are supplemented by Maynard and Stegemerten with: Complete Survey of All Operations Performed on Part, Method, and Common Possibilities for Job Improvement.[1] When all these points are considered in studying each individual operation, attention is focused on the items most likely to produce improvement. All of these points will not be applicable to each activity appearing on the flow chart, but usually it will be found that more than one should be considered. The method of analysis recommended is to take each step in the present method individually and analyze it with a specific approach toward improvement clearly in mind, giving consideration to all key points of analysis. Then follow with the same procedure on succeeding operations, inspections, moves, storages, etc., shown on the chart. After each element has been thus analyzed, it is well to consider the product being studied

---

[1] H. B. Maynard and G. J. Stegemerten, *Operation Analysis* (New York: McGraw-Hill Book Co., Inc., 1939).

as a whole rather than in the light of its elemental components and to reconsider all points of analysis with thought toward over-all improvement possibilities. There are usually unlimited opportunities for methods improvement in every plant. The best technique for developing the maximum savings is in the careful study of individual and collective operations as outlined. Wherever this procedure has been followed by competent engineers, beneficial results have always been realized.

PURPOSE OF OPERATION

Probably the most important of the ten points of operation analysis used for improving an existing method or planning a new job is the purpose of the operation. A cardinal rule that the analyst should observe is to try to eliminate or combine an operation before improving it. In my experience, as much as 25 per cent of the operations being performed by diversified American industry can be eliminated if sufficient study be given the design and the process.

Unnecessary operations are frequently a result of improper planning at the time the job was first set up. Once a standard routine is established, it is difficult to make a change, even if such a change would allow the elimination of a portion of the work and make the job easier. When new jobs are planned, the planner usually will include an extra operation if there is any question as to the possibility of rejection of the product without the extra work. For example, if there is some question as to whether to take two or three cuts in turning a steel shaft in order to maintain a 40 micro-inch finish, invariably the planner will specify three cuts, even though proper maintenance of cutting tools, supplemented with ideal feeds and speeds, would allow the job to be done with two cuts. Likewise, if there is some question as to the ability of a drill press to hold a .005 inch tolerance on a ¼ inch drilled hole, the planner, when setting up the job, will call for a reaming operation. Actually, the drilling operation would be adequate if all variable factors (speed, feed, cutting lubricant, drill size) are controlled.

Many times an unnecessary operation may develop because of the improper performance of a previous operation. A second operation must be done in order to touch up or make acceptable the work done by the first operation. For example, in one plant, armatures were previously spray-painted in a fixture which made it impossible to cover the bottom of the armature with paint in that the fixture shielded the bottom from the spray blast. It was necessary to touch up the armature bottoms after spray-painting. A study of the job resulted in a redesigned fixture which held the armature and still allowed complete coverage. The new fixture permitted spray-painting of seven armatures simultaneously, whereas the old method called for spray-painting one at a time. Thus, it was possible to eliminate the touch-up operation by giving consideration to the thought that an unnecessary operation may develop because of the improper performance of a previous operation.

In the manufacture of large gears it was necessary to introduce a hand-scraping and lapping operation in order to remove waves in the teeth after they had been hobbed. An investigation disclosed that contraction and expansion brought about by temperature changes in the course of the day were responsible for the waviness in the teeth surface. By inclosing the whole unit and installing an air-conditioning system within the enclosure, proper temperature was maintained during the whole day. Immediately the waviness disappeared, and it was no longer necessary to continue the hand-scraping and lapping operations.

Sometimes unnecessary operations develop because an operation was introduced in order to facilitate an operation which followed. For example, it was thought necessary to twist each pair of wires when wiring commutators in order to keep the correct pair of wires together and also increase the strength. It was found, however, after analysis that the correct pair of wires could be placed in the proper slot without twisting.

FIG. 4–2. *Above:* Painted armature as removed from old fixture and as removed from improved fixture. *Below:* Armature in spray-painting fixture allowing complete coverage of armature bottom.

Also, observation revealed that twisting caused the wires to be unequal in length, and the uneven tension in the twisted wire weakened rather than strengthened the wires. It was discovered that the winding of the wire was unnecessary when someone asked: "Can a change in assembly eliminate the need for a previous operation?"

In endeavoring to eliminate operations, the analyst should consider the question: Is an additional operation justified by savings it will effect in a subsequent operation? For example, a brush holder was originally planned so that two holes were drilled and tapped in each holder. One hole was drilled and tapped in the bottom, another was drilled an tapped in the top. The brush holder was assembled in such a manner that alternately a holder with the drilled and tapped hole in the bottom and with the hole tapped in the top were used. Since all parts had tapped holes in both the bottom and top, it was merely a matter of positioning the part for assembly. By questioning the need for both tapped holes in each piece, it was discovered to be more economical to have two parts —one with the hole tapped in the top, the other with the hole tapped in the bottom. The two parts were then assembled alternately. Drilling and tapping a hole in each brush holder was eliminated because someone questioned the necessity of performing this operation.

Again, an unnecessary operation may develop because it was thought it would give the product greater sales appeal. One company originally used cast brass name plates for various lines of its products. Although the cast name plate was attractive, it was found that by using instead an

FIG. 4-3. Large gear completely housed so as to maintain constant temperature during hobbing operation.

etched steel name plate the appearance was still kept attractive, and cost was notably reduced.

In order to have a smooth joint in the production of electric fan guards, it was thought necessary to perform a coining operation where the ends of the wire cage were joined by butt welding. By slightly modifying the design, it was possible to place the joined wire ends directly in back of the crossbars of the fan guard, making it impossible to see the joined ends. Since the butt-welded ends could not be seen, it was no longer necessary to perform the coining operation. This design made it difficult to reach the butt-welded portion so that there was no chance of scratching the hands on the rough welded area.

Frequently an unnecessary operation will exist because of inadequate or outmoded tools and equipment. In one shop, an eight-hole jig was used for drilling the holes on a fan-cooled motor frame. This jig was also used for locating and drilling eight of the sixteen holes necessary on an explosion-proof motor. The remaining eight holes had to be laid out prior to drilling. By adopting a new sixteen bushing drill jig, the hand-laying-out operation was eliminated. By asking and answering the question, Can better tooling eliminate an operation?, it was possible to inaugurate improvement.

In an effort to eliminate, combine, or shorten each operation, the analyst should ask and answer the following question: Does an outside supplier's tooling enable him to perform the operation more economi-

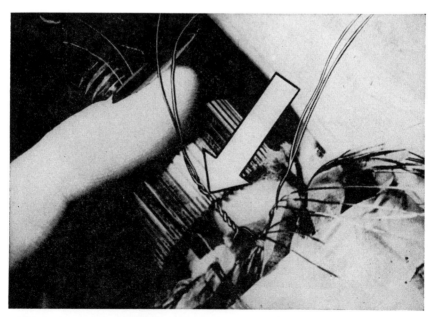

FIG. 4–4. Twisting of wires during commutator winding operation was found unnecessary as correct pair of wires could be placed in proper slot without twisting.

cally? Ball bearings purchased from an outside vendor had to be packed in grease prior to assembly. A study of bearing vendors revealed that "sealed-for-life" bearings could be purchased from another supplier, and at lower cost.

The above examples highlight the desirability of establishing the purpose of each operation before endeavoring to improve the operation. Once the necessity of the operation is determined, then determine how it can be improved by giving consideration to the remaining nine approaches to operation analysis.

Summary: Purpose of Operation

Many operations being performed by every manufacturing establishment and business are unnecessary and can be eliminated if sufficient study be given the procedure or process. Before accepting any operation as being absolutely necessary, the analyst should determine the purpose of the operation. While determining the purpose of the operation "check list" questions should be asked and answered so as to stimulate ideas that may result in the elimination of the operation being studied or some component of it.

DESIGN OF PART

The methods engineer often is inclined to feel that once a design has been accepted his only recourse is to plan its manufacture in the most economical way. Granted, it is usually difficult to introduce even a slight change in design, still a good methods analyst should review every design for possible improvements. Designs are not permanent; they can be changed, and if improvement is the result and the activity of the job is significant, then the change should be made.

To improve the design, the analyst should keep in mind the following pointers for lower-cost designs:

1. Reduce the number of parts, thus simplifying the design.
2. Reduce the number of operations and length of travel in manufacturing by joining parts better and making the machining and assembly easier.
3. Utilize a better material.
4. Rely for accuracy upon "key" operations rather than upon series of closely held limits.

These general observances should be kept in mind as consideration is given to design analysis on each component and each subassembly.

The General Electric Company has summarized the following ideas to be kept in mind for developing minimum cost designs:[2]

---

[2] Reprinted from *American Machinist*, reference sheets (12th ed.; New York: McGraw-Hill Publishing Co., Inc.).

Castings

1. Eliminate dry sand (baked-sand) cores.
2. Minimize depth to obtain flatter castings.
3. Use minimum weight consistent with sufficient thickness to cast without chilling.
4. Choose simple forms.
5. Symmetrical forms produce uniform shrinkage.
6. Liberal radii—no sharp corners.
7. If surfaces are to be accurate with relation to each other, they should be in the same part of the pattern, if possible.
8. Locate parting lines so that they will not affect looks and utility, and need not be ground smooth.
9. Specify multiple patterns instead of single ones.
10. Metal patterns are preferable to wood.
11. Permanent molds instead of metal patterns.

Moldings

1. Eliminate inserts from parts.
2. Design molds with smallest number of parts.
3. Use simple shapes.
4. Locate flash lines so that the flash does not need to be filed and polished.
5. Minimum weight.

Punchings

1. Punched parts instead of molded, cast, machined or fabricated parts.
2. "Nestable" punchings to economize on material.
3. Holes requiring accurate relation to each other to be made by the same die.
4. Design to use coil stock.
5. Punchings designed to have minimum sheared length and maximum die strength with fewest die moves.

Formed Parts

1. Drawn parts instead of spun, welded or forged parts.
2. Shallow draws if possible.
3. Liberal radii on corners.
4. Bent parts instead of drawn.
5. Parts formed of strip or wire instead of punched from sheet.

Fabricated Parts

1. Self-tapping screws instead of standard screws.
2. Drive pins instead of standard screws.
3. Rivets instead of screws.
4. Hollow rivets instead of solid rivets.
5. Spot or projection welding instead of riveting.
6. Welding instead of brazing or soldering.
7. Use die-castings or molded parts instead of fabricated construction requiring several parts.

Machined Parts

1. Use rotary machining processes instead of shaping methods.
2. Use automatic or semi-automatic machining instead of hand-operated.

3. Reduce the number of shoulders.
4. Omit finishes where possible.
5. Use rough finish when satisfactory.
6. Dimension drawings from same point as used by factory in measuring and inspecting.
7. Use centerless grinding instead of between-center grinding.
8. Avoid tapers and formed contours.
9. Allow a radius or undercut at shoulders.

Screw-Machine Parts

1. Eliminate second operation.
2. Use cold-rolled stock.
3. Design for header instead of screw machine.
4. Use rolled threads instead of cut threads.

Welded Parts

1. Fabricated construction instead of castings or forgings.
2. Minimum sizes of welds.
3. Welds made in flat position rather than vertical or overhead.
4. Eliminate chamfering edges before welding.
5. Use "burn-outs" (torch-cut contours) instead of machined contours.
6. Lay out parts to cut to best advantage from standard rectangular plates and avoid scrap.
7. Use intermittent instead of continuous weld.
8. Design for circular or straight-line welding to use automatic machines.

Treatments and Finishes

1. Reduce baking time to minimum.
2. Use air drying instead of baking.
3. Use fewer or thinner coats.
4. Eliminate treatments and finishes entirely.

Assemblies

1. Make assemblies simple.
2. Make assemblies progressive.
3. Make only one assembly and eliminate trial assemblies.
4. Make component parts RIGHT in the first place so that fitting and adjusting will not be required in assembly.
   This means that drawings must be correct, with proper tolerances, and that parts be made according to drawing.

General

1. Reduce number of parts.
2. Reduce number of operations.
3. Reduce length of travel in manufacturing.

When one observes almost any article and thinks back only a few years, the changes of design that have taken place begin to become apparent. The automobile, refrigerator, typewriter, telephone, washing machine, home, watch, toothbrush, lead pencil, all have gone through significant design changes in the past ten years—even the last five years. It is a poor policy to think of any design as being permanent. It is much better to consider that all designs are wrong, and that the only reason they are in effect is because a better design or process has not been discovered.

Figures 4–5 and 4–6 give some examples of good and poor casting and forging design.

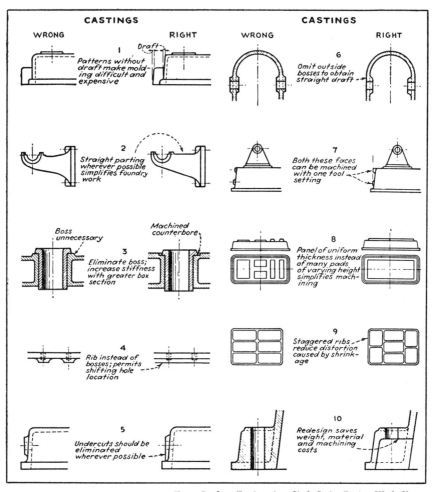

From *Product Engineering*, Sixth Series Design Work Sheets (McGraw-Hill Publishing Co., Inc., 1941), p. 16.

FIG. 4–5. The rights and wrongs of details of castings and forgings.

One manufacturer always used cast-iron brackets on its motors. A methods analyst questioned this design, and this led to the redesign of the bracket, making it from welded sheet steel. Not only was the new design stronger, lighter, and more eye-appealing, but it was less expensive to produce.

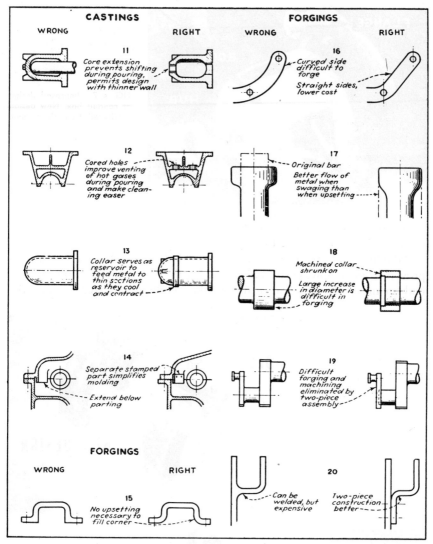

From *Product Engineering*, Sixth Series Design Work Sheets
(McGraw-Hill Publishing Co., Inc., 1941), p. 17.

FIG. 4–6. The rights and wrongs of details of castings and forgings.

A similar design improvement was in the construction of conduit boxes. Originally, they were built of cast iron, whereas, the improved design, making a stronger, neater, lighter, and less expensive conduit box, was fabricated from sheet steel.

In another instance a brass cam switch used in control equipment was made as a brass die casting. By slightly altering the design, the less expensive process of extruding was utilized. The extruded sections were cut to desired length to produce the cam switch.

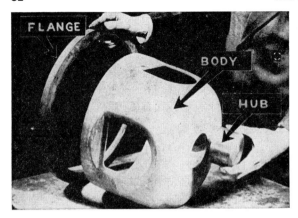

FIG. 4–7. Improved design of conduit box. New design fabricated from sheet steel.

All the above improvements were brought about by considering a better material in an effort to improve the design.

Attaching nuts were originally arc welded to transformer cases. This proved to be a slow, costly operation. Furthermore, the resulting design had an unsightly appearance due to the overflow and spatter from the

FIG. 4–8. *Above:* Redesigned brass cam switch allowing part to be made from extrusion. *Below:* New design shown cut to length from section of brass extrusion.

FIG. 4–9. Projection welding of nuts to surface provides neat-appearing and inexpensive method of joining.

arc-welding process. By projection-welding nuts to the transformer case, not only were time and money saved but the resulting design had considerably more sales appeal.

FIG. 4–10. Mounting bracket changed so that spot welding may be used rather than arc welding. Illustration of bracket arc welded to resistor tube indicates unsightly appearance necessitated through the old method.

A similar improvement was brought about by changing from arc welding to spot welding to join mounting brackets to resistor tubes.

Another example of design simplification through joining parts better was in the assembly of terminal clips to their mating conductors. It had been the policy to turn the end of the clip up to form a socket. This socket was filled with solder, and the wire conductor was then tinned

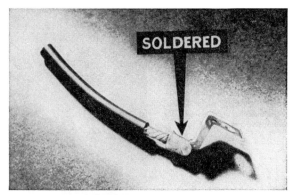

FIG. 4–11. Improved design illustrating resistance welded clip to wire conductor. Old design required tinned and soldered connection.

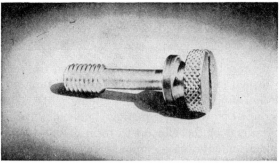

FIG. 4–12. Old design and improved one-piece design of motor cover thumb screw.

and inserted in the solder-filled socket and held until the solder solidified. By altering the design to call for resistance welding the clip to the wire conductor, both the forming and dipping operations were eliminated.

A motor cover thumb screw was originally made of three parts: head, pin, and screw. These components were assembled by joining the head to the screw with the pin. A much less costly thumb screw was developed by redesigning the part for an automatic screw machine which was able to turn out the part complete, with no secondary operations. A simplified design resulted in a less expensive part that still met all service and operating requirements.

The foregoing examples are characteristic of the possibilities for improvement when the design of the part is investigated. It is wise to always check the design for improvement because design changes can be valuable. In order to be able to recognize good design, the methods engineer should have had some training and practical experience in this area. Good designs do not just happen; they are the result of broad experience and creative thinking, tempered with an appreciation of cost.

Summary: Design of Part

Designs should never be regarded as being permanent. Experience has shown that practically every design can be improved. The method analyst should question the present design in order to determine if it is possible to improve it. He should learn to recognize good design and if he encounters poor design, he should assume the responsibility of reporting his findings to the product design department. He should then follow through to assure that the proposed design improvements are carried out.

TOLERANCES AND SPECIFICATIONS

The third of the ten points of operation analysis to be considered in an improvement program is tolerances and specifications. Many times this point is considered in part when reviewing the design. This, however, usually is not adequate, and it is well to consider tolerances and specifications independent of the other approaches to operation analysis.

There is a natural tendency for designers to incorporate more rigid specifications than necessary when developing a product. This is brought about by one or both of two reasons:

1. Lack of appreciation for the elements of cost.
2. The feeling that it is necessary to specify closer tolerances and specifications than actually needed in order to have the manufacturing departments produce to the required tolerance range.

The methods analyst should be versed in the aspects of cost and be fully aware of what unnecessarily close specifications can do to the selling price. If it appears that designers are being needlessly "tight" in establishing tolerances and specifications, it may be wise for management to embark on a training program in which the economies of specifications are clearly presented.

The analyst must be on the alert for too liberal specifications, as well as those that appear too restricted. By closing up a tolerance, it is often possible to facilitate an assembly operation or some other subsequent step. This may be economically sound, even though the time required to perform the present operation has been increased by reducing a manufacturing tolerance.

Beyond the principle of operating economies through correct tolerances and specifications is the consideration of establishing the ideal inspection procedure. Invariably, inspection is a verification of the quantity, the quality, the dimensions, and the performance. Inspection in all of these areas usually can be performed by numerous methods and techniques. One way is usually better, not only from the standpoint of quality control, but also from the time and cost consideration. The methods engineer should question the present way with thought toward improvement.

The possibilities for installation of spot inspection, lot-by-lot inspection or statistical quality control should be considered.

Spot inspection is a periodic check to assure that established standards are being realized. For example, a nonprecision blanking and piercing operation setup on a punch press should have a spot inspection to assure maintenance of size and the absence of burrs. As the die begins to wear or deficiencies in the material being worked begin to show up, the spot inspection would catch the trouble in time to make the necessary changes without the generation of any scrap.

Lot-by-lot inspection is a sampling procedure in which a sample is examined in order to determine the quality of the production run or lot. The size of the sample selected is dependent on the allowable per cent defective and the size of the production lot under check.

Statistical quality control is an analytical tool which is employed to control the desired quality level of the process.

If a 100 per cent inspection is being encountered, it is well to consider the possibility of spot inspection or lot-by-lot inspection. One hundred per cent inspection refers to the process of inspecting every unit of product and rejecting the defective ones. Experience has shown that this type of inspection does not assure a perfect product. The monotony of screening tends to create fatigue, and thus lowers operator attention. There is always a good chance that the inspector will pass some defective parts as well as reject good parts. Because a perfect product is not assured under 100 per cent inspection, acceptable quality may be realized from the considerably more economical methods of either lot-by-lot or spot inspection.

Usually, any elaborate quality control procedure is not justified if the product does not require close tolerances, if its quality is easily checked, and if the generation of defective work is unlikely.

Just as there are several mechanical methods for checking a .500″/.502″ reamed hole, so there are several over-all policy procedures that can be adopted as a means of a control. The methods analyst must be alert and well grounded in the various techniques, so that he can make sound recommendations for improvement.

In one shop a certain automatic polishing operation was found to have a normal rejection quantity of 1 per cent. It would have been quite expensive to subject each lot of polished goods to 100 per cent inspection. It was decided, at an appreciable saving, to consider 1 per cent the allowable per cent defective, even though this quantity of defective material would go through to plating and finishing only to be thrown out in the final inspection before shipment.

The analyst must always be aware of the fact that the reputation and demand for his company's product depend upon the care taken in establishing correct specifications and in maintaining them. Once quality standards are established, no deviations will be permitted. In general, tolerances and specifications can be investigated in these three ways:

1. Are they absolutely correct?
2. Are ideal inspection methods and inspection procedures being used?
3. Are modern quality control techniques being exercised?

One manufacturer's drawings called for a .0005″ tolerance on a shoulder ring for a DC motor shaft. Original specifications called for a 1.8105″ to 1.8110″ tolerance on the inside diameter. It was thought necessary to hold this close tolerance, as the shoulder ring was shrunk on the motor shaft.

An investigation revealed that a .003″ tolerance was adequate for the shrink fit. The drawing was immediately changed to specify a 1.809″ to 1.812″ inside diameter. A reaming operation was saved because someone questioned the absolute necessity of a close tolerance.

In another instance, it was possible to introduce an automatic control on an external cylindrical grinder. Formerly, it was necessary to manually feed the grinding wheel to the required stop. Each piece had to be carefully inspected to assure maintenance of tolerance on the outside diameter. With the automatic machine control, the feed is tripped and the piece released upon completion of the in-feed. The automatic machine control made the operator free to do other work because some methods analyst endeavored to develop an ideal inspection procedure.

In an automatic screw machine shop, it was thought necessary to inspect 100 per cent parts coming off the machine because of the critical tolerance requirements. However, it developed that adequate quality control would be maintained by inspecting every sixth piece. This sampling procedure allowed one inspector to service three machines rather than one machine.

By investigating tolerances and specifications and taking action when desirable, costs of inspection will be reduced, scrap will be minimized, repair costs diminished, and quality will be kept high.

Summary: Tolerances and Specifications

The methods analyst, because of his familiarity with shop operations, is in an ideal position to question the tolerances and specifications as-

FIG. 4–13. Automatic control attached to external cylindrical grinder.

signed to a product. He should well understand the additional cost incurred through establishing close tolerances. Frequently, tolerances and specifications can be liberalized so as to decrease unit cost with no detrimental effects on quality.

In other instances, tolerances and specifications should be made more rigid in order to facilitate certain manufacturing operations.

Occasionally, the method of inspection as well as the inspection procedure can be changed so as to effect savings.

Tolerances and specifications must be investigated carefully by the analyst in order to be assured of a successful operation analysis program.

MATERIAL

One of the first questions an engineer considers when he is designing a new product is, "What material shall I use?" Since the ability to choose the right material is based upon the engineer's knowledge of materials and since it is difficult to choose the correct material because of the great variety of materials available, many times it is possible and practical to incorporate a better and more economical material in an existing design.

There are five considerations that the methods analyst should keep in mind relative to direct and indirect materials utilized in a process. These are:

1. Finding a less expensive material.
2. Finding materials easier to process.
3. Using materials more economically.
4. Possible use of salvage materials.
5. Economical use of supplies and tools.

Finding a Less Expensive Material

Prices of materials can be compared by their basic costs. Monthly publications available to all engineers summarize the approximate cost per pound of steel sheets, bars, and plates, and the cost of cast iron, cast steel, cast aluminum, cast bronze, and other basic materials (see

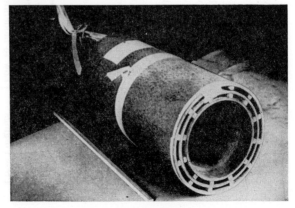

FIG. 4–14. Glass tubing substituted for rectangular micarta bars to separate windings of transformer coils provides substantial savings.

TABLE I

Fabricated Form	Raw Material Costs	Tool and Die Costs	Optimum Lot Sizes
Sand Castings	2½¢ per lb. for iron to 20¢ per lb. for magnesium.	Pattern costs are low as compared to making dies and molds.	Wide range—from 100 to 10,000.
Permanent Mold Castings	Medium cost—aluminum, copper, magnesium alloys most used—iron and steel sometimes used.	Moderate—less than die casting, but more than for other casting methods.	Large quantities—in the thousands.
Plaster Mold Castings	Medium—16¢ aluminum; 18¢ bronze, etc.	Medium—between permanent mold and sand castings.	Short runs—100 to 2,000.
Die Castings	Medium—about 13½¢ per lb. for zinc, other materials somewhat higher.	High—more than other casting methods. Typical dies cost $200 to $5,000.	Large quantities—1,000 to hundreds of thousands.
Precision Castings	High generally—the process is best suited to special alloys which are usually costly.	Low—if model is available; moderate if model must be made.	Wide range, although best for quantities of from 10 to 1,000.
Drop Forgings	Low to moderate—most used steels at a few cents per lb., but alloys up to 55¢ per lb. or more are used.	High—dies must be carefully made to withstand heat and impact—$100 to $1,000 or more.	Lge. quantities—10,000 to 100,000 or more, but used on small quantities when properties are required.
Press Forgings	Low to moderate—compares with drop forgings.	High—but usually somewhat lower than dies for drop forgings.	Medium to high production lots.
Upset Forgings	Low to moderate—as with press and drop forgings.	High—often because of large number of impressions or difficult design.	Medium to high lot production best.
Cold Headed Parts	Low to moderate—6 or 7¢ per lb. for steel wire, up to 35 or 40¢ for other materials.	Medium—sometimes to a few hundred dollars.	Large lots are best.
Stampings, Formed Parts	Low to moderate, ranging from ordinary steel to stainless.	High—$600 to $1,200 is common for dies for small parts—more for large parts.	Large lots—over 10,000 best.

Fabricated Form	Raw Material Costs	Tool and Die Costs	Optimum Lot Sizes
Spinnings	Low to moderate. Steel 3 to 4¢ per lb., up to stainless steel sheet 39 to 50¢ per lb.	Low—form can cost from $25 up to $200.	Quantities under 1,000.
Screw Machine Parts	Low to medium—steel (4 to 5¢ per lb.) most common up to brasses (34 to 50¢), with a few more expensive materials.	Medium—$50 to $200 common tooling cost range.	Large lots best—more than 1,000 essential—the higher the quantity the better.
Powder Metal Parts	Medium to high—powders run 13 to 90¢ per lb. for iron; 20 to 25¢ for copper, 22½ to 30¢ for brass, etc.	Medium—usually more than $100, range $100 to $2,000.	Large lots best to amortize die costs—10,000 pieces. However, small runs may be necessary.
Electro-Formed Parts	Low to high, depending upon the material used: iron lowest, chromium highest.	Medium—master mold doesn't wear out. However, due to small lots die costs may be relatively high.	Best where small lots are involved.
Sectional Tubing	High—invariably 20¢ per lb. or over; some tubing much higher.	Low—cutting is done with simple tools.	Wide range—good for small lots as well as large quantities.
Cut Extrusions	High—usually over 20¢ per lb.	Low—cutting is done with simple tools.	Wide range—useful for large and small quantities.
Impact Extrusions	Moderate—mostly used for aluminum, zinc, lead.	Medium—dies often cost less than $100.	Wide range—quantities can vary from thousands to millions.
Welded or Brazed Assemblies	Low cost materials can be used (carbon, steel, etc.).	Low to moderate—assembly jigs sometimes required.	Small quantities best, although small assemblies can be mass produced at low cost.
Molded Plastics	Medium to high—material varies from 10 to 15¢ per lb. to over $1.00 per lb.	Medium to high—depending upon type of mold or die required; from $100 up, generally.	Large lots—over 5,000 pieces best.
Molded Non-metallic	Moderate to high.	Medium—molds are often rather simple.	Wide—because of need for parts of some materials, quantities must be low.

Courtesy: *Materials and Methods*

Table I). These costs can be used as anchor points from which one can judge the application of new materials. Developments of new processes for producing and refining materials are continuously taking place. Thus, a material that was not competitive in price yesterday may be so today.

In one company, micarta spacer bars were used between windings of transformer coils. They were placed so as to separate the windings and permit circulation of air between the windings. An investigation revealed that glass tubing could be substituted for the micarta bars at a saving. Not only was the glass tubing less expensive, but it met service requirements better because the glass could withstand higher temperatures. Furthermore, the hollow tubing permitted more air circulation than the solid micarta bars.

Another example of starting with a less expensive material that still meets service requirements was in the production of distribution transformers. Originally, a porcelain plate was used to separate and hold the wire leads coming out of the transformers. A fuller board plate was substituted which stood up just as well in service, yet was considerably less expensive.

The methods analyst should keep in mind that such items as valves, relays, air cylinders, transformers, pipe fittings, bearings, couplings, chains, hinges, hardware, and motors can usually be purchased at less cost than they can be manufactured.

FIG. 4–15. Fuller board plate makes economical and effective substitute for porcelain plate to hold wire leads from distribution transformers. Fuller board illustrated below.

Finding a Material Easier to Process

One material is usually more readily processed than another. By referring to handbook data of the physical properties, it is usually easy to discern which material will react most favorably to the process that it must be subjected to in its transposition from raw material to finished product. For example, machinability varies inversely with hardness and hardness usually varies directly with strength.

FIG. 4–16. Packing ivory bars before methods change.

The partial list of properties of materials shown in Table II form the basis on which a material is chosen. The tabulation shows the relation between various materials and properties when one of the variables, such as thickness, stiffness, strength or weight, is held constant.

By keeping the thought in mind of selecting a material that is easy to process, one methods analyst was able to show real savings when he changed the procedure of producing stainless steel bearing shells. Originally, they were made by drilling and boring to size cut lengths of stain-

FIG. 4–17. Packing ivory bars after methods change.

TABLE II

USING STEEL AS 100 FOR COMPARISON

Basis of Comparison	Material	Thickness	Stiffness	Strength	Weight
Equal Thickness......	Structural Steel	100	100	100	100
Equal Thickness......	Alum–52S ½ H	100	34	81	36
Equal Thickness......	Mag. FS–1a	100	22	53	23
Equal Thickness......	Titanium	100	52	200	57
Equal Stiffness.......	Structural Steel	100	100	100	100
Equal Stiffness........	Alum–52S ½ H	143	100	164	51
Equal Stiffness.......	Mag. FS–1a	165	100	143	37
Equal Stiffness.......	Titanium	125	100	312	72
Equal Strength.......	Structural Steel	100	100	100	100
Equal Strength.......	Alum–52S ½ H	111	47	100	40
Equal Strength.......	Mag. FS–1a	137	59	100	31
Equal Strength.......	Titanium	71	19	100	41
Equal Weight........	Structural Steel	100	100	100	100
Equal Weight........	Alum–52S ½ H	281	765	647	100
Equal Weight........	Mag. FS–1a	444	1,954	1,040	100
Equal Weight........	Titanium	173	270	600	100

Source: Data taken from B. W. Niebel and E. N. Baldwin, *Designing for Production.*

less steel bar stock. By specifying stainless steel tubing as a material source, material was conserved, rate of production was increased, and cost of manufacture was reduced.

Using Material More Economically

A fertile field for analysis is the possibility of using material more economically. If the ratio of scrap material to that actually going into the product is high, then consideration should be given to greater utilization.

For example, if a part required 18 inches of 2-inch × 14-gage seamless steel tubing (including the width of the cut-off tool) and random lengths had been supplied, it would be well to specify to the source that this tubing should be delivered in exact multiple lengths of 18 inches. This procedure would prevent short ends being left over.

In the production of stampings from sheet, if the skeleton seems to contain an undue amount of scrap material, it may be possible to go to the next higher standard width of material and utilize a multiple die. If a multiple die is used, care should be exercised in the arrangement of the cuts to assure greatest utilization of material. Figure 4–18 illustrates how careful nesting of parts permit maximum utilization of flat stock.

At one time the Procter and Gamble Company packed bars of Ivory soap into boxes with the opening on the largest face of the cardboard box. This operation is shown in Figure 4–16. Flaps on the four edges of the open case fold over to form a double cover over that part of the box during packing. As the result of a method study, consideration was given to using material more economically. It was found that the bars could be packed satisfactorily, with no increase in time, by passing them

FIG. 4–18. Method of torch cutting heavy gear case side plates. Note nesting of the point and the heel for most effective use of plate.

through an open end. This permitted redesign of the case so that the overlapping of the flaps was at the smallest face of the case, using much less box board. The end packing is shown in Figure 4–17. This change resulted in a substantial reduction in the cost of the container.

Another example of economical use of material is in compression molding of plastic parts. By preweighing the amount of material put into the mold, only the exact amount of material required to fill out the cavity will be used and excessive flash will be eliminated.

Salvage Materials

The possibility of salvaging materials that would otherwise be sold as scrap should not be overlooked. Sometimes by-products resulting from the unworked portion or scrap section offer real possibilities for savings. One manufacturer of stainless steel cooling cabinets had sections of stainless steel 4 to 8 inches wide left as cuttings on the shear. An analysis brought out a by-product of electric light switch plate covers.

Another manufacturer, after salvaging the steel insert from defective bonded rubber wringer rolls, was able to utilize the cylindrical hollow rubber roll as bumpers for protecting motor and sail boats while moored. Figure 4–19 illustrates how one manufacturer used pieces of circular plate scrap to produce needed components.

Courtesy: General Electric Co.

FIG. 4–19. Circular piece is scrap from motor frame head fabrication part. This scrap part is used to produce gusset support pieces for locomotive platform. Lower photo shows Airco No. 50 Travo-graph 8 torch burner cutting gusset support pieces from scrap blank.

If it is not possible to develop a by-product, then scrap materials should be segregated for top scrap prices. Separate bins should be provided in the shop for tool steel, steel, brass, copper, aluminum, and chip haulers and floor sweepers should be instructed to keep the scrap segregated.

It is usually wise to salvage items such as electric light bulbs if large quantities are used. The brass socket should be stored in one area, and after breaking and disposing of the glass bulb, the tungsten filament should be removed and stored separately for greatest residual value.

Wooden boxes from incoming shipments should be saved and the boards sawed to standard lengths for use in making smaller boxes for outgoing shipments. This practice is always economical and is being followed by many large industries today as well as service maintenance centers.

Full Use of Supplies and Tools

Full use of all shop supplies should be encouraged. One manufacturer of dairy equipment introduced the policy that no new welding rod was to be distributed to workers without return of old tips under two inches long. The cost of welding rods was reduced immediately by more than 15 per cent.

It is usually economical to repair by brazing or welding expensive cutting tools such as broaches, special form tools, and milling cutters. If it has been company practice to discard tools of this nature, once broken, it would be well to investigate the potential savings brought about by a tool salvage program.

The unworn portion of grinding wheels, emery discs, and so forth, should be checked for possible use in the plant. Such items as gloves and rags should not be discarded once they are soiled. It is less expensive to store the dirty items in containers to await laundering than to replace them.

Waste of material benefits no one. The methods analyst can make a real contribution to his company by preventing material wastes which today claim about one fifth of our material.

Summary: Material

In every manufacturer's shop, materials constitute a large percentage of the total costs of the products of production. Consequently, the proper selection and use of materials is important, not only from the standpoint of giving the customer a more satisfactory product, but also because by selecting a material which is more economical to process, production will be performed at a lower cost.

Whether the product being produced is chemical, vegetable, or mineral, the chances are that material costs can be reduced and product quality can be improved by asking and answering these questions:

1. Have you re-examined materials specifications for chances to use:

   a. Less expensive materials?

   Eliminate "special" grades whenever possible.

   b. Lighter-gage or less strong materials? Less pure materials?

   Such techniques as corrugating metal sheet to increase rigidity, or changing processing methods to hold dilution of chemicals to a minimum, may achieve real savings.

   c. Stronger materials and more concentrated chemicals?

   This is the reverse of question "*b*," but both possibilities rate consideration.

   d. Lighter-weight materials that can save on handling and shipping?

   Even if they've been considered before, it's worth taking another look at such materials as aluminum, magnesium, resin-impregnated glass fibers, and paper.

   e. Other forms of materials that can cut handling costs?

   For instance, sugar in liquid form can be piped around the plant. It is much easier to handle than bulk sugar in bags, so should be considered even when initial cost is higher.

   f. Standard grades, gages, and formulations in place of special materials that are harder to get—and often harder to process?

   Often a very slight change in part size or shape will make it possible to cut scrap to a minimum while using standard sheet or strip.

   g. Fewer varieties of each material?

   For example, standardizing on half a dozen colors instead of specifying a rainbow can reduce paint and pigment inventory, minimize chances for error, and make matching of colors easier.

   h. Disposable or expendable materials that not only reduce original cost, but save on maintenance and repair?

2. Have you re-examined sources of supply for chances to:

   a. Obtain materials in more convenient quantities?

   b. Obtain better prices, better delivery?

   c. Get help in design and processing?

   d. Work with vendors to help them slice their costs and improve quality?

   e. Buy parts now made in the plant; or make parts now bought?

   Changing labor and equipment situation may have reversed price and production picture which existed when decision on a given part was originally made.

3. Have you re-examined scrap and waste for chances to:

   a. Use waste material in making another part or product?

   b. Replace materials whose scrap cannot be re-used with those which have usable scrap?

   For example, replace thermosetting plastics with thermoplastics that can be remelted.

   c. Use dark-colored and other less easily contaminated materials in place of the light-colored, easily contaminated ones?

   d. Turn waste material into usable by-products?

   For instance, waste sulphur dioxide from refineries is being recovered as usable sulphur; waste pickle liquor is being made into wall board.

4. Are you paying special attention to materials which are easily contaminated, or which evaporate or deteriorate on storage?

   a. Is it possible to eliminate use of such materials?

   b. Could better containers and better storage methods be devised?

   For instance, materials which evaporate should be stored in containers with tight-fitting covers that close automatically.

c. Would a slight change in product specifications and processing methods make it possible to convert such materials into a more stable form as soon as they arrive in the plant?

d. Is corrosion resistance of processing equipment now being used taken into account when new materials are considered?

TEXT QUESTIONS

1. Give a complete definition of operation analysis.
2. How is operation analysis related to methods engineering?
3. Does increased competition submerge the necessity for operation analysis? Explain.
4. Explain the relationship between market price and volume as related to production.
5. What is the major obstacle in the path of the methods engineer?
6. How do unnecessary operations develop in an industry?
7. What four thoughts should the analyst keep in mind in order to improve design?
8. Explain why it may be desirable to "tighten up" in tolerances and specifications.
9. What is meant by lot-by-lot inspection?
10. When is an elaborate quality control procedure not justified?
11. What five points should be considered when endeavoring to reduce material cost?
12. Explain why corrugated metal sheet is more rigid than flat sheet of the same material.
13. How does a changing labor and equipment situation affect the cost of purchased components?

GENERAL QUESTIONS

1. Formulate a check list that would be helpful in improving operations.
2. Show the calculations that indicate that Titanium is .19 as stiff as a section of steel having equal strength when loaded as a beam. Both bars have equal width.
3. Explain how conservation of welding rod can result in 20 per cent material savings.
4. Investigate the operations required to convert waste sulphur dioxide to usable sulphur.

CHAPTER 5

Operation Analysis (Continued)

PROCESS OF MANUFACTURE

JUST AS THERE ARE A GREAT number of materials to select from when designing a part, so there are almost an unlimited number of manufacturing processes to choose from when planning for its production. New and improved methods are constantly being developed. A new process may be developed in one plant to satisfy a particular design or project. Investigation will often reveal several other places in the plant where it could be used to advantage over the existing process. For example, to finish the outside diameter of a product, a setup on an infeed centerless grinder may have been developed. A survey may disclose that the centerless grinding can produce other products faster that were formerly turned down on a lathe, and still have a better machine finish.

No methods analyst can ever expect to learn every process and be informed on the various operations of the equipment and its limitations as to tolerance, capacities, and various applications. However, by keeping the basic fundamentals in mind, he will be in a position to foresee opportunities for improved processes throughout his organization. For example, the requirements of clean surface, proper fusion temperature at joint, and pressure to force the metal together and hold it while cooling, are applicable to forge welding, butt welding, flash welding, spot welding, projection welding, seam welding, and percussion welding.

If the methods analyst understands these fundamental requirements, he will be in a position not only to see possibilities for developing better joining techniques, but will be able to clear up troubles encountered in welding processes. Thus, the methods analyst will find that by grouping

71

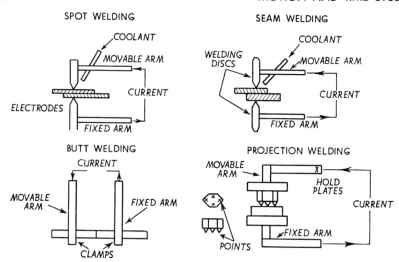

FIG. 5–1. Methods of resistance welding.

the processes under fundamental principles and requirements, the vast varieties of processes can be understood without knowing the detailed construction or characteristics of the process equipment.

It is wise for the methods engineers to review current technical peri-

TABLE III

SIMILAR AND DISSIMILAR METAL COMBINATIONS THAT MAY BE SPOT WELDED

	Aluminum	Ascoloy	Brass	Copper	Gal. Iron	Iron	Lead	Monel	Nickel	Nichrome	Tin Plate	Zinc	Phos. Bronze	Nickel Silver
Aluminum............	o	...	...	...	...	...	...	...	...	...	o	o	...	...
Ascoloy..............	...	o	o	o	o	o	...	o	o	o	o	...	o	o
Brass................	...	o	o	o	o	o	o	o	o	o	o	o	o	o
Copper..............	...	o	o	o	o	o	...	o	o	o	o	o	o	o
Galvanized Iron......	...	o	o	o	o	o	o	o	o	o	o	...	o	o
Iron.................	...	o	o	o	o	o	...	o	o	o	o	...	o	o
Lead................	...	...	...	o	...	o	...	...	...	...	o	o	...	o
Monel...............	...	o	o	o	o	o	...	o	o	o	o	...	o	o
Nickel...............	...	o	o	o	o	o	...	o	o	o	o	...	o	o
Nichrome............	...	o	o	o	o	o	...	o	o	o	o	...	o	o
Tin Plate............	o	o	o	o	o	o	o	o	o	o	o	...	o	o
Zinc.................	o	...	o	o	...	...	o	...	...	...	o	o	...	...
Phos. Bronze.........	...	o	o	o	o	o	...	o	o	o	o	...	o	o
Nickel Silver.........	...	o	o	o	o	o	o	o	o	o	o	...	o	o

Note: The "o" means the metals can be spot welded.

odicals, as ideas for method improvement are often crystallized when he sees "what the other fellow is doing." Possible application for improvements should be clipped and filed for future reference, and in time an invaluable manufacturing methods library can be developed.

By systematically questioning and investigating manufacturing processes, new and better methods will be evolved. It is well for the methods analyst to adopt the philosophy, "There is no best way to do a job—there is always a better way."

From the standpoint of improving the processes of manufacture, investigation should be made in four ways:

1. When changing an operation, consider possible effects on other operations.
2. Mechanize manual operations.
3. Utilize more efficient facilities on mechanical operations.
4. Operate mechanical facilities more efficiently.

Effects on Subsequent Operations by Changing Present Operation

Before changing any operation, it is wise to consider detrimental effects that may result on subsequent operations down the line. Reducing costs of one operation can result in higher costs on others. For example, the following change in manufacturing of A.C. field coils resulted in higher costs and was, therefore, not practical. The field coils were made of heavy copper bands which were formed and then insulated with mica tape. The mica tape was hand wrapped on the already coiled parts. It was thought advantageous to machine wrap the copper bands prior to coiling. This did not prove practical as the forming of the coils cracked the mica tape, and time-consuming repairs were necessitated prior to acceptance.

Rearranging operations often results in savings. The flange of a motor conduit box required four holes to be drilled—one in each corner. Also, the base had to be smooth and flat. Originally, the job was planned by first grinding the base, then drilling the four holes in a drill jig. The drilling operation threw up burrs which had to be removed in the next step. By rearranging operations so that the holes were drilled first, and the base then ground, it was possible to eliminate the deburring operation. The base grinding operation automatically removed the burrs.

By combining operations, costs can usually be reduced. Formerly, the fan motor supports and outlet box of electric fans were completely fabricated, painted separately, and then riveted together. By riveting the outlet box and fan motor support together prior to painting, and then painting the assembly, appreciable savings in time was effected on the painting operation.

Mechanize Manual Operation

Any time heavy manual work is encountered, consideration should be given to possible mechanization. To clean insulation and dried varnish from armature slots, one company resorted to tedious hand filing. By questioning this process of manufacture, an end mill placed in a power air drill was developed. This not only took most of the physical effort out of this job, but allowed a considerable higher rate of production.

The utilization of power assembly tools, such as power nut and screw drivers, electric or air hammers, and mechanical feeders, often are more economical than hand-tool methods.

FIG. 5–2. Machine-wrapped copper bands prove unsatisfactory in manufacture of A.C. field coils. *Top:* Method of forming heavy copper bands. *Center:* Handwrapped field coils. *Bottom:* Cracked insulation in coils machine wrapped prior to forming.

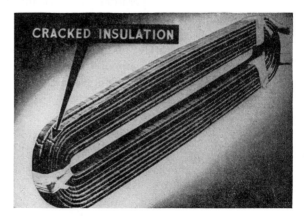

FIG. 5–3. Grinding after drilling automatically removes burrs thrown up in the drilling operation.

FIG. 5–4. This tedious hand-filing operation was improved by performing the operation with an end mill placed in a power air drill.

Utilize More Efficient Machine

Can a more efficient method of machining be used? is a question that should be foremost in the analyst's mind. If the operation is done mechan-

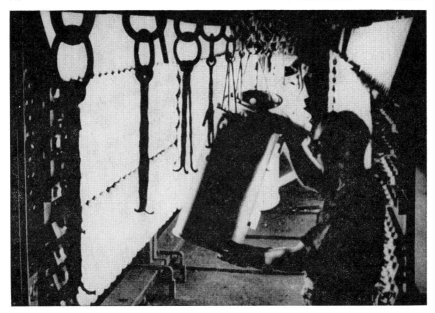

FIG. 5–5. Infrared lamps for drying transformer tanks after painting permitted drying in one twelfth the time of the former method.

ically, there is always the possibility of a more efficient means of mechanization. Let us look at some examples. Turbine blade roots were machined by performing three separate milling operations. Cycle time was high, as well as costs. By means of external broaching, all three surfaces were finished at once. A pronounced saving was the result.

The possibility of utilizing press operation should never be overlooked. This process is one of the fastest for forming and sizing operations. A stamped bracket had four holes that were drilled after the bracket was formed. By designing a die to pierce the holes, the work was performed in a fraction of the drilling time.

Another applicable example of utilizing a more efficient machine was conversion of steam-heated ovens to banks of infrared lamps for drying transformer tanks after painting. The change allowed drying of the same volume of tanks in one twelfth the time.

Operate Mechanical Facilities More Efficiently

A good slogan for the methods analyst to keep in mind is, "Design for two at a time." Usually, multiple die operation in presswork is more economical than single stage operation. Again, multiple cavities in die casting, molding, and similar processes, should always be given consideration when there is sufficient volume.

On machine operations, the analyst should be sure that proper feeds and speeds are being used. He should investigate the grinding of cutting tools so that maximum performance will result. He should check to see if the cuttings tools are properly mounted, if the right lubricant is being used, and if the machine tool is in good condition and is being adequately maintained. Many machine tools are being operated at a fraction of their possible output. Always endeavoring to operate mechanical facilities more efficiently will pay dividends.

Summary: Process of Manufacture

There are usually a number of ways to produce a part. Better production methods are continually being developed. By systematically questioning and investigating manufacturing processes, the analyst is bound to find a more efficient method. Always question the process of manufacture with an idea toward improvement. There is no best way to do a job—there is always a better way.

SETUP AND TOOLS

One of the most important elements which applies to all forms of work holders, tools, and setup is the economic one. The amount of "tooling up" that proves most advantageous depends on:

1. The quantity to be produced.
2. The chance for repeat business.
3. The amount of labor involved.
4. Delivery requirements.
5. Amount of capital required.

One of the most prevalent mistakes made by planners and toolmakers is to tie up money in fixtures which may show a large saving when in use, but which are seldom used. For example, a saving of 10 per cent in direct labor cost on a job in constant use would probably justify greater expense in tools than an 80 or 90 per cent saving on a small job appearing only a few times per year on the production schedule. The economic advantage of lower labor costs is the controlling factor in the determination of the tooling; consequently, jigs and fixtures may be desirable even where only small quantities are involved. Other considerations, such as improved interchangeability, increased accuracy, or reduction of labor trouble, may provide the dominant reason for elaborate tooling, although this usually is not the case.

For example, the production engineer in a machining department has under study a job which is being machined in the shop now. He has devised two alternate methods involving different tooling for this same job. Data on the present and proposed methods follow. Which method would be the most economical in view of the activity? The base pay rate is $1.20 per hour. The estimated activity is 50,000 pieces per year. Fixtures are capitalized and depreciated in five years.

Method	Time Value	Fixture Cost	Tool Cost	Average Tool Life
Present Method........	3.50 min. each	None	$ 6.00	10,000 pieces
No. 1 Alternate........	2.80 min. each	$300.00	$20.00	20,000 pieces
No. 2 Alternate........	1.85 min. each	$600.00	$35.00	5,000 pieces

A cost analysis of the above data would reveal that a unit total cost of $0.0464 represented by alternate method No. 2 is the most economical for the quantity anticipated. The elements of cost entering into this total are as follows:

Method	Unit Direct Labor Cost	Unit Fixture Cost	Unit Tool Cost	Unit Total Cost	Annual Cost
Old Method..........	$0.070	$0	$0.0006	$0.0706	$3,530.00
No. 1 Alternate.......	$0.056	$0.0012	$0.0010	$0.0582	$2,910.00
No. 2 Alternate.......	$0.037	$0.0024	$0.0070	$0.0464	$2,320.00

Once the amount of tooling is determined, or if tooling already exists, the ideal amount needed is determined, then specific points should be kept in mind in order to produce the most favorable designs. Colvin and Haas summarize the following points:[1]

Will the fixture be similar to some other that has been used to advantage? If so, can you improve upon it?

Has the part undergone any previous operations? If so, can you use any of these points to step from?

Is it absolutely necessary to work from any previously bored or finished surface?

Will a table of clamping schemes help you?

Can any stock castings be used for making the fixture?

Would it be of advantage to make a special pattern?

Can the part be quickly placed in the fixture?

Can the part be quickly removed from the fixture?

Is the part held firmly so that it cannot work loose, spring, or chatter while the cut is on?

Always bear in mind that the cut should be against the solid part of the fixture and not against the clamp.

Can more than one part be placed in the fixture and so increase the output?

Can the chips be readily removed from the face of the fixture upon which the part is located or clamped?

Are the clamps on the fixture strong enough to prevent them from buckling when they are tightened down on the work?

In using cams or wedges for binding or clamping the work, always bear in mind that through the vibration or chatter of the fixture or work they are apt to come loose and cause a great deal of damage.

Are there any special wrenches to be designed to go with the fixture?

---

[1] F. H. Colvin and L. L. Haas, *Jigs and Fixtures* (5th ed.; New York: McGraw-Hill Book Co., Inc., 1948), pp. 14–17.

Can you use a reversible key in the milling fixture, and will it fit the millers on which the fixture is to go?

Can a gage be designed, or hardened pins added, to help the operator set the milling cutters or check up on the work?

Must special milling cutters, arbors, or collars be designed to go with the fixture?

Is there plenty of clearance for the arbor collars to pass over the work without striking?

If the fixture is of the rotary type, have you designed an accurate indexing arrangement?

Can the fixture be used on a standard rotary indexing head?

Is the fixture strong enough to prevent any vibration while the cutters are in action?

Can the fixture be made to take in more than one operation? If so, would it be advisable to have it do so, instead of making two fixtures?

Have you, in the designing of the fixture, brought the work as close to the table of the miller as possible?

Can the part be milled in a standard miller vise by making up a set of special jaws and thus doing away with an expensive fixture?

If the part is to be milled at an angle, could the fixture be simplified by using a standard adjustable milling angle?

Is there any danger of injury to the operator through the faulty design of the fixture?

Can lugs be cast on part to be machined to enable you to hold it?

What arrangements have you made to prevent the clamps from turning while they are being tightened on the work?

How many different-sized wrenches must the operator have in order to tighten all clamps? Why will one not do?

Can the work be gaged in the fixture, or must the fixture be cut away so that a micrometer, or snap gage, can be used?

Can you use jack pins to help support the work while it is being milled?

Will a reciprocating fixture be of advantage in getting out production?

Can a profile be used to help the operator in accurately locating the part?

Have you placed springs under all clamps?

In the building up of the fixture are all parts properly screwed and doweled in place? Is there any danger of their working loose?

Are all steel contact points, clamps, etc., hardened?

What kind or class of jigs are you going to design? Will any of the standard jig designs shown help you?

Has the part undergone any previous operation? If so, can you utilize any of these points to start from?

If locating against rough or unfinished surface, is it advisable to have locating points adjustable?

Can any of the clamping schemes shown be used to hold the part securely while it is being drilled and reamed?

Can any of the standard stock castings or patterns shown be used in making the jig, or must you make a special pattern?

Can the work be held down by any of the methods illustrated?

If so, will the results after drilling and reaming be accurate enough?

What takes the thrust of the drill? Can you use any jack pins or screws to support the work while it is being drilled?

Can a drilling angle, as shown, be used to advantage to take care of a hole that is on an angle?

Can the standard wrenches and handles be used with the jig?

Are there any gages to be designed to help the operator get quick and accurate results from the jig?

Can you use a double or triple thread on the screw that holds the work in the jig, so that it will take fewer turns to get the screw out of the way in order to remove the part more quickly?

Are there any loose parts of the jig, such as clamps, that could be made integral with the jig and thus prevent their getting lost?

Have you made a note on the drawing, or have you stamped all loose parts with a symbol indicating the jig that they were made for so that in case they are lost or misplaced they can be returned to the jig when found?

Are all necessary corners rounded?

Is there any danger of the operator's being injured through the faulty design or make-up of the jig?

Can the toolmaker make the jig?

Are your drill bushings so long that it will be necessary to make up extension drills?

Are the legs on the jig long enough to allow the drill, reamer, or pilot of the reamer to pass through the part a reasonable distance without striking the table of the drill press?

Have you provided against clamps turning?

Are all clamps located in such a way as to resist or help resist the pressure of the drill?

Will a profile on the base of the jig help you to locate accurately the part to be drilled?

Have you provided springs under clamps or bushings?

Is the work apt to spring when tightening down on clamps?

If the jig is a rotary jig, is the indexing positive and accurate?

Can you use a straight index pin instead of a tapered one?

If the part can be tapped or spot-faced in the jig to advantage, have you provided large enough slip bushings?

Has the counterbore been provided with stop collars?

Has the drill press the necessary speeds for drilling and reaming all holes? Must it have a tapping attachment also?

Always remember that it is not practical to have several small holes and only one large one to be drilled and reamed in the jig, for the reason that quicker results can be obtained by drilling the small holes on a small drill press, while, if there is only one large one, it would require the jig to be used on a large machine. The question then arises, is it cheaper to drill the large hole in another jig, and will the result, after so drilling, be accurate enough?

Is the jig too heavy to handle?

Setup ties in very closely with the tooling consideration in that the tooling of a job invariably determines the setup and tear-down time. When we speak of setup time, we usually include such items as punching in on the job; procuring instructions, drawings, tools, and material; preparing work stations so that production can begin in the prescribed manner (setting up tools, adjusting stops, setting feeds, speeds, depth of cut, etc.); tearing down the setup; returning tools to crib; cleaning work stations; and punching out on job.

It can readily be seen that setup operations are of extreme importance in the job shop when production runs tend to be small. Even if this type of shop had modern facilities and high effort were put forth, it would still be difficult to meet competition if setups were long because of poor planning and sloppy tooling. When the ratio of setup time to production-run time is high, then the methods analyst will usually be able to develop possibilities for setup and tool improvement.

To develop better methods, the analyst should investigate the setup and tools in these three ways:

1. Reduce setup time by better planning and production control.
2. Design tooling to utilize the full capacity of the machine.
3. Introduce more efficient tooling.

Reduce Setup Time by Better Planning and Production Control

The time spent between making the last piece of the present run and the first piece of the next run represents setup time, and since this time is often difficult to control, it is the portion of the workday that is usually performed least efficiently. This time often can be reduced through effective production control. By making the dispatch section responsible for seeing that the tools, gages, instructions, and materials are provided at the correct time, and that the tools are returned to their respective cribs after job completion, the need for the operator to leave his work area will be eliminated. Thus, the operator will have to perform only the actual setting up and tearing down of the machine. The clerical and routine function of providing drawings, instructions, and tools can be performed by those more familiar with this type of work. Thus, large numbers of requisitions for these requirements can be performed simultaneously and setup time will be minimized.

Another function of production control that should be carefully reviewed for possible improvement is that of scheduling. Considerable setup time can be saved by scheduling like jobs in sequence. For example, if a 1-inch bar stock job is scheduled to a No. 3 Warner and Swasey turret lathe, from the standpoint of setup time, it would be economical to have other 1-inch round bar stock work scheduled to immediately follow the first 1-inch job. This would eliminate collect changing time, and probably minimize the number of tool changes in the square and hex turrets.

Usually, it is advisable to provide duplicate cutting tools for the operator rather than to make him responsible for sharpening his own tools. When it becomes necessary for the operator to get a new tool, the dull one should be turned in to the tool crib attendant and replaced with a sharp one. The benefits of standardization cannot be realized when tool sharpening is the responsibility of the operator.

To minimize down-time, there should be a constant backlog of work ahead of each operative. There should never be any question as to what each operator's next work assignment will be. A technique frequently used to keep the work load apparent to the operator, supervisor, and superintendent is to provide a board over each production facility with three wire clips or pockets to receive work orders. The first clip contains all work orders scheduled ahead, the second clip holds the work orders currently being worked on, while the last clip holds the completed orders. As the dispatcher issues work orders, they are placed in the "work ahead" station. At the same time, he picks up all completed job tickets from the "work completed" station and delivers them to the scheduling department for record. It is obvious that this system assures the operator of a perpetual load in front of him and does not require him to go to his supervisor for his next work assignment.

By making a record of difficult recurring setups, considerable setup time can be saved when repeat business is received. Perhaps the simplest and yet most effective way to compile a record of a setup is to take a photograph of the setup once it is complete. The photograph should be either stapled and filed with the production operation card, or else be placed in a plastic envelope and attached to the tooling prior to storage in the tool crib.

Design Tooling to Utilize the Full Capacity of the Machine

In considering the second point of setup and tools, the analyst should ask, can the work be held to permit all machining operations in one setup? A careful review of many jobs will bring out possibilities for multiple cuts, thus utilizing a greater share of the machine's capacity. For example, it was possible to change a milling setup of a toggle lever so that the six faces were simultaneously milled by five cutters. The old setup required the job to be done in three steps. The part had to be placed in a separate fixture three different times. The new setup reduced the total machining time and increased the accuracy of the relationship between the six machined faces.

Another thought to be kept in mind is the possibility of positioning one part while another is being machined. This opportunity exists on many milling machine jobs where it is possible to conventional mill on one stroke of the table and climb mill on the return stroke. While the operator is loading a fixture at one end of the machine table, a similar fixture is holding a piece being machined by power feed. As the table of the machine returns, the first piece is removed from the machine and the fixture is reloaded. While this internal work is taking place, the machine is cutting the piece in the second fixture.

Introduce More Efficient Tooling

Everyone is aware of the vast number of designs of screw drivers. Each design provides an efficient driver under a particular set of conditions. A screw driver that is efficient under one set of conditions may be very inefficient under another group of conditions.

The analyst should investigate to see if the proper hand tools are being provided and are being used.

More important than proper hand tools are the proper cutting tools. Grinding wheels should be carefully checked to be sure that the right wheel is being used on the job. Excessive grinding wheel wear, poor finish, and slow rate of cutting are characteristics of having selected the wrong wheel.

Carbide tooling offers large savings over high-speed steel tools on many jobs. For example, a 60 per cent saving was realized by changing the milling operation of a magnesium casting. Formerly, the base was milled complete in two operations, using high-speed steel milling cutters. An analysis resulted in employing three carbide-tipped fly-cutters mounted in a special holder so as to mill parts complete. Faster feeds and speeds were possible and surface finish was not impaired.

Selection of the correct drill is important. Just as there are a variety of hand tools—each designed for a specific task, so there are broad varieties of cutting tools—each having its own limited range of application.

The old method for drilling a hole one-half inch in diameter and seven inches deep in a hard steel shaft with a high-speed twist drill resulted in considerable difficulty. It was necessary to back out the drill about twenty times in order to remove the chips and cool the drill. It was not possible to get the coolant to the cutting edge because of the depth of the hole. By utilizing a carbide-tipped V-shaped gun drill with a hole in

FIG. 5–6. This milling machine equipped with three carbide-tipped fly-cutters resulted in a 60 per cent saving over the old milling method.

FIG. 5–7. Carbide-tipped V-shaped gun drill with hole through center for coolant answers deep-hole drilling problem.

the center through which the coolant was pumped, it was possible to drill the hole in about one third the time.

Again, it was possible to greatly reduce the costs of die maintenance

FIG. 5–8. More than 600,000 pieces are produced on this die before resharpening is necessary.

by considering the use of carbide as a die-cutting edge material. To produce a certain stamping, it was necessary to resharpen a die with tool steel cutting edges after every 50,000 pieces. A study of die-cutting edges resulted in an improved die with edges of tungsten carbide. Now, more than 600,000 pieces are produced before resharpening is necessary.

In the introduction of more efficient tooling, develop better methods for holding the work. Be sure that the work is held so that it can be positioned and removed quickly. A quick-acting bench vise has been developed, utilizing the feet to open and close the vise while the hands are engaged in doing useful work. The vise is opened by kicking one foot pedal and is closed by pressing the other foot pedal. Another example of quick clamping is the use of a foot-operated air vise which holds a ball race in position for drilling. As another piece is inserted in the air vise, the finished piece is pushed out.

Summary: Setup and Tools

The extent of tooling justified for any job is determined largely by the number of parts to be produced. On low-activity jobs, only elementary tooling is justified; on high activity, special tooling is required because cost of tooling is prorated over the large number of units. On high-activity work, it is important to bring unit production time down to an absolute minimum. Good setup and tool practice produces worthwhile benefits; it makes the job easier, simpler, and less fatiguing. Time used in analysis of setup and tools will result in better production and improved products at minimum costs.

WORKING CONDITIONS

The methods analyst should accept as part of his responsibility the provision of good, safe, comfortable working conditions. Experience has proved conclusively that plants providing good working conditions will outproduce those that maintain poor conditions. The economic return provided through investment in improved working environment is usually significant. Ideal working conditions will improve the safety record, reduce absenteeism and tardiness, raise employee morale, and improve public relations, in addition to increasing production.

Some common considerations for improving working conditions follow:

1. Improve lighting.
2. Control temperature.
3. Provide for adequate ventilation.
4. Control sound.
5. Promote orderliness, cleanliness, and good housekeeping.

6. Arrange for immediate disposal of irritating and harmful dusts, fumes, gases, and fogs.
7. Provide guards at nip points and points of power transmission.
8. Provide, at cost when necessary, personal protection equipment.
9. Sponsor and enforce a well-formulated first-aid program.

Improve Lighting

The intensity of light required depends primarily on what operations are being performed in the area. It is obvious that a toolmaker or an inspector requires greater intensity of light than would be needed in a storeroom. Glare, quality of light, location of light source, contrasts in color and brightness, flicking and shadows, all must be considered in addition to intensity. Some characteristics of good lighting are as follows:

1. Reduce glare by installing a large number of sources of light to give the total required light output.
2. Enclose filament-type bulbs in opalescent bowls which will reduce glare by spreading the light output over a greater surface.
3. White light, or the composition of average sunlight, is generally considered ideal. A satisfactory approximately white light for most uses can be produced by a filament-type bulb or by a single white fluorescent unit.
4. The correct level of illumination should be provided at all points of the work station which will prohibit all shadow.

The Bausch & Lomb Company reports through its Industrial Vision Service Division that it has been proven to be possible, with a sound vision program, to increase quantity and quality of production by amounts varying between 15 and 20 per cent. If this additional amount of production can be achieved through correct placement of visually skilled individuals, then it follows that at least this amount of production may be sacrified by an outdated lighting program.

Control Temperature

The human body endeavors to maintain a constant temperature of about 98° F. When the body is exposed to unusually high temperatures, large amounts of perspiration evaporate from the skin. During the perspiration process, sodium chloride is carried through the pores of the skin and is left on the skin surface as a residue when evaporation takes place. This represents a direct loss to the system and may create a disturbance to the normal balance of fluids in the body. The result is heat fatigue and heat cramps, with accompanying slowdown in production.

Conversely, detailed time studies have repeatedly brought to attention the loss in production when working conditions are unduly cold. Temperature should be controlled so that it will be between 65 and 75° F. the year round. If this level can be maintained, losses and slowdowns from heat fatigue, heat cramps, and lack of manipulative dexterity will be kept to a minimum.

Provide for Adequate Ventilation

Ventilation also plays an important role in the control of accidents and operator fatigue. It has been found that disagreeable fumes, gases, dusts, and odors cause fatigue that definitely taxes the physical efficiency of the worker and often creates a mental tension. Laboratory findings indicate that the depressing influence of poor ventilation is associated with air movement as well as temperature and humidity.

When humidity increases, evaporative cooling decreases rapidly, thus reducing the ability of the body to dissipate heat. Under these conditions high heart rates, high body temperatures, and slow recovery after work result in pronounced fatigue.

The New York State Commission of Ventilation disclosed that in heavy manual labor 15 per cent less work was done at 75° F. with 50 per cent relative humidity than was done at 68° F. with the same humidity; and 28 per cent less work was done at 86° F. with 80 per cent relative humidity. It was also brought out that 9 per cent less work was accomplished in stagnant air than in fresh air when the temperature and humidity remained constant. Further experiments showed a reduced work capacity of 17 per cent at 75° F. and 37 per cent at 86° F. when compared with work done at 68° F.

Similar experiments made by the American Society of Heating and Ventilating Engineers show similar gains in production, safety, and employee morale that follow when ideal ventilation is introduced to the production floor.

Control Sound

Both loud and monotonous noises are conducive to worker fatigue. Constant and intermittant noise also tends to excite the worker emotionally, resulting in loss of temper and difficulty in doing precision work. Quarrels and poor conduct on the part of workmen often can be attributed to disturbing noises. Tests have proven that irritating noise levels heighten the pulse rate and blood pressure and result in irregularities in heart rhythm. The nervous system of the body, in order to overcome the effect of noise, is strained, resulting in neurasthenic states.

Noise levels should be controlled in order to maintain good worker efficiency and morale. It is difficult to control the noise on many operations such as pneumatic hammers, steam forging presses, and woodworking machinery such as planers and jointers. In some instances more quietly operating facilities may be substituted for those operating at a higher noise level. For example, a hydraulic-operated riveter may be substituted for pneumatic equipment, or electrically operated apparatus may be quieter than steam. In any case, noise levels can be controlled to some extent by insulating the surrounding walls and ceiling and the equipment itself to prevent the telegraphing of noise and to control vibration. Insulated noisy work areas free the surrounding work areas from distracting sounds.

Promote Orderliness, Cleanliness, and Good Housekeeping

A good industrial housekeeping program will:

1. Diminish fire hazards.
2. Reduce accidents.
3. Conserve floor space.
4. Improve employee morale.

Industrial accident statistics indicate that a large percentage of accidents are the result of poor housekeeping practice. Many times the phrase, "A place for everything, and everything in its place," has been cited as the basis for orderliness. This is true, and the methods analyst should be sure that a place is provided for everything and, if necessary, follow through with supervision to see that everything is in its place.

When the general layout of a plant shows management and supervision's desire to have orderliness, cleanliness, and good housekeeping, then the employees will tend to follow the example set for them, and they will practice good housekeeping themselves.

Arrange for Disposal of Irritating and Harmful Dusts, Fumes, Gases, and Fogs

Dusts, fumes, gases, vapors, and fogs generated by various industrial processes constitute one of the major dangers encountered by the workmen. The following classification of dusts alone, prepared by the National Safety Council, gives an indication of the problem:

1. Irritating dusts, such as metal and rock dusts.
2. Corrosive dusts, such as from soda and lime.
3. Poisonous dusts, such as from lead, arsenic, or mercury.
4. Dusts from fur, feathers, and hair may carry disease germs which may infect the worker.

All of these maladies can be either removed or rendered harmless by employing such methods as exhaust systems, complete enclosing of process, wet or absorbing techniques, and complete protection of operator through personal respiratory protective equipment. Probably the most effective measure for controlling dust and fumes is through local exhaust systems wherein a hood is installed for collection of the substance to be removed right at the point of generation. A fan draws the contaminated air through metal pipes or ducts to the outside or to some properly provided place for disposal. The diameter of the exhaust pipe is an important detail that must be determined in order to insure a satisfactory installation. Generally, the larger the exhaust pipe, the more costly the initial installation. However, larger pipes allow increased efficiency of the motive system since they require less power for the exhaust of air (see Table IV).

TABLE IV

Diameter of Buffing Wheels	Maximum Grinding Surface Sq. In.	Minimum Diameter of Pipe In.
6 in. or less, not over 1 in. thick......................	19	3
7 to 9 in., inclusive, not over 1½ in. thick............	43	3½
10 to 16 in., inclusive, not over 2 in. thick............	101	4
17 to 19 in., inclusive, not over 3 in. thick............	180	4½
20 to 24 in., inclusive, not over 4 in. thick............	302	5
25 to 30 in., inclusive, not over 5 in. thick............	472	6

Source: National Safety Council Safe Practices Pamphlet No. 32.

The analyst can consider the utilization of the dust or fumes that are collected. Perhaps wood dust can be used as a source of heat as can blast furnace gases and others containing carbon monoxide. One manufacturer in the lead industry claims that he salvages enough lead annually to more than pay for the operation of his exhaust system.

Provide Guards at Nip Points and Points of Power Transmission

In the majority of the states, the employer is legally responsible for the proper guarding of his facilities, so that his employees may be protected. Guards must be designed correctly if they are to provide protection and still not hinder production. The general requisites of good guarding are:

1. Effectively protects employee.
2. Permits normal operation of the facility at a pace equal to, or greater than, that used prior to the guard installation.
3. Permits normal maintenance to the facility.

Since the machine tool builder is in an ideal position to provide satisfactory guards, it is usually advantageous to purchase necessary guards at the same time that the machines are procured. Although many homemade guards are doing an excellent job, they are not usually as efficient, attractive, or as inexpensive as a purchased unit.

Production workers are fully aware that unguarded machinery is hazardous. If they are exposed to such working conditions, there will be a natural tendency to execute at low effort as a precautionary measure. Also, an employer who fails to spend any reasonable amount to remove a visible hazard cannot expect full co-operation from his employees.

Provide at Cost Necessary Personal Protective Equipment

It is not always possible to eliminate certain hazards by revision of methods, equipment, and tools because of economic considerations. When this condition occurs, the operator can often be fully protected by personal protective equipment. Representative personal protective equipment would include goggles, faceshields, welding helmets, aprons, jackets, trousers, leggings, gloves, shoes, and respiratory equipment.

So as to be assured that operating personnel will conscientiously use protective equipment, it should either be furnished to the employee at cost, or be provided for him at no expense. The policy of the company to absorb completely the cost of personal protective equipment is be-

Courtesy: L. & J. Press Corp.

FIG. 5–9. Work station showing a press operation. Notice sweep guard which prevents operators' hands from being in the danger zone when the die is closed. Also note light which allows adequate illumination at work station.

coming more and more common. Ernest Dunnick, Chief Industrial Engineer of the Titan Metal Company, reports that eye injuries have almost been eliminated in his plant since goggles furnished by the company have become mandatory throughout the operating divisions. Innumerable cases can be cited where personal protective equipment has saved an eye, hand, foot, and a life. For example, one steel company reported that twenty fatalities were prevented in one year by enforced wearing of company-provided helmets. A northwest lumber company reported, too, that six serious head injuries were prevented within a twenty-day period through the use of protective hats.

Sponsor and Enforce a Well-formulated First-aid Program

The most advanced program in industrial safety will never be able to eliminate completely all accidents and injuries. In order to care adequately for the injuries that do occur, a well-formulated first-aid program is essential. This will include training and publicity, so that the employees will be fully aware of the danger of infection and ease of avoidance of infection through first aid. Also, a complete procedure to be followed in case of injury must be arranged, with proper instruction to all supervisory levels. A well-equipped first-aid room must be provided to care for injured and ill employees until medical aid is available.

Summary: Working Conditions

Working conditions are continually being improved to make plants clean, healthy, and safe. Good working conditions are reflected in health, output, quality of work, and workers' morale. A better place to work results in better products at lower prices.

MATERIAL HANDLING

The eighth primary approach to operation analysis is material handling. Material handling is not new. Through the years, industry has recognized the application of the old principles of mechanics—the lever, the wheel, and the inclined plane to make the job of moving, shifting, lifting, and carrying easier and faster. Today, material handling has grown into a full science of methods and equipment, which ties together productive and nonproductive operations and makes them a large production unit. The American Material Handling Society defines material handling as being the "art and science involving the movement, packaging, and storing of substances in any form." It will be noted that this definition takes into consideration the smallest particle to the largest unit that can be moved. The methods analyst must realize that the handling of material is an essential part of an operation, and usually consumes the major share of the time of that operation. Also, material handling adds nothing but cost to the product, and the more of it that can be diminished, the more competitive will be the product.

The tangible and intangible benefits of material handling can be reduced to four major objectives, as outlined by the American Material Handling Society. These are:

1. Reduction of handling costs
    a) Reduction of labor costs
    b) Reduction of material costs
    c) Reduction of overhead costs
2. Increase of capacity
    a) Increase of production
    b) Increase of storage capacity
    c) Improved layout
3. Improvement in working conditions
    a) Increase in safety
    b) Reduction of fatigue
    c) Improved personnel comforts
4. Better distribution
    a) Improvement in handling system
    b) Improvement in routing facilities
    c) Strategic location of storage facilities
    d) Improvement in user service
    e) Increase in availability of product

An axiom that the methods analyst should always keep in mind is that the best handled part is the least manually handled part. Whether distances of moves are large or small, the methods analyst should study them with thought toward improvement. By giving considerations to these four points, it is possible to reduce the time and energy spent in the handling of material:

1. Reduce the time spent in picking up material.
2. Reduce material handling by using mechanical equipment.
3. Make better use of existing handling facilities.
4. Handle material with greater care.

Reduce Time Spent in Picking up Material

Many people think of material handling only as transportation and neglect to consider positioning at the work station. It is equally important, and since it is often overlooked, it may offer even greater opportunities for savings than transportation. The job of reducing time spent in picking up material is to minimize tiring, costly manual handling at machine or workplace. It gives the operator a chance to do his job faster and with less fatigue and also with greater safety.

Consider the possibility of avoiding loose piling on the floor. Perhaps the material can be stacked directly on pallets or skids after being processed at the work station. This can result in substantial reduction of terminal transportation time (time material handling equipment stands

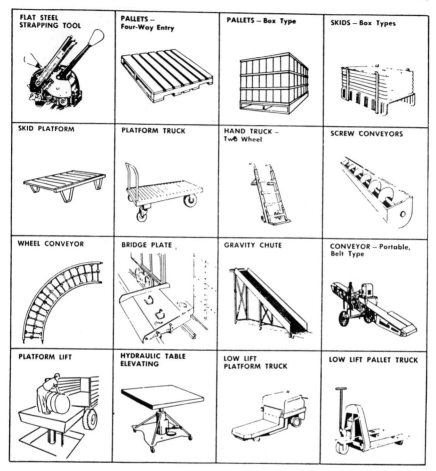

FIG. 5–10. Typical handling equipment used in industry today.

idle while loading and unloading take place). In fact, a good axiom to remember is, if terminal time is long in the transportation of any material, then an improved material handling installation is needed. A good example of reducing terminal time to a minimum is utilization of an electromagnet on a crane to lift ferrous loads. The crane is tied up a negligible amount of time at the terminal points. Usually, some type of conveyor or mechanical fingers can be used to bring material to the work station and thus avoid or reduce the time spent in picking up the material. Often gravity conveyors, used in conjunction with automatic removal of finished parts, can be installed, thus minimizing material handling at the work station.

Several types of positioning equipment are available to reduce the time spent in handling material to and from the work station. Hydraulic

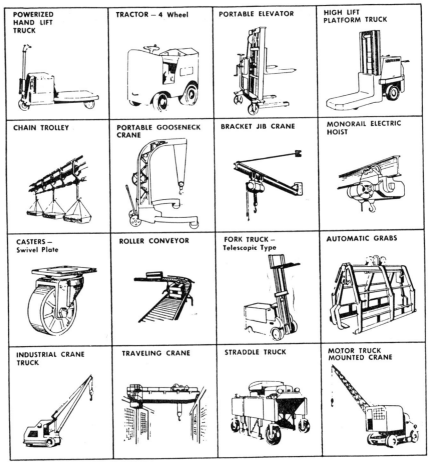

Courtesy: The Material Handling Institute

FIG. 5–11. Typical handling equipment used in industry today.

tables that can place sheets of material at proper feeding height for shears, presses, brakes, and other machines, as well as transport, and bring to position dies and other heavy tools, often have application. The portable elevator or positioning truck is an elevating mechanism supported on a truck mast and base. The hoisting unit is either motorized or has a winch mechanism. Another well-known positioning aid is the welding positioner. Latest models provide for powered rotation and elevation of materials to permit downhand welding motions.

The Bethlehem Steel Company in their Lebanon, Pennsylvania, plant recently installed a strip-feeding table to position metal strip at the shear punch in their cold rolled department.[2] The twenty-four foot table is

---

[2] "Handling Shorts," *Factory Management and Maintenance*, Plant Operation Library No. 134, *Better Material Handling, a $2-Billion Target*.

expected to pay for itself within four years. Again, the Erie Malleable Iron Company of Erie, Pennsylvania, by installation of a positioning table was able to reduce the man-minutes required to load a stack of annealing pots from thirty to ten.[3]

Reduce Material Handling by Using Mechanical Equipment

By mechanizing the handling of material, labor costs will usually be reduced, safety improved, fatigue alleviated, and production increased. However, care must be exercised on proper selection of equipment and methods. Standardization of equipment is important because operator training is simplified, interchangeability of equipment is provided, and less stocking of repair parts is needed.

The savings possible through mechanization of material handling equipment are typified by the following examples. One plant installed a monorail hoist over two workplaces and a paint basin. Formerly, 25 tons of tools in process were transported weekly by hand. The return of the monorail installation investment was estimated at 200 per cent the first year. In another instance, a 100 per cent investment return was realized by moving one heavy cut-off saw close to another cut-off saw, and then furnishing a jib crane to service the two saws.

Make Better Use of Existing Handling Facilities

In order to assure greatest return from material handling equipment, it must be used effectively. By palletizing material in temporary and permanent storage, greater quantities can be transported and can be transported faster than when stored without the use of pallets. The United Wallpaper, Inc., was able to realize the following gross direct labor savings through palletizing and mechanical material handling:

1. Reduced labor cost of warehousing finished stock 66 per cent.
2. Reduced labor cost of assembling and shipping finished goods orders 30 to 65 per cent.
3. Reduced labor cost of unloading and warehousing raw stock 80 per cent.
4. Reduced labor cost of unloading and warehousing other raw materials 40 per cent.[4]

Sometimes, it may be possible to design special racks so that the material can be handled in larger or more convenient units. When this is done, the compartments, hooks, pins, or supports for holding the work should be in multiples of ten for ease of count during processing and final inspection.

If any material handling equipment is used only a portion of the time,

[3] Donald W. Pennock, "Positioners: for Better Handling at the Workplace," *Factory Management and Maintenance*, Plant Operation Library No. 134, *Better Material Handling, a $2-Billion Target*.

[4] Philip F. Cannon, "Palletizing Makes New Warehousing System Really Work," *Factory Management and Maintenance*, Plant Operation Library No. 134.

consider possibilities for putting it to use a greater share of the time. By relocating production facilities or adapting material handling equipment for diversified areas of work, greater utilization may be achieved.

Handle Parts with Greater Care

Industrial surveys indicate that approximately 40 per cent of plant accidents are a result of material handling operations. Of this, 25 per cent are caused by the lifting and shifting of material. When care is exercised in the handling of material and when the physical effort of material handling is transferred to mechanical mechanisms, fatigue and accidents are reduced. Records prove that the safe factory is also an efficient factory. Although it is factual knowledge that the greater the amount of mechanized material handling, the safer the factory is, the analyst must consider the possibility of making the handling equipment safer, too. Safety guards at points of power transmission, safe operating practices, good lighting, and good housekeeping are essential to make material handling equipment safer.

It is often wise to consider the reduction of product damage by better handling. If the number of reject parts is at all significant in the handling of parts between work stations, then this area should be investigated. Usually, damage to parts in handling can be kept to a minimum if specially designed racks or trays are fabricated to hold the parts immediately after being processed. For example, one manufacturer of aircraft engine parts incurred a sizable number of damaged external threads on one component that was stored in metal tote pans after completion of each operation. When the tote pans filled with parts were moved to the next work station by two-wheeled hand trucks, the machined forgings bumped against each other and the sides of the metal pan to such an extent that they became badly damaged. Someone investigated the cause of the rejects and suggested making wooden racks with individual compartments to support the machined forgings. This prevented the parts from bumping against one another and against the sides of the metal tote pan. Production runs were also more easily controlled in view of faster counting of parts and rejects.

Summary: Material Handling

The analyst should always be on the alert to eliminate inefficient handling of material. Harry E. Stocker covers the following principles that should be considered in doing a better job in materials handling:[5]

1. Maximum economy is obtained in handling materials by reducing the terminal time of materials handling equipment to the minimum.
2. Economy in handling obtained as the size of the handling unit is in-

[5] Harry E. Stocker, *Materials Handling* (2nd ed.; New York: Prentice-Hall, Inc., 1951).

creased, whether this be the package prepared by the shipper or a handling unit made up at the terminal by the shipping company.

3. Economy in materials handling is determined by performance, which is measured by comparative expense per unit of material handled.
4. The determination of the best practice under particular conditions is necessary to maximum economy.
5. Economy is obtained when equipment and methods are replaced by new equipment and methods, if the expense of the replacement is exceeded by economies effected within a reasonable time.
6. Economy in materials handling is obtained by the use of equipment and methods that are capable of a variety of uses or application.
7. Economy is obtained as the speed of the materials handling equipment is increased, provided the cost of the increased speed is exceeded by the savings effected.
8. Economy is obtained as the ratio of dead weight of equipment to load carried is reduced.
9. Productivity of equipment is increased by the provision of automatic couplers, nonfriction bearings, rubber tires, and other equipment details best suited to conditions.
10. The productivity of equipment is increased if repairs and replacements are anticipated.
11. Productivity is increased as safe working conditions are provided.
12. Economy in handling materials is obtained if they are moved in a straight line.
13. The productivity of men is increased as fatigue is reduced by provision of mechanical equipment and other aids to the reduction of fatigue.
14. The unit expense of handling materials decreases as the quantity to be handled increases.
15. The unit expense of material handling increases as the quantity to be transported exceeds the capacity of the plant.
16. Economy is obtained when materials are moved by gravity.

It may be well to reiterate that the predominant principle to be kept in mind is that the less a material is manually handled, the better it is handled.

PLANT LAYOUT

Good plant layout involves designing a plan to place the right equipment in a manner and location that will introduce maximum economy during manufacturing processing.

Although it is difficult and costly to make changes in arrangements that already exist, the methods analyst should be trained to review with a critical eye every portion of every layout that he comes in contact with. Poor plant layouts result in major costs, and unfortunately, most of these costs are hidden and, consequently, cannot be readily exposed. Indirect labor expense of long moves, backtracking, delays, and work stoppage due to bottlenecks are characteristic of a plant that has an antiquated plant layout.

Layout Types

In general, all plant layouts represent one or a combination of two basic types of layout. These are product or straight-line layouts and process or functional arrangements. In the straight-line layout, the machinery is located so that the flow from one operation to the next is minimized for any product class. Thus, in an organization that utilizes this technique, it would not be unusual to see a surface grinder located between a milling machine and a turret lathe with an assembly bench and plating tanks in the immediate area. This type of layout for certain mass-production manufacture is quite popular because material handling costs are lower than when process grouping of facilities is practiced.

There are some distinct disadvantages of product grouping which should be kept in mind before making any major change in plant layout. Since a broad variety of occupations are represented in a small area, employee discontent can readily be fostered. This is especially true when the different opportunities carry a significant money rate differential. Because unlike facilities are grouped together, operator training becomes more cumbersome since no experienced employee on a given facility may be located in the immediate area to train the new man. The problem of finding competent supervisors is also enhanced, due to the variety of facilities and jobs that must be supervised. Then, too, this type of layout invariably necessitates greater initial investment in view of duplicate service lines required, such as air, water, gas, oil, and power. Another disadvantage of product grouping that can result in indirect costs is the fact that this arrangement of facilities tends to give the casual observer the thought that disorder and chaos prevail. With these conditions, it is often difficult to promote good housekeeping.

In general, the disadvantages of product grouping are more than offset by the advantages if production requirements are substantial.

Process or functional layout is the grouping of similar facilities. Thus, all turret lathes will be grouped in one section, department, or building. Milling machines, drill presses, and punch presses would also be grouped in their respective sections.

This type of arrangement gives a general appearance of neatness and orderliness, and tends to promote good housekeeping. Another advantage of functional layout is the ease with which a new man can be trained. Since he is surrounded by experienced men operating similar machines, he has the opportunity to learn from them. The problem of finding competent supervisors is lessened because the job demands are not as great with this type of grouping. Since a man need be familiar with but one general type or class of facilities, his background does not have to be nearly as extensive as that of a supervisor in a shop using product grouping.

Of course, the obvious disadvantage of process grouping is the chance for long moves and backtracking on jobs that require a series of operations on diversified machines. For example, if the operation card of a job specified a sequence of drill, turn, mill, ream, and grind, the movement of the material from one section to the next could prove extremely costly. Another major disadvantage of process grouping is the great volume of paper work required to issue orders and control production between sections.

Usually, if production quantities of similar products are limited and the plant is "job" or special order in form, then a process type of layout will be more satisfactory.

No two plants have completely identical layouts, even though the nature of their operations are similar. Many times, a combination of process grouping and product grouping is in order. Regardless of what type of grouping is contemplated, the analyst should consider the following principal points for layout improvement:

1. For straight-line mass production—material laid aside should be in position for the next operation.
2. For diversified production—the layout should permit short moves and deliveries, and the material should be convenient to the operator.
3. For multiple machine operations—equipment should be grouped around the operator.
4. For efficient stacking—storage areas should be arranged to minimize searching and rehandling.
5. For better worker efficiency—service centers should be located close to production areas.

Making the Layout

Before a new layout can be designed or an old one corrected, the methods analyst will have to accumulate all facts that directly and indirectly influence the layout. These will include many, if not all, of the following:

1. Present and anticipated sales volume of each product, line or class.
2. Labor content of each operation on each product.
3. Complete inventory of existing machines and material handling equipment.
4. Status of existing facilities from the standpoint of condition and book value.
5. Possible changes in product design.
6. Drawings of existing plant indicating location of all service facilities, windows, doors, columns, and reinforced areas.

Once all of these facts are gathered, the analyst should then construct a flow process chart (see Chapter 3), which in itself gives the general form the layout will take. In the construction of the flow chart, suggestions should be encouraged from operators, inspectors, material handlers, and line supervisors. These men are closer to the production work than anyone else, and they will often provide valuable suggestions. Then, too, if they are brought into the picture at an early stage, they will be a lot more enthusiastic when the revised layout is actually introduced.

In the making of the proposed layout, templates must be prepared of all facilities. There are several possibilities in the construction of the templates which are usually constructed to a scale of one-fourth inch equals one foot, unless the size of the project is quite large, when a scale of one-eighth inch equals one foot may be used. If an existing layout is available, a blueprint can be made of it and all facilities are cut out of the print for use as templates. If no layout exists, two-dimensional templates can be purchased in printed form, as illustrated in Figure 5–12. Of course, the analyst can draw his own templates on a good grade of stiff cardboard and cut them out. The advantages of using stiff cardboard are apparent if the same templates are to be used several times.

The American Society of Mechanical Engineers has recommended the adoption of national standards on plant layout templates and models. These recommendations are herewith stated:[6]

PART I. TEMPLATES

1) *Scale.* All template shall be drawn to a scale of ¼″ equal to 12″ of full scale or ¼″ equal to 1 ft., U.S. measure. All dimensions shall be shown in feet and inches.

2) *General Outline.* Outline of the equipment in heavy line indicating the contour as it would be described on the floor if a plumb line held at a height of 7 ft. above the floor were to be followed around the periphery of the equipment and touching every extremity point when making a complete circle of the equipment, except for wheels or handles, etc., which should be indicated as a detail. (See recommended lines below.)

Thick	Fixed outline of machine tool or equipment from floor level to 7′–0″ elevation above floor level
Thin	Detail parts and substructures
Thick Dash	Clearances for moving parts of machine tools or equipment
Medium Dot and Dash	Overhead or underground elements—foundations, pits, service clearances and other elements important to the template
Thin Center Line	Center lines

3) *Detail.* Particularly on machine tools and mechanical equipment, center lines, loading points, control points, and operating points should be indicated using a lighter line than used for the machine outline. Enough detail of plan view features should be included within the outline of the template to make it clearly distinguishable and important points easily located.

---

[6] Extracted from *ASME Plant Layout Templates and Models, 1949, Standard*, with permission of the publisher, The American Society of Mechanical Engineers, 29 West 39th St., New York, N.Y.

4) *Clearance.* All clearance lines including movable parts, service access points and clearances required for feeding or operating should be shown in broken dash lines. Space allowed for material storage and other purposes, not required specifically for the equipment installation, service or operation *should not* be included in the template.

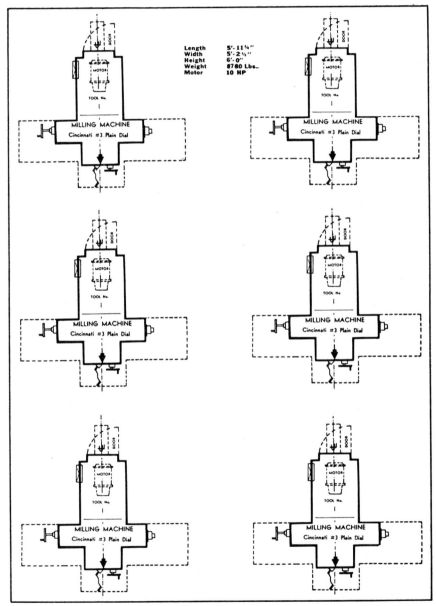

Courtesy: Triometric, Inc.

FIG. 5–12. Standard templates of Cincinnati No. 3 plain dial milling machine.

5) *Interferences.*   Parts or structures above the 7 ft. height, or foundations or substructures below floor level, should also be indicated. These are usually of importance to the installation or operation of the machine or might serve as obstructions. It is usually required that they be shown on final drawings. These features should be drawn in light broken lines of a different character than clearance lines.

6) *Data.*   On templates of equipment with top surface of varying height, the point of maximum height should be indicated on the templates with a suitable symbol. The over-all length, width, and height, including machine travel clearances, but not including operating or feeding clearances, also weight and horsepower, should be specified on or adjacent to the template.

7) *Identification.*   Space should be provided on the template to specify the name, style or model, size, and user's identifying number.

8) *Miscellaneous.*   Indication of controls, service facilities, connection points, or conduit or pipe risers, operator's position, and any other special feature should also be included on the template or included in the data. The operator's position should be indicated by a heavy arrow (⟶).

9) *Printing.*   Templates should be printed on both white and colored stock of at least 110 lb. weight, index bristol or equivalent. Various classes of equipment should be printed with black ink on stock of distinctive colors to permit ease of perception. Colors for colored stock templates are:

Class	*Color*
Machine tools, mechanical equipment, and similar devices	Salmon
Office equipment; stationary equipment, such as benches, bins, racks, lockers; service facilities, such as lavatories, toilets, etc.	Green
Material handling equipment	Yellow
Space occupying portable auxiliaries used for material handling or temporary storage (such as skids, tote pans, pallets, trays, etc.)	Red

PART II.   MODELS

10) *Scale.*   All models shall be made to a scale of ¼ in. equal to 12 in. of full scale or ¼ in. equal to 1 ft., U.S. measure.

11) *Detail.*   The amount of detail to be designed into the model shall be governed by its utilitarian value. Sufficient detail as to form, shape, contours, special design features, etc., should appear to make the model readily distinguishable as representative of the actual equipment. Unless no other means of detailing are possible, no moving parts should be designed into the model. All points of control should be clearly indicated. Hazard areas should be clearly indicated. All normally moving parts should be shown in mid-point or neutral positions. Models should in no way be distorted from actual appearance of the equipment represented.

12) *Finishes.*   All models prepared for distribution commercially shall be finished with materials and in colors, duplicating as nearly as practical the finishes most frequently used in the object represented. Where there is a multiplicity of finishes normally used, models can be finished correspondingly. (Example, office furniture.) In the case of machine tools, the manufacturer's standard should be followed insofar as practical or the recommendations of the Machine Tool Builders Association.

In the case of equipment having machined surfaces, these can be indicated with aluminum paint.

Control points can be indicated by application of light-buff paint as recommended for two-tone painting of equipment for better visibility and safety.

Where models are made and/or used exclusively by one company or client, their particular practice should be followed.

13) *Allowances and Clearances.* No dimensions should be exaggerated in the model to allow for clearances. With each three-dimensional model shall be provided a two-dimensional template showing all clearances required under extreme operating and service conditions of the machine proper. The template shall not show requirements of operator, materials, auxiliaries not fixed to the machine, or other conditions not required in the basic machine or equipment. The template shall be imprinted with all pertinent information required by the planning engineer and shall include or provide for at least the following information: Name or description, model number, type, size, owner's identification number, maximum clearance dimensions (length, width, height), center lines and weight. Where the template is too small practically to contain all the foregoing information, the name and model number only shall be provided. Where possible, data on overhead or underground requirements should be shown.

NOTE: See Part I (of the Standard) covering plant layout templates.

14) *Materials and Construction.* Models shall be made of any suitable material that will permit normal handling without distortion or damage to finish. It should resist fracture or spalling when coming in contact with other models or materials in general. It should resist breakage or distortion when dropped from a height of 2 ft. onto a solid hard surface. Models should have sufficient weight and balance to remain in position when normally arranged and subject to slight jarring or vibrations. The base of the model should be so designed as to permit it to remain in a position once placed or to be fitted with pins to permit fastening in position. These are to be optional with the user.

Where pins are used, the template should be pierced with holes to allow the model to become accurately located in relation to the template, and the entire assembly held in position on board by the pins fitted to the model base.

15) *Identification.* Models shall bear the name and/or trade-mark of the equipment represented. The model number or size description should also be included, if possible. Abbreviations or initials should be used where practical. The markings should be made in the most suitable place, rather than attempting to place them in the same position as on the actual equipment. ·

16) *General.* Models shall be so designed and constructed to permit them to be used in conjunction with standard templates designed to represent the same identical items of equipment.

The establishment of the above standards should prove quite helpful to plant layout and methods engineers by eliminating misunderstandings and consequent errors that have developed in the past through misinterpretation of varying techniques of plant layout templates and models.

During the early part of World War II, scale models were developed as an aid to plant layout. These models give the third dimension to plant layouts, and are especially helpful to the analyst when he is endeavoring to sell his contemplated layout to a top executive who has neither the time nor the familiarity to grasp all details of the layout when it has been constructed on a two-dimensional basis.

Once all necessary templates have been made, a trial layout can be prepared. By giving consideration to the principal points for efficient layout and by providing adequate output capacity at each work station

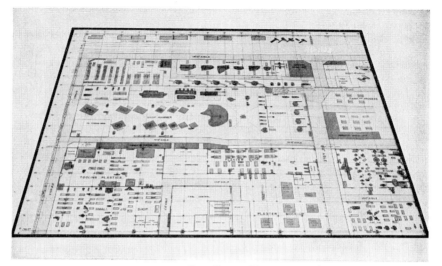

From *Factory Management and Maintenance*, Oct., 1952

FIG. 5–13.   Template layout of portion of a large industrial plant.

without introducing bottlenecks and without interrupting the flow of production, good layouts will be evolved.

After an ideal layout has been designed, it is well to construct a flow chart of the proposed plan so that reduction of distances traveled, storages, delays, and over-all savings will be highlighted. This will greatly facilitate final approval of the design. A good technique for testing the layout is to wind colored thread around the map tacks holding down the templates, and with the thread follow the flow of the product from its raw material components to its transformation into a finished product. By using a different colored thread for every line of product produced, the flow of all work can be visualized quite rapidly. This pictorial presentation, supplemented with the flow chart, will bring to light most flaws of the proposed method.

Making the Floor Plan

After the layout has been approved, it is converted in final detail on plant layout drawings prior to going ahead with the physical move. No standards have been accepted on either a national or an industrial basis as to just what information should be included on the layout drawing. Too much detail will obviously confuse the interpreters; too little detail is even worse because many questions that come up will be unanswered. Randolph W. Mallick and Armand T. Gaudreau[7] have summarized fourteen items which every layout drawing should include. These are:

---

[7] Randolph W. Mallick and Armand T. Gaudreau, *Plant Layout Planning and Practice* (New York: John Wiley & Sons, Inc.), p. 110.

1. Title and scale of the drawing.
2. Sketch number.
3. Approval space.
4. Detail notations for use of plant engineer.
5. Construction notations for architects and detail engineers.
6. Notations on heating, lighting, ventilation, and communication facilities.
7. Directional locations and orientation on plant site.
8. Transportation and handling facilities.
9. Overhead obstructions, and obstructions below floor levels where foundations or superstructures are necessary.
10. Machine-tool and equipment identification number.
11. Column numbers.
12. Service outlets for gas, electricity, water, air, and other utilities.
13. Fire protection and other safety apparatus notes.
14. Signature and date.

If all these items are included on the plant layout drawing, it can be used with assurance for the installation of machinery and equipment.

Photographic copies are frequently substituted for drawings in the reproduction of template layouts. This method saves the laborious scaling and detailed drawing of machinery and other facilities. One company[8] uses flexible, plastic templates, which are colored, translucent, and matte-finished and their layout sheets are flexible, matte-finished, clear plastic. Templates are made with a photosensitive matte film, thus allowing one drawing of a facility to serve as a master to reproduce templates for all identical equipment. Once the layout is completed, a transparency is made directly from the layout by running it through a standard printing machine.

Summary: Plant Layout

Possibilities for plant layout improvement are most likely to be uncovered if they are looked for systematically. Work stations and machines should be arranged to permit the most efficient processing of a product with a minimum of handling. Do not make a change in layout until a careful study of all factors involved has been made. The methods analyst should learn to recognize poor layout and present the facts to the plant engineer for his consideration.

PRINCIPLES OF MOTION ECONOMY

The last of the ten primary approaches to operation analysis has to do with improving the arrangement of parts at the workplace and of the motions required to perform the task. In Chapter 7, considerable detail is given to the laws of motion economy. At this point, consideration will be given only to investigation of motion economy as practiced by the

---

[8] G. L. Thuering, "How to Get Faster, Better, Less Expensive Plant Layout Drawings Without Drafting," *Factory Management and Maintenance*, Vol. 110, No. 10.

methods analyst. When studying work performed at a work station, the analyst should ask:

1. Are both hands working at the same time and in opposite symmetrical direction?
2. Is each hand going through as few motions as possible?
3. Is the workplace arranged so that long reaches are avoided?
4. Are both hands being used effectively and not being used as a holding device?

If the answer to any of the above questions is no, then there are opportunities for improvement of the work station.

Both Hands Should Work at the Same Time

The left hand, in right-handed people, can be used just as effectively as the right hand and should be given just as much consideration for use. It is common knowledge that a boxer learns to jab more effectively with his left than with his right hand. A stenographer will be just as proficient with one hand as the other. In a large number of instances, work stations can be designed to do "two at a time." This is a good slogan for the methods analyst to keep in mind. By providing dual fixtures so as to hold two components, it is often possible to have both hands working at the same time and making symmetrical moves in opposite directions.

For example, a production increase of 100 per cent was made possible by developing a fixture that utilized two-handed operation and permitted grinding two motor brushes at a time. The old method involved a one-handed operation, as only one piece was done during each grinding cycle.

Each Hand Should Go Through As Few Motions As Possible

It is just common sense that the more motions the hands make while performing a task, the longer it will take to do the work. All hand motions are a series of reaches, moves, grasps, positions, and releases, and the more of these fundamental motions that can be eliminated or reduced, the more satisfactory will be the work station.

For example, by providing drop delivery and gravity chutes, it is possible to eliminate certain moves and positions and reduce release time. Likewise, installation of a belt conveyor to bring material to the work station and carry away the processed part will usually result in reduced "move" time. Position is usually a time-consuming basic division of accomplishment that in many instances can be minimized through well-designed fixtures. By the use of tapered channels and pilots, two mating parts can readily be assembled with considerable reduction or elimination of the positioning element.

FIG. 5–14. Work station and fixture designed to allow productive work with both hands. Operator is marking two bulb bases simultaneously.

The Workplace Should Be Arranged to Avoid Long Reaches

The time required to pick up an article is dependent to a great extent on the distance the hand must move. Likewise, move time is definitely related to distance. If at all possible, the workplace should be arranged so that all parts are in easy reach of the operator. If all components can be reached while both elbows are close to the body, then the work will be performed in the "normal" working area. This normal area represents the space within which work can be accomplished in a minimum time.

The work, tools, and parts should not be located beyond the reach of the hands when the arms are fully extended. The area encompassed with the arms fully extended in both the horizontal and vertical planes represents the maximum working area, and the analyst should be on the alert for work stations that demand work to be performed beyond this area.

Avoid Using Hand As a Holding Device

If either hand is ever used as a holding device during the processing cycle of a part, then useful work is not being performed by that hand. Invariably, a fixture can be designed which will satisfactorily hold the work, thus allowing both hands to do useful work. Many times foot-operated mechanisms can be introduced which permit utilization of both hands for productive work. The therblig, "hold," represents an inef-

Courtesy: Alden Systems Co.

FIG. 5–15.   Ideal assembly work station with all components arranged so as to avoid long reaches and moves.

fective basic division of accomplishment and should be eliminated, if practically possible, from all work stations.

Summary: Principles of Motion Economy

It is not necessary for the methods analyst to make a frame-by-frame analysis, characteristic of the micromotion procedure, in order to analyze a work station from the standpoint of applying principles of motion economy. He will be able to introduce many improvements by carefully watching the operator perform at the work station and subject each phase of the operator's work cycle to the questions related to motion economy. These principles should be kept in mind when "tooling up" any new job. If this is done, the work station will inevitably be quite proficient, and the necessity of restudying in order to effect improvements will be diminished.

Summary: Ten Primary Approaches to Operation Analysis

Regardless of the nature of the work, whether continuous or intermittent, process or job shop, soft or hard goods, when systematic operation analysis is applied by competent personnel, real savings will result. It must be remembered that these principles are just as applicable in the planning of new work as in the improving of work already in production. A flow diagram of the analysis procedure will help crystallize the technique discussed in this chapter and Chapter 4.

Increased output is the outcome of operation analysis, but it also distributes benefits of improved production to all workers and helps de-

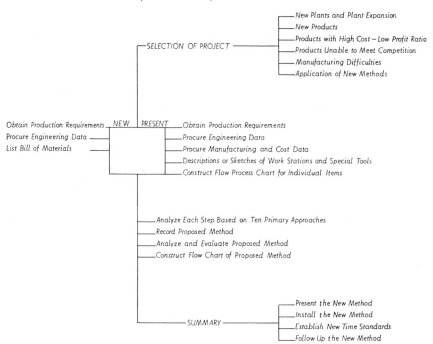

FIG. 5–16.   General flow of analysis procedure.

velop better working conditions and methods, so that the worker can do more work at the plant, do a good job, and still have energy to enjoy life.

A representative case history which follows the method of analysis referred to, was that of the production of an Auto-Starter, a device for starting A.C. motors by reducing the voltage through a transformer. A subassembly of the Auto-Starter is the Arc Box. This part sits in the bottom of the Auto-Starter and acts as a barrier between the contacts so that there will be no short circuits. The present design consists of the following components:

Asbestos barriers with three drilled holes................ 6
Spacers of insulating tubing 2″ long.....................15
Steel rods threaded at both ends........................ 3
Pieces of hardware.....................................18
    Pieces Total....................................42

In assembling these components the operator places a washer, lock washer, and nut on one end of each rod. The rods are then inserted through the three holes in the first barrier. Then one spacer is placed on each of the rods (three in all), and another barrier added. This is repeated until six barriers are on the rods and separated by the tubing.

It was suggested that the six barriers be made with two slots—one at each end—and that two strips of asbestos for supporting the barriers be made with six slots in each.

These would be slipped together and placed in the bottom of the Auto-Starter as needed. The manner of assembly would be the same as that used in putting together the separator in an egg box.

A total of fifteen suggested improvements resulted after the analysis was completed, with the following results:

Old Method	New Method	Savings
42 parts................... 8		34
10 work stations.......... 1		9
18 transportations......... 7		11
7,900 feet of travel........200		7,700
9 storages................ 4		5
0.45 hours time........... 0.11 hours time		0.34 hours
$1.55 costs............... $0.60		$0.95

A program of operation analysis resulted in a 17,496-ton annual saving for one Ohio company. By forming a mill section into a ring and welding it, an original rough-forged ring weighing 2,198 pounds was replaced. The new mill section blank weighed but 740 pounds. The saving of 1,458 pounds of high-grade steel, amounting to twice the weight of the finished piece, was brought about by the simple procedure of reducing the excess material that had been cut away in chips.

An analytical laboratory in a New Jersey plant has applied the principles of operation analysis with gratifying results. New workbenches have been laid out in the form of a cross so that each chemist has an L-shaped worktable. This arrangement allows the chemist to reach any part of his work station by taking but one stride.

The new workbench has consolidated equipment, thus saving space and duplication of facilities. One glassware cabinet services two chemists. A large four-place fume head allows multiple activity in this area that formerly was a bottleneck. All utility outlets are relocated for maximum efficiency.

A state government activity, in an effort to streamline its organization, developed a program of operation analysis that resulted in an estimated annual savings of more than 50,000 hours. This was brought about by combining, eliminating and redesigning all paper-work activities, improving the plant layout, and developing paths of authority.

Application of method improvement is equally as effective in office procedures as in production operations. One industrial engineering department of a Pennsylvania company[9] was given the problem of simplifying the paper work necessary for shipping molded parts manufactured in one of their plants to an outlying plant for assembly. A new method was developed that reduced the average daily shipment of 45 orders from 552 sheets of paper forms to 50 sheets. The annual savings

---

[9] From a talk by Lynell Cooper, Manufacturing Engineer of Westinghouse Electric Corporation, to the central Pennsylvania chapter of the Society for Advancement of Management.

TABLE V
Reduction in Work Performed

Section	Work Station	Eliminate	Comments
Z.............	Inspection Production Production Packing group	Hand-written inspection tag #15208 Hand-written works delivery #5501 Typing check list of daily shipments Less matching of paper work—speeds up movement of shipments	540 entries on 45 tags (daily) 585 entries on 45 forms (daily) 180 entries on 1-letter (daily) 45 matching operations reduced to 5
WS-2.........	Office Packing floor	Typing of preaddressed label #18123 Typing of preaddressed shipping notice #23922 Folding and stuffing packing list in envelope Glue label on each carton Attach packing list on each carton	45 entries on 45 labels (daily) 630 entries on 45 forms (daily) (daily) (daily)
2-E...........	Interworks	Identify customer and indicate receiving section and indicate shipment serial number.	135 check written entries on 45 orders checked daily
General.......	Various	Fewer forms to check, distribute, file, etc.	552 sheets reduced to 50

in paper alone brought about by this change was $366.60. In addition, Table V indicates the reduction in work performed.

TEXT QUESTIONS

1. Can nickel be spot welded to lead? To Monel? To zinc?
2. In what four ways should investigation be made in order to improve process of manufacture?
3. Explain how rearranging operations can result in savings.
4. What process is usually considered the fastest for forming and sizing operations?
5. How should the analyst investigate the setup and tools in order to develop better methods?
6. Why should the methods analyst accept as part of his responsibility the provision of good working conditions?
7. Give the requisites of effective guarding.
8. What are the two general types of plant layout? Explain each in detail.
9. To what scale are templates usually constructed?
10. What is the best way to test a proposed layout?
11. What questions should the analyst ask himself when studying work performed at a work station?
12. For what purpose is operation analysis used?
13. Explain the advantage of using a check list.
14. What are the primary approaches to operation analysis?
15. On what does the extent of tooling depend?
16. How can planning and production control affect setup time?
17. Do working conditions appreciably affect output? Explain.
18. How can you best handle a material?
19. Explain the effect of humidity on the operator.
20. What are some of the physical effects on the workmen when exposed to intermittent noise?

GENERAL QUESTIONS

1. Where would you find application for a hydraulic elevating table?
2. What is the difference between a skid and a pallet?
3. Explain the significance of the colored code for stock templates.
4. When would you recommend the use of three-dimensional models in layout work?
5. What is the general flow of analysis procedure when applied to a product that has never been manufactured?
6. In a process like operation analysis is it necessary to determine the point of diminishing returns? Why?

CHAPTER 6

Man and Machine, Gang, and Operator Process Charts

ONCE AN OPERATION HAS BEEN found necessary through analysis of the operation and flow process chart, it may frequently be improved through further analysis. The three process charts discussed in this chapter are helpful tools for further analyzing certain operations under specific conditions. These process charts are:

1. Man and machine process chart.
2. Gang process chart.
3. Operator process chart.

Man and Machine Process Charts

While the operation and flow process charts are used primarily to explore a complete process or series of operations, the man and machine process chart is used to study, analyze, and improve but one work station at a time. This chart shows the exact relationship in time between the working cycle of the man and the operating cycle of his machine. With these facts clearly presented, possibilities for a fuller utilization of both idle man and machine time and better balancing of the work cycle exist.

Today, many of our machine tools are either completely automatic, such as the automatic screw machine, or are partially automatic, such as the turret lathe. In the operation of these types of facilities, the operator is often idle a portion of the cycle. The utilization of this idle time can increase operator earnings and improve the efficiency of the production. The practice of having one employee operate more than one machine is known as "machine coupling." Machine coupling is not new. One plant, during the depression of the middle 1930's, was unable to justify the amount of incentive earnings being turned in by the second shift in one of the machining departments. Investigation revealed that the operators were practicing machine coupling on their own initiative.

Today, some industries have encountered resistance from organized labor to the practice of machine coupling. The idea of "one operator for each machine" is to some extent a holdover from early World War II days when an acute scarcity of machine tools existed. At that time, it was essential that each machine tool be run to its full capacity every shift each day of the week. To accomplish this, one operator per machine was the logical answer.

The best way to sell machine coupling is to demonstrate the opportunity for added earnings. Since machine coupling will increase the percentage of "effort" time during the operating cycle, the opportunity for greater incentive earnings is enhanced.

Construction of the Man and Machine Process Chart

In the construction of the man and machine process chart, the analyst should first identify the chart in the usual fashion by indicating at the top of the sheet "Man and Machine Process Chart." Immediately below this heading, the following information should be included: part number, drawing number, description of operation being charted, present or proposed method, date, and name of person doing the charting.

Since man and machine charts are always drawn to scale, the analyst should next select a distance in inches to conform with a unit of time so that his chart can be neatly arranged on his paper. The longer the cycle time of the operation being charted, the shorter the distance will be per decimal minute of time. Once exact values have been established for distance in inches per unit of time, the analyst can begin his charting. On the left-hand side of the paper, the operations and time for the man are shown, and to the right of the man time is shown graphically the working and idle time of the machine or machines as the case may be. Working time on the part of the man is represented by a solid line drawn vertically. A break in the vertical man-time line signifies idle time. Likewise, a solid vertical line under each machine heading indicates machine operating time, and a break in the vertical machine line designates idle machine time. Loading and unloading machine time is shown by a dotted line under the machine column, indicating that the machine is neither idle nor is production work being accomplished at the moment (see Figure 6–1).

All elements of occupied and idle time for both the man and the machine he operates are charted until the termination of the cycle. At the foot of the chart is shown the total working time of the man plus his total

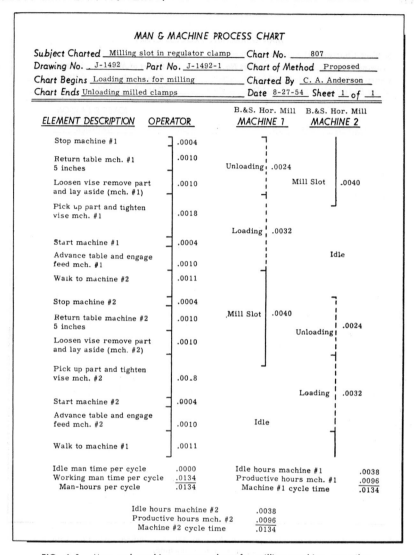

FIG. 6–1. Man and machine process chart for milling machine operation.

idle time. Likewise, the total working time of each machine plus each machine idle time is charted. The productive time of the man plus idle man time must equal the productive time plus idle time of each machine he operates.

It will be noted that accurate elemental time values are necessary before the man and machine chart can be constructed. These time values should represent standard times[1] which include an acceptable manufacturing allowance to take care of fatigue, unavoidable delays, and personal

[1] See Chapter 17.

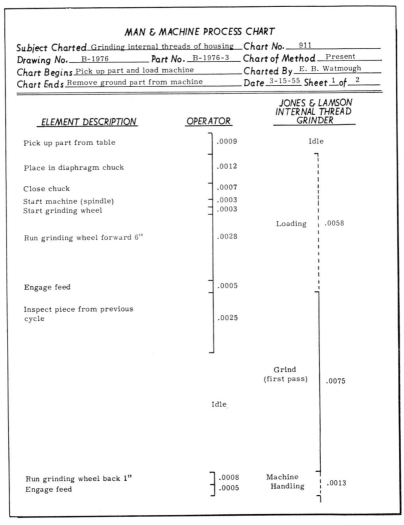

MAN & MACHINE PROCESS CHART

Subject Charted Grinding internal threads of housing Chart No. 911
Drawing No. B-1976   Part No. B-1976-3 Chart of Method Present
Chart Begins Pick up part and load machine   Charted By E. B. Watmough
Chart Ends Remove ground part from machine   Date 3-15-55 Sheet 1 of 2

ELEMENT DESCRIPTION	OPERATOR	JONES & LAMSON INTERNAL THREAD GRINDER
Pick up part from table	.0009	Idle
Place in diaphragm chuck	.0012	
Close chuck	.0007	
Start machine (spindle)	.0003	
Start grinding wheel	.0003	
		Loading .0058
Run grinding wheel forward 6"	.0028	
Engage feed	.0005	
Inspect piece from previous cycle	.0025	
		Grind (first pass) .0075
	Idle	
Run grinding wheel back 1"	.0008	Machine Handling .0013
Engage feed	.0005	

FIG. 6–2. Man and machine process chart of thread-grinding operation with one man operating one machine.

delays. In no case should over-all stop-watch readings be used in the construction of the chart.

The completed man and machine process chart clearly shows both idle machine and man time. These areas are generally a good place to start effecting improvements.

The analyst must be careful not to be deceived by what looks like an appreciable amount of idle man time. In many instances, it is far more economical to have a man idle a portion of a cycle rather than chance an expensive piece of equipment or process being idle even a small portion of the time. In order to be sure that his proposal is the best solution, the

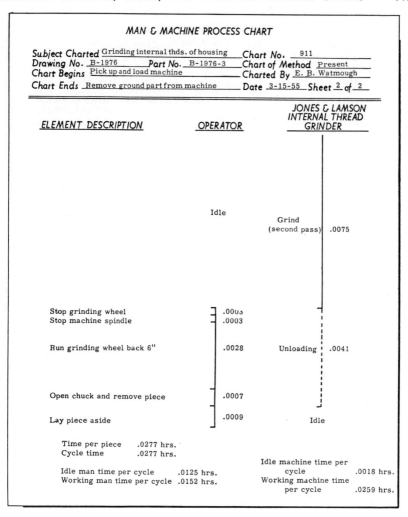

FIG. 6–2 (continued)

analyst must know the cost of the idle facility as well as the cost of the idle man. It is only when total cost is considered that one can safely recommend one method over another. Figure 6–3 illustrates a man and machine chart that represents economies over the one shown in Figure 6–2.

Using the Man and Machine Process Chart

The analyst will construct a man and machine process chart when his preliminary investigation reveals that the working cycle of the operator is somewhat shorter than the operating cycle of the machine. Once he has completed the chart, the logical place to consider improvement

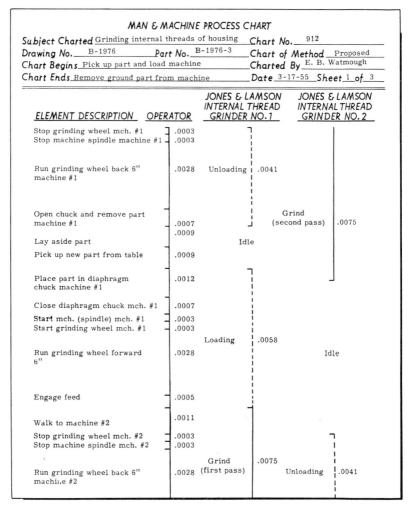

FIG. 6–3. Man and machine process chart of thread grinding operation with one man operating two machines.

possibilities is during the idle portion of the man's cycle. Considering the amount of this time, he should investigate:

1. The possibility of operating a second machine during this idle time.
2. The possibility of performing some bench or manual operation such as filing burrs or gaging part during the idle time.

Sometimes more available operator time can be obtained by reducing the speed and feed of the machine. This may permit machine coupling where otherwise it would not have been possible, and thus reduce total costs. As mentioned earlier, it is not always advisable to practice machine coupling, as idle machine time introduced may more than offset the idle

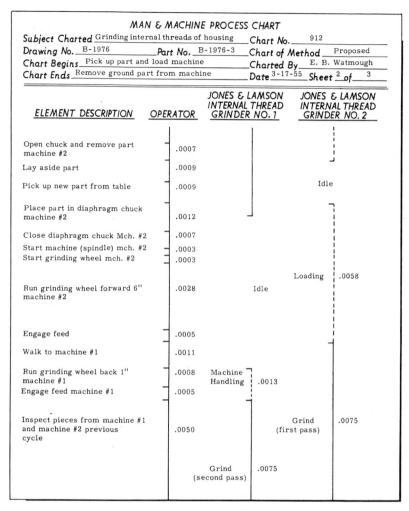

ELEMENT DESCRIPTION	OPERATOR	JONES & LAMSON INTERNAL THREAD GRINDER NO. 1		JONES & LAMSON INTERNAL THREAD GRINDER NO. 2	
MAN & MACHINE PROCESS CHART					
Subject Charted Grinding internal threads of housing Chart No. ___912___					
Drawing No. B-1976 _____ Part No. B-1976-3 ___Chart of Method ___Proposed___					
Chart Begins__Pick up part and load machine____Charted By__E. B. Watmough__					
Chart Ends__Remove ground part from machine____Date 3-17-55 Sheet 2 of 3					

ELEMENT DESCRIPTION	OPERATOR	JONES & LAMSON INTERNAL THREAD GRINDER NO. 1		JONES & LAMSON INTERNAL THREAD GRINDER NO. 2	
Open chuck and remove part machine #2	.0007				
Lay aside part	.0009				
Pick up new part from table	.0009			Idle	
Place part in diaphragm chuck machine #2	.0012				
Close diaphragm chuck Mch. #2	.0007				
Start machine (spindle) mch. #2	.0003				
Start grinding wheel mch. #2	.0003				
				Loading	.0058
Run grinding wheel forward 6" machine #2	.0028	Idle			
Engage feed	.0005				
Walk to machine #1	.0011				
Run grinding wheel back 1" machine #1	.0008	Machine Handling	.0013		
Engage feed machine #1	.0005				
Inspect pieces from machine #1 and machine #2 previous cycle	.0050			Grind (first pass)	.0075
		Grind (second pass)	.0075		

FIG. 6–3 (continued)

operator time saved. The only sure way to make the analysis is on a total cost basis.

Man and machine charts are effective in determining the extent of coupling justified in order to assure a "fair day's work for a fair day's pay." They are valuable for determining how idle machine time may be more fully utilized.

Gang Process Charts

The gang process chart, in a sense, is an adaptation of the man and machine chart. After completing a man and machine process chart, the analyst should be able to determine the most economical number of machines to be operated by one man. However, several processes and facilities are of such magnitude that it is not a question of how many machines should a man operate, but a problem as to how many men should it take to man the machine effectively. The gang process chart shows the exact relationship between the idle and operating cycle of the machine and the idle and operating time per cycle of the men who service it. This chart shows clearly the possibilities for improvement by reducing both idle man and machine time.

Construction of the Gang Process Chart

After heading the gang process chart, "Gang Process Chart," and completely identifying the process being plotted with part number, drawing number, description of operation being charted, present or proposed

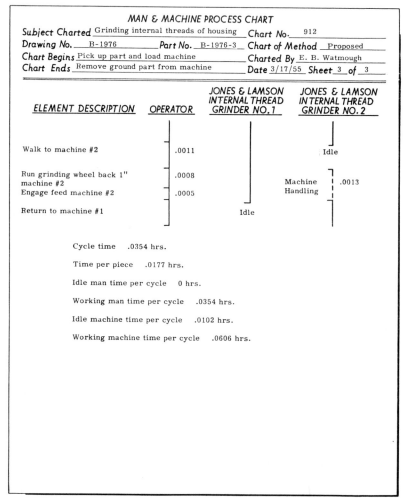

FIG. 6–3 (concluded)

method, date, and name of person doing the charting, the analyst should select a time scale to give a neat-appearing chart on the paper being used. As in the man and machine process chart, the gang process chart is always drawn to scale.

On the left-hand side of the paper is shown the operations being performed on the machine or process. Immediately to the right of the operation description, the loading, operating, and idle time of the machine is represented graphically. Further to the right, the operating and idle time of each operator manning the process is illustrated by flow lines in a vertical direction. A solid vertical line indicates productive work being done, while a dotted vertical line in connection wtih the facility shows that either loading or unloading operations are taking place. A void in the vertical flow line reveals idle time, and the length of the void determines the duration of the idle time. In the case of the operators, solid vertical lines show that work is being done, while breaks in the solid lines demonstrate that idle time is prevailing. Figure 6–4 illustrates a gang process chart, and it is apparent that a large number of idle man-hours exist. A better loading of the same process is shown on the gang process chart illustrated in Figure 6–5. The saving of sixteen hours per shift was easily developed through the use of the gang process chart.

Using the Gang Process Chart

The analyst usually constructs the gang process chart when his initial investigation of a given operation indicates that more men are being used to operate a facility or process than is necessary. If he suspects this, he will find that the gang process chart is a useful tool for determining the exact number of operators needed to service a machine or process effectively. Once the chart has been constructed, the hours of idle man time can be analyzed to determine the possibility of utilizing one man to perform the work elements currently performed by two or more.

For example, in the gang process chart shown in Figure 6–4, the company is employing two more men than needed. This is apparent when it is shown that under this process, 18.4 idle man-hours are involved in every 8-hour turn.

By relocating some of the controls of the process, it was possible to reassign the elements of work so that four, rather than six, men effectively operated the extrusion press.

Figure 6–5 illustrates a gang process chart of the proposed method using but four operators and so making savings of 16 man-hours per shift. Without the gang process chart, this solution would have been quite difficult.

From the example given in Figures 6–4 and 6–5, it can be seen that the gang process chart aids in dividing the available work among the members of the team that operate the equipment, and then clearly de-

GANG PROCESS CHART OF PRESENT METHOD

HYDRAULIC EXTRUSION PRESS   DEPT. 11

BELLEFONTE PA. PLANT

CHARTED BY B.W.N.   4-15-

CHART NO. G-85

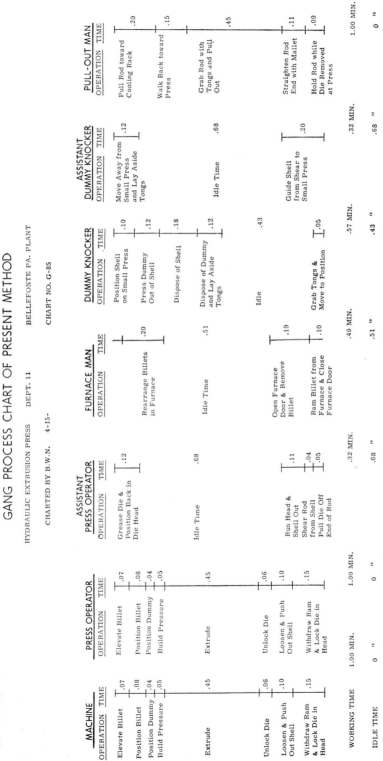

MACHINE		PRESS OPERATOR		ASSISTANT PRESS OPERATOR		FURNACE MAN		DUMMY KNOCKER		ASSISTANT DUMMY KNOCKER		PULL-OUT MAN	
OPERATION	TIME	OPERATION	TIME	OPERATION	TIME	OPERATION	TIME	OPERATION	TIME	OPERATION	TIME	OPERATION	TIME
Elevate Billet	.07	Elevate Billet	.07	Grease Die & Position Back in Die Head	.12			Position Shell on Small Press	.10	Move Away from Small Press and Lay Aside Tongs	.12	Pull Rod toward Cooling Rack	.20
Position Billet	.08	Position Billet	.08			Rearrange Billets in Furnace	.20	Press Dummy Out of Shell	.12				
Position Dummy	.04	Position Dummy	.04									Walk Back toward Press	.15
Build Pressure	.05	Build Pressure	.05					Dispose of Shell	.18				
Extrude	.45	Extrude	.45	Idle Time	.68	Idle Time	.51	Dispose of Dummy and Lay Aside Tongs	.12	Idle Time	.68	Grab Rod with Tongs and Pull Out	.45
Unlock Die	.06	Unlock Die	.06					Idle	.43				
Loosen & Push Out Shell	.10	Loosen & Push Out Shell	.10	Run Head & Shell Out	.11	Open Furnace Door & Remove Billet	.19			Guide Shell from Shear to Small Press	.20	Straighten Rod End with Mallet	.11
Withdraw Ram & Lock Die in Head	.15	Withdraw Ram & Lock Die in Head	.15	Shear Rod from Shell	.04	Ram Billet from Furnace & Close Furnace Door	.10	Grab Tongs & Move to Position	.05			Hold Rod while Die Removed at Press	.09
				Pull Die Off End of Rod	.05								
WORKING TIME	1.00 MIN.	WORKING TIME	1.00 MIN.		.32 MIN.		.49 MIN.		.57 MIN.		.32 MIN.		1.00 MIN.
IDLE TIME	0 "	IDLE TIME	0 "		.68 "		.51 "		.43 "		.68 "		0 "

IDLE TIME = 2.30 MAN-MINUTES PER CYCLE = 18.4 MAN-HOURS PER EIGHT-HOUR DAY

FIG. 6-4.

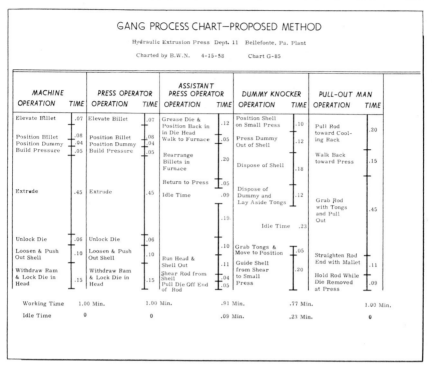

FIG. 6-5. Gang process chart of proposed method of operation of hydraulic extrusion process.

termines the job assignment of all involved. Through the construction and use of the gang process chart, equipment will be operated to capacity, labor costs will be reduced, and employee morale will be improved as a result of equitable distribution of work assignments.

Operator Process Chart

The operator process chart, sometimes referred to as a "left- and right-hand" process chart is, in effect, a tool of motion study. This chart shows all movements and delays made by both the right and left hands, and the relationship between the relative basic divisions of accomplishment as performed by the hands. The purpose of the operator process chart is to present a given operation in sufficient detail so that by means of an analysis the operation can be improved. Usually it is not practical to make a detailed study through the operator process chart unless a highly repetitive manual operation is involved. Through motion analysis of the operator chart, inefficient motion patterns become apparent and violation of the laws of motion economy (see Chapter 7) is readily observed. This chart will facilitate changing a method so that a balanced two-handed operation can be achieved and ineffective motions either reduced or eliminated. The result will be a smoother, more rhythmic cycle which will keep both delays and operator fatigue to a minimum.

Construction of the Operator Process Chart

Although Frank and Lillian Gilbreth state that there are seventeen fundamental motions, and that every operation consists of a combination of some of these elements, the methods analyst will find it practical when plotting operator process charts to use but eight basic divisions of accomplishment. These elemental motions with their symbols are:

Reach	Re	Use	U
Grasp	G	Release	Rl
Move	M	Delay	D
Position	P	Hold	H

See Chapter 7 for detailed description of each of these basic divisions of human work.

Although there are several different types of delays, such as unavoidable delay, avoidable delay, rest to overcome fatigue, and "balancing delay,"[2] the methods analyst need only indicate in the operator process chart a cessation of work with the identification "delay." Often, delays will not occur to both hands simultaneously. Thus, an operator hand-feeding the cross slide of his lathe would be performing "use" with his right hand while his left hand would be delayed. Other examples of delays would be interruptions of work due to a coughing spell of the operator or his sitting down to rest. In both of these examples, the right hand as well as the left hand would be shown as being delayed. Delays should always be investigated with thought toward eliminating or minimizing them.

The operator process chart should be headed "Operator Process Chart" and this should be followed with all necessary identifying information which would include part number, drawing number, operation or process description, present or proposed method, date, and the name of the person doing the charting. Immediately below the identifying information should be a sketch of the work station drawn to scale. The sketch will materially aid in presenting the method under study. A typical operator process chart form, with a section of the sheet laid out in co-ordinate form in order to facilitate sketching is shown in Figure 6–6.

After the analyst has completely identified the operation and made a sketch of the work station showing dimensional relationships, he is ready to begin construction of the operator process chart. Since this chart is drawn to scale, the analyst should determine by observation the duration of the cycle. Then he can readily determine the amount of time represented by each ¼ inch of vertical space on the chart. For example, if it developed that the operation to be studied had a cycle time of .70 min-

---

[2] S. M. Lowry, H. B. Maynard, and G. J. Stegemerten, *Time and Motion Study and Formulas for Wage Incentives* (3rd ed.; New York: McGraw-Hill Book Co., Inc., 1940).

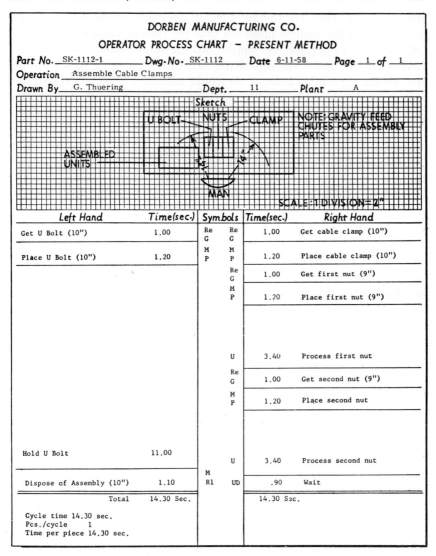

DORBEN MANUFACTURING CO.

OPERATOR PROCESS CHART – PRESENT METHOD

Part No. SK-1112-1   Dwg. No. SK-1112   Date 6-11-58   Page 1 of 1
Operation   Assemble Cable Clamps
Drawn By   G. Thuering   Dept.   11   Plant   A

Sketch

U BOLT   NUTS   CLAMP   NOTE: GRAVITY FEED CHUTES FOR ASSEMBLY PARTS

ASSEMBLED UNITS

MAN

SCALE: 1 DIVISION = 2"

Left Hand	Time(sec.)	Symbols		Time(sec.)	Right Hand
Get U Bolt (10")	1.00	Re G	Re G	1.00	Get cable clamp (10")
Place U Bolt (10")	1.20	M P	M P	1.20	Place cable clamp (10")
			Re G	1.00	Get first nut (9")
			M P	1.20	Place first nut (9")
			U	3.40	Process first nut
			Re G	1.00	Get second nut (9")
			M P	1.20	Place second nut
Hold U Bolt	11.00		U	3.40	Process second nut
Dispose of Assembly (10")	1.10	M R1	UD	.90	Wait
Total	14.30 Sec.			14.30 Sec.	

Cycle time 14.30 sec.
Pcs./cycle   1
Time per piece 14.30 sec.

FIG. 6–6. Operator process chart of assembly of cable clamps.

utes and there were 7 vertical inches of available charting space, then each ¼ inch of chart space would equal .025 minutes.

It is usually less confusing to chart completely the activities of one hand, and then chart all the basic divisions of accomplishment performed by the other hand. Although there is no fixed rule as to what part of the work cycle should be used as a starting point, it is usually best to start plotting immediately after the "release" of the finished part. If this release be done with the right hand, the next movement that would normally take place would be the first motion shown on the operator process chart. This, for the right hand, probably would be "reach for new part." If the analyst observed that the "reach" element took about .025 minutes to perform, he would indicate this duration by drawing a horizontal line across the right-hand side of the paper ¼ inch from the top. Under the symbol column, he would indicate a "Re" for "reach" and this would be shown in black pencil, indicating that an effective motion had been accomplished. Immediately to the right of the symbol would be a brief description of the event, such as "Reach 20" for a half-inch nut. Immediately below, the next basic division would be shown, and so on until completion of the cycle. The analyst would then proceed to plot the activity of the left hand during the cycle. While plotting the left hand, it is a good idea to verify that end points of the therbligs actually occur at the same point as the chart indicates. This is a good check for over-all errors in plotting.

It should be noted that elements must be large enough to be measured, since it is not possible in most instances to obtain with the stopwatch the time required for individual therbligs. For example, in Figure 6–6, the first element performed by the left hand was classified as "get U bolt." This element was comprised of the therbligs, "reach" and "grasp." It would not have been possible with a stopwatch to determine the time required to perform either of these therbligs. Only the moving picture camera could disclose time values as short as these (see Chapter 9).

The observer in Figure 6–6 was using a decimal second watch and, by observing one element at a time, was able to break elements into periods as short as one second.

After the activities of both the right and the left hand are charted, a summary should be shown at the bottom of the sheet, indicating the cycle time, pieces per cycle, and time per piece.

Using the Operator Process Chart

After the operator process chart of an existing method has been completed, the analyst should see what improvements can be introduced. The "delays" and "holds" are good places to begin. For example, in Figure 6–6 it can be seen that the left hand was used as a holding device for almost the entire cycle. An analysis of this condition would suggest the development of a fixture to hold the U bolt. Further consideration of how to get balanced motions of both hands would suggest that, when the fixture holds the U bolts, then the left hand and the right hand would each assemble completely a cable clamp. Additional study of this chart might result in the introduction of an automatic ejector and gravity chute which would eliminate the final cycle element of "dispose of assembly."

The best way of doing a job is through systematic analysis of all the detailed elements that comprise that job. The operator process chart clearly reveals the work done by each hand in performing an operation and shows the relative time and relationships of all motions performed by the hands. The operator process chart is an effective tool to:

1. Balance motions of both hands and reduce fatigue.
2. Eliminate and/or reduce nonproductive motions.
3. Shorten the duration of productive motions.
4. Train new operators in the ideal method.
5. Sell the proposed method.

The methods analyst should learn to make and use operator process charts in order to bring about improvements.

Summary: Man and Machine, Gang, and Operator Process Charts

The methods analyst should know the specific functions of the man and machine, gang, and operator process charts so that he can select the appropriate one for improving operations. The operator chart is adapted to all work where the operator goes through a series of manual motions. The man and machine and gang process charts are used only when machines or facilities are used in conjunction with the operator or operators. Frequently, where an operator is employed in running a machine, it will be worthwhile to make a study both from the standpoint of possible coupling and improvement of motion pattern. Thus, it may be helpful to construct both a man and machine and an operator process chart. In summary, the functions of these three charts are:

1. Man and Machine Chart—Used to analyze idle man and idle machine time. Ideal for determination of the amount of machine coupling to be practiced.
2. Gang Process Chart—Used to analyze idle facility time and idle time of operators servicing the facility or process. Ideal for determining labor requirements of a production facility.
3. Operator Process Chart—Used to analyze work station for proper layout, proper operator motion pattern, and best sequence of elements. Best chart to use for improvement of repetitive manual motions.

TEXT QUESTIONS

1. When is it advisable to construct a man and machine process chart?
2. Why should the man and machine process chart be drawn to scale?
3. How does the gang process chart differ from the man and the machine process chart?
4. What is the purpose of the operator process chart?
5. What symbols are used in the construction of the operator process chart?

6. Explain how you would sell machine coupling to union officials who were strongly opposed to the technique.

7. In what way does an operator benefit through machine coupling?

GENERAL QUESTIONS

1. Why cannot average elemental times be used in construction of the man and machine process chart?

2. Should base rates of pay be increased when an operator is asked to operate two turret lathes as a result of a man and machine analysis, whereas he operated only one turret lathe prior to the study? Why?

CHAPTER 7

Motion Study

MOTION STUDY IS THE CAREFUL analysis of the various body motions employed in doing a job, for the purpose of eliminating or reducing ineffective movements, and facilitating and speeding effective movements. Through motion study, the work is performed more easily and the rate of output is increased. The Gilbreths pioneered the study of manual motion and developed basic laws of motion economy that today are considered fundamental. They were also responsible for the motion-picture technique for making detailed motion studies known as micromotion studies, which have proved invaluable in the study of very highly repetitive manual operations.

Motion study, in the broad sense, covers two degrees of refinement that have wide industrial application. These are visual motion study and micromotion study.

Visual motion study has considerably the broader application, due to the fact that the activity of the work need not be as great to justify its use economically. This type of study involves a careful observation of the operation and construction of an operator process chart, and a probing analysis of the chart, giving consideration to the laws of motion economy.

The micromotion procedure (see Chapter 8), in view of its much higher cost, is usually practical only on extremely active jobs where the life and repetitiveness are great. The two types of studies may be compared to viewing a part under a magnifying glass and viewing it under a microscope. The added detail revealed by the microscope finds application on only the most productive job.

The Fundamental Motions

The basic division of accomplishment concept, developed by Frank Gilbreth in his early work, applied to all production work performed by

129

the hands of the operator. He called these fundamental motions "ther-bligs" (Gilbreth spelled backward), and concluded that any and all operations are made up of a series of these seventeen basic divisions. These seventeen fundamental hand motions, modified somewhat from Gilbreth's summary, and their symbols and color designations are shown in Table VI.

TABLE VI

THERBLIG NAME	SYMBOL	COLOR DESIGNATION	SYMBOL
SEARCH	S	BLACK	⌒
SELECT	SE	GRAY, LIGHT	→
GRASP	G	LAKE RED	∩
REACH	RE	OLIVE GREEN	⌣
MOVE	M	GREEN	⌣
HOLD	H	GOLD OCHRE	⌂
RELEASE	RL	CARMINE RED	⌒
POSITION	P	BLUE	9
PRE–POSITION	PP	SKY–BLUE	𝖻
INSPECT	I	BURNT-OCHRE	0
ASSEMBLE	A	VIOLET, HEAVY	#
DISASSEMBLE	DA	VIOLET, LIGHT	⧣
USE	U	PURPLE	U
UNAVOIDABLE DELAY	UD	YELLOW OCHRE	⌒o
AVOIDABLE DELAY	AD	LEMON YELLOW	⌐o
PLAN	PL	BROWN	β
REST TO OVERCOME FATIGUE	R	ORANGE	ℓ

Definitions of Basic Divisions of Accomplishment

The Management Research and Development Division of the Society for Advancement of Management in its "Glossary of Terms Used in Methods, Time Study, and Wage Incentives" has provided definitions of the various therbligs. These definitions, in part, are included in the following summary.

1. *Search.* Search is the basic operation element employed to locate an object. It is that part of the cycle during which the eyes or hands are groping or feeling for the object. It begins the instant the eyes move in an effort to locate an object and ends the instant they are focused on the found object.

Search is a therblig that the analyst should always endeavor to eliminate. Well-planned work stations allow work to be performed continuously so that it is not necessary for the operator to perform this element. Providing an exact location for all tools and parts is the typical way to eliminate search from a work station.

A new employee, or one that is not familiar with his job, will find it necessary to use search periodically until his skill and proficiency develop.

The well-trained motion analyst will ask himself the following questions in order to eliminate or reduce "search" time:

1. Are articles properly identified? Perhaps labels or color could be utilized.
2. Can transparent containers be used?
3. Will a better layout of the work station eliminate searching?
4. Is proper lighting being used?
5. Can tools and parts be prepositioned?

2. *Select.* Select is the therblig that takes place when the operator chooses one part over two or more analogous parts. This therblig usually follows search and even with a detailed micromotion procedure, it is difficult to determine the exact ending of search and the beginning of select. Select does occur without search when selective assembly is being encountered. In this case, it is usually preceded by inspect. Select can also be classified as an ineffective therblig and should be eliminated from the work cycle by better layout of the work station and control of parts.
   In order to eliminate this therblig, the analyst should ask:

1. Are common parts interchangeable?
2. Can tools be standardized?
3. Are parts and materials stored in the same bin?
4. Can a rack or tray be used so that parts will be prepositioned?

3. *Grasp.* Grasp is the elemental hand motion of closing the fingers around a part in an operation. Grasp is an effective therblig and usually cannot be eliminated, but in many instances it can be improved. It occurs the instant the fingers of either or both hands begin to enclose around an object in order to maintain control of it and ends the moment control has been obtained. Grasp is usually preceded by reach and followed by move. Detailed studies have concluded that there are many types of grasp, some taking three times as much time to perform as others. The number of grasps occurring during the work cycle should be kept to a minimum and the parts to be picked up should be arranged in such a manner that the most simple type of grasp can be used. This is done by having the object by itself in a fixed location and positioned in such a manner that no interference takes place with the worktable, bin, or surrounding environment.
   These therblig check questions may help improve the "grasps" performed during a cycle:

1. Would it be advisable for the operator to grasp more than one part or object at a time?
2. Can a contact-grasp be used rather than a pick-up grasp? In other words, can objects be slid instead of carried?
3. Will a lip on the front of bins simplify the grasping of small parts?
4. Can tools or parts be prepositioned for easy grasp?
5. Can a vacuum, magnet, rubber fingertip, or other device, be used to advantage?
6. Can a conveyor be used?
7. Has the jig been designed so that the part may easily be grasped when removing it?

8. Can previous operator preposition tool or work thus simplifying grasp for the following operator?
9. Can tools be prepositioned on a swinging bracket?

4. *Reach.* Reach represents the motion of an empty hand, without resistance, toward or away from an object. The basic division reach was known as "transport empty" in Gilbreth's original summary. However, the shorter term is generally accepted by methods men today. Reach begins the instant the hand moves toward an object or general location and ends the instant hand motion stops upon arrival at the object or destination. Reach is usually followed by grasp and preceded by a release. Obviously, the time required to perform a reach is dependent upon the distance of the hand movement. As in the case of grasp, reach can be classified as an objective therblig, and usually cannot be eliminated from the work cycle. However, it can be reduced by shortening the distances required for reaching. By keeping this elementary principle in mind, work stations can be developed that will keep reach time to a minimum.

5. *Move.* Move is the basic division to signify a hand movement with a load. The load can be in the form of pressure. Move was originally known as "transport loaded." This therblig begins the instant the hand under load moves toward a general location and ends the moment motion stops upon arrival at the destination. Move is usually preceded by a grasp and is usually followed by either a release or a position.

The time required to perform move is dependent on distance, weight to be moved, and type of move. Move is an objective therblig, and it is difficult to remove this basic division from the work cycle. Nevertheless, the time to perform move can be diminished by reducing the distances to be moved, lightening the load, and improving the type of move by providing gravity chutes or a conveyor at the terminal point of the move, so that it will not be necessary to bring the object being moved to a specific location. Experience has proved that moves to a general location are performed more rapidly than to an exact location.

Both reach and move therbligs may be improved by asking and answering the following questions:

1. Can either of these therbligs be eliminated?
2. Can distances be shortened to advantage?
3. Are the best means being used? i.e., conveyors, hand, tongs, tweezers, etc.
4. Is the correct body member used? i.e., fingers, wrist, forearm, shoulder.
5. Can a gravity chute be employed?
6. Can transports be effected through mechanization and foot-operated devices?
7. Will time be reduced by transporting in larger units?
8. Is time increased because of the nature of the material being moved or because of a subsequent delicate positioning?
9. Can abrupt changes in direction be eliminated?

6. *Hold.* Hold is the basic division of accomplishment that occurs when either hand is supporting or maintaining control of an object while the other hand does useful work. Hold is an ineffective therblig and can usually be removed from the work cycle by designing a jig or fixture to hold the work rather than using the hand. The hand is seldom considered an efficient holding device, and the methods analyst should always be on the alert to prevent hold from being a part of any work assignment.

Hold begins the instant control is exercised by the hand on the object and ends at the instant the other hand completes its work on the object. A typical example of hold would occur when the left hand holds a stud while the right hand runs a nut on the stud. During the assembly of the nut to the stud, the left hand would be utilizing the therblig hold.

Hold can often be eliminated by asking and answering these questions:

1. Can a mechanical jig such as a vise, pin, hook, rack, clip, or vacuum be used?
2. Can friction be used?
3. Can a magnetic device be used?
4. Should a twin holding fixture be used?

7. *Release.* Release is the basic division that occurs when the object of the operator is to relinquish control of the object. Release takes the least amount of time of all the therbligs, and little can be done to influence the time required for this objective therblig.

Release begins the instant the fingers begin to move away from the part held and ends the instant all fingers are clear of the part. This therblig is usually preceded by a move or a position and is usually followed by a reach.

To make improvements on release, the motion analyst should ask:

1. Can the release be made in transit?
2. Can a mechanical ejector be used?
3. Are the bins that will contain the part after release of the proper size and design?
4. At the end of the therblig release load, are the hands in the most advantageous position for the next therblig?
5. Can multiple units be released?

8. *Position.* Position is an element of work consisting of locating an object in such a way that it will be properly oriented in a specific location.

The therblig position occurs as a hesitation while the hand or hands are endeavoring to place the part in such a manner that further work may be more readily performed. Actually, position may be a combination of several very rapid motions. The locating of a contoured piece in a die would be a typical example of position. Position is usually preceded by a move and followed by a release. Position begins the instant the controlling hand or hands begin to agitate, twist, turn, or slide the part in order to orient it to the correct place and ends as soon as the hand begins to move away from the part.

Position frequently can be eliminated or improved through the answering of these and similar check questions:

1. Can such devices as a guide, funnel, bushing, stop, swinging bracket, locating pin, recess, key, pilot, or chamfer be used?
2. Can tolerances be changed?
3. Can the hole be counterbored or countersunk?
4. Can a template be used?
5. Are burrs increasing the problem of positioning?
6. Can the article be pointed so as to act as a pilot?

9. *Preposition.* Preposition is an element of work which consists of positioning an object in a predetermined place in such a way that it may be grasped in the position in which it is to be held when it is needed.

Preposition often occurs in conjunction with other therbligs, one of which is usually move. It is the basic division that arranges a part so that it can be conveniently placed upon arrival. The time required to preposition is difficult to measure since the therblig itself can seldom be isolated. Preposition would take place if a screw driver was being aligned while being moved to the screw it was going to drive.

These check questions will assist the analyst in studying preposition therbligs.

1. Can holding device be used at work station so that tools may be kept in their proper position and their handles kept in upright position?
2. Can tools be suspended?
3. Can a guide be used?
4. Can a magazine feed be used?
5. Can a stacking device be used?
6. Can a rotating fixture be used?

10. *Inspect.* Inspect is an element included in an operation in order to assure acceptable quality through a regular check by the employee performing the operation.

Inspect takes place when the predominant purpose is to compare some object with a standard. It usually is not difficult to detect when inspect is encountered, as the eyes are focused upon the object and a delay between motions is noted while the mind decides either to accept or reject the piece in question. The time taken for inspect is determined primarily by the severity of the standard and the amount of deviation of the part in question. Thus, if an operator were sorting out all blue marbles from a bin, little time would be consumed in deciding what to do with a red marble. However, if a purple marble were picked up, there would be a longer hesitation for the mind to evaluate the marble and decide if it should be accepted or rejected.

These questions, when answered by the analyst, may result in improvements on inspect therbligs:

1. Can inspection be eliminated or combined with another operation or therblig?
2. Can multiple gages or tests be used?
3. By increasing the illumination, will inspection time be reduced?
4. Are the articles being inspected the correct distance from the workmen's eyes?
5. Will a shadowgraph facilitate inspection?
6. Does an electric eye have application?
7. Does the volume justify automatic electronic inspection?
8. Would a magnifying glass facilitate the inspection of small parts?
9. Is the best inspection method being used? Has consideration been given to polarized light, template gages, sound tests, performance tests, etc.?

11. *Assemble.* Assemble is the basic division that occurs when two mating parts are brought together. This is another objective therblig and can more readily be improved than eliminated. Assemble is usually preceded either by a position or a move and is usually followed by a release. It begins the instant the two mating parts come in contact with one another and ends upon completion of the uniting element.

12. *Disassemble.* Disassemble is just the reverse of assemble and occurs when two mating parts are disunited. The basic division is usually preceded by a grasp and is usually followed by either a move or a release. Disassemble is objective in nature, and improvement possibilities are more likely than complete elimination of the therblig. Disassemble begins the moment either or both hands have control of the object after grasping it, and ends as soon as the disassembly has been completed, usually evidenced by the beginning of a move or the beginning of a release.

13. *Use.* Use is a completely objective therblig and occurs when either or both hands have control of an object during that part of the cycle when productive work is being performed. When both hands are holding a casting up against a grinding wheel, "use" would be the therblig that would correctly indicate the action of the hands. After a screw driver had been positioned in the slot of the screw, use would occur as the screw is being driven home. The duration of this therblig depends on the operation as well as the performance of the operator. It is quite easily detected, as this therblig "always advances the operation toward the ultimate objective."[1]

In studying the three objective therbligs, assemble, disassemble and use, thought should be given to the following questions:

1. Can a jig or fixture be used?
2. Does the activity justify automated equipment?

_____

[1] L. P. Alford and J. R. Bangs, *Production Handbook* (New York: Ronald Press Co., 1944).

3. Would it be practical to make the assembly in multiple units?
4. Can a more efficient tool be used?
5. Can stops be used?
6. Is the tool being operated at the most efficient feeds and speeds?
7. Should a power tool be employed?

14. *Unavoidable Delay.* Unavoidable delay is an interruption beyond the control of an operator in the continuity of an operation. It represents idle time in the work cycle experienced by either hand or both hands because of the nature of the process. Thus while an operator is hand feeding a drill with his right hand to a part held in a jig, the left hand would be unavoidably delayed. Since the operator has no control over unavoidable delays, in order to remove them from the cycle, the process will have to be changed in some manner.

15. *Avoidable Delay.* Any idle time that occurs during the cycle for which the operator is solely responsible, either intentionally or unintentionally, is classified as an avoidable delay. Thus, if an operator developed a coughing spell during a work cycle, this delay would be avoidable, as normally it would not appear in the work cycle. The majority of avoidable delays encountered can be avoided by the operator without changing the process or method of doing the work.

16. *Plan.* The therblig plan is a mental process, when the operator pauses to determine the next action. Plan may take place during any part of the work cycle and is usually readily detected as a hesitation after all components have been located. This therblig is characteristic of a new employee and usually can be removed from the work cycle through proper operator training.

17. *Rest to Overcome Fatigue.* This delay seldom appears in every cycle, but is evidenced periodically in order for the operator to recover from fatigue caused by his work. The duration of rest to overcome fatigue will vary not only with the class of work but also with the individual performing the work.

In order to reduce the number of occurrences of the therblig rest, the analyst should consider:

1. Is the best order-of-muscles classification being used?
2. Are temperature, humidity, ventilation, noise, light, and other working conditions satisfactory?
3. Are benches the proper height?
4. Can the operator alternately sit and stand while performing his work?
5. Does the operator have a comfortable chair of the right height?
6. Are mechanical means being used for heavy loads?

Principles of Motion Economy

Beyond the basic division of accomplishment concept, as first set forth by the Gilbreths, are the principles of motion economy also developed by them and added to by others, notably Ralph M. Barnes. These laws of motion economy are not all applicable to every job, and several find application only through the tool of micromotion study as discussed in Chapter 8. However, those that apply to visual motion study, as well as the micromotion technique, that should always be considered are broken down into three basic subdivisions: (1) use of the human body, (2) arrangement and conditions of the workplace, and (3) design of tools and equipment.[2]

The methods analyst should become familiar with the visual laws of motion economy so that he will be able to detect inefficiencies in the method by briefly inspecting the workplace and the operation. These basic principles, under their respective divisions are as follows:

I. Use of the human body

    a) Both hands should begin and end their basic divisions of accomplishment simultaneously and should not be idle at the same instant, except during rest periods.

    b) The motions made by the hands should be made symmetrically and simultaneously away and toward the center of the body.

    c) Momentum should be employed to assist the worker wherever possible, and it should be reduced to a minimum if it must be overcome by muscular effort.

    d) Continuous curved motions are preferable to straight-line motions involving sudden and sharp changes in direction.

    e) The least number of basic divisions should be used, and these should be confined to the lowest possible classifications. These classifications, summarized in ascending order of time and fatigue expended in their performance, are:
1. Finger motions
2. Finger and wrist motions
3. Finger, wrist, and lower arm motions
4. Finger, wrist, lower arm, and upper arm motions
5. Finger, wrist, lower arm, upper arm, and body motions

    f) Work that can be done by the feet should be arranged so that it is done simultaneously with work being done by the hands.

II. Arrangement and conditions of the workplace

    a) Fixed locations should be provided for all tools and materials so as to permit the best sequence and to eliminate or reduce the therbligs search, select, and find.

    b) Gravity bins and drop delivery should be used to reduce reach and move times; also ejectors should be provided wherever possible to remove finished parts automatically.

    c) All materials and tools should be located within the normal area in both the vertical and horizontal planes.

    d) A comfortable chair should be provided for the operator and the height so arranged that the work can be efficiently performed by the operator alternately standing and sitting.

    e) Proper illumination, ventilation, and temperature should be provided.

---

[2] *Ibid.*

    f) Visual requirements of the workplace should be considered so that eye fixation demands are minimized.

    g) Rhythm is essential to the smooth and automatic performance of an operation, and the work should be arranged to permit an easy and natural rhythm wherever possible.

III. Design of tools and equipment

    a) Multiple cuts should be taken whenever possible by combining two or more tools in one, or by arranging simultaneous cuts from both feeding devices if available (cross slide and hex turret).

    b) All levers, handles, wheels, and other control devices should be readily accessible to the operator and should be designed so as to give the best possible mechanical advantage.

    c) Holding parts in position should be done by fixtures.

    d) Always investigate the possibility of powered or semiautomatic tools, such as power nut and screw drivers, speed wrenches, etc.

EXPLANATION OF LAWS OF MOTION ECONOMY

Both hands should begin and end their basic divisions of accomplishments simultaneously and should not be idle at the same instant except during rest periods.

When the right hand is working in the normal area to the right of the body and the left hand is working in the normal area to the left of the body, there is a feeling of balance which tends to induce rhythm in the performance of the operator that leads to maximum performance. When one hand is working under load and the other hand is idle, the body exerts an effort to put itself in balance. This usually results in greater fatigue than if both hands were employed doing useful work. This law can readily be demonstrated by reaching out with the right hand about 14 inches, picking up an object weighing about a half pound and moving it 10 inches toward the body before releasing it. The operation should then be immediately repeated, only this time the part is moved away from the body. Repeat the cycle about 200 times and note the discomfort in the body induced by "balance fatigue." Now repeat the operation using both hands simultaneously. Have the left hand reach out radially to the left of the body and the right hand reach out radially to the right of the body, grasp the objects, move both objects toward the body, and release them simultaneously. Repeat the cycle 200 times and note that the body feels less fatigued, even though twice as much load was handled.

The motions made by the hands should be made symmetrically and simultaneously away and toward the center of the body.

It is natural for the hands to move in symmetrical patterns: deviations from symmetry in a two-handed work station result in slow, awkward movements of the operator. The difficulty of patting the stomach with the left hand while rubbing the top of the head with the right hand is familiar to many. Another experiment that can readily be tried to illustrate the difficulty of performing nonsymmetrical operations is to draw a circle with the left hand while the right hand is drawing a square. Figure 7–1 illustrates an ideal work station that allows the operator to assemble a typewriter by going through a series of symmetrical motions made simultaneously away and toward the center of the body.

Momentum should be employed to assist the worker wherever possible, and it should be reduced to a minimum if it must be overcome by muscular effort.

As the hands progress through the elements of work comprising the operation, momentum will be developed during reach and move therbligs and will be overcome during position and release therbligs. In order to make full use of the momentum that is built up, work stations should be designed so that a finished part can be released in a delivery area while the hands are on their way to get component parts or tools to begin the next work cycle. This allows the hands to perform their reaches with the aid of momentum and makes the therblig easier and faster to perform.

Courtesy: Royal Typewriter Company

FIG. 7–1. An ideal work station that permits the operator to assemble a typewriter by going through a series of symmetrical motions made simultaneously away from and toward the center of the body.

Detailed studies have proven conclusively that both reaches and moves are performed faster if the hand is in motion at the beginning of the therblig.

Continuous curved motions are preferable to straight-line motions involving sudden and sharp changes in direction.

This law is very easily demonstrated by moving either hand in a rectangular pattern, and then moving it in a circular pattern of about the same magnitude. The greater amount of time required to make the abrupt ninety degree directional changes is quite apparent. In order to make a directional change, the hand must decelerate, change direction, accelerate until it is time to decelerate preparatory to the next directional change. Continuous curved motions do not require deceleration, and consequently are performed faster per unit of distance.

The least number of basic divisions should be used and these should be confined to the lowest practicable classifications.

In order to become fully aware of the significance of this fundamental law of motion economy, it is first necessary to be able to identify the various classifications of motions.

1. The finger motion is the fastest of the five motion classes and is readily recognized, as it is made by moving the finger or fingers while the remainder of the arm is kept stationary. Typical finger motions are running a nut down on a stud, depressing the keys of a typewriter, grasping a small part, etc. Usually there is a significant difference in time required to perform finger motions with the various fingers. The index finger in most cases will be able to move considerably faster than the other fingers, and in the design of work stations this should be taken into consideration. Although with practice the fingers of the left hand (in right-handed people) can be trained to move with the same rapidity as the fingers of the right hand, detailed studies have shown that the fingers of the left hand will move somewhat slower. R. E. Hoke made a study of the "universal" keyboard used on typewriters and found that 88.9 taps could be made with the fingers of the left hand for every 100 made with the right hand.[3]

The analyst should recognize that the finger motion is the weakest of the five motion classes. Consequently, care should be exercised in designing work stations involving great manual effort so that higher classifications than finger motion may be employed.

2. Finger and wrist motions are made by movements of the wrist and fingers while the forearm and upper arm are stationary. In the majority

[3] R. E. Hoke, *The Improvement of Speed and Accuracy in Typewriting* (The Johns Hopkins University Studies in Education No. 7) (Baltimore: The Johns Hopkins Press, 1922).

of cases, finger and wrist motions consume more time than strictly finger motions. Typical finger and wrist motions occur when positioning a part in a jig or fixture or when assemblying two mating parts. Reach and move therbligs usually cannot be performed by motions of the second class unless the transport distances are very short.

3. The finger, wrist, and lower arm motions are commonly referred to as "forearm" motions and include those movements made by the arm below the elbow while the upper arm is stationary. Since the forearm includes a strong muscle, this motion is usually considered efficient, as it is not fatiguing. The time required to make forearm motions for a given operator is dependent on the distance moved and the amount of resistance overcome during the movement. By designing work stations so that these third-class motions will be used to perform the transport therbligs rather than fourth-class motions, the analyst will minimize cycle times.

4. The finger, wrist, lower arm, and upper arm motion, commonly known as the fourth-class or shoulder motion, is probably used more than any one single motion class. The fourth-class motion for a given distance takes considerably more time than the three lower classes just described. Fourth-class motions are required to perform transport therbligs of parts that cannot be reached without extending the arm. The time required to perform fourth-class motions is dependent primarily on the distance of the move and the resistance to the move.

5. Fifth-class motions include body movements and those of course are the most time consuming. Body motions include ankle, knee, and thigh motions as well as body trunk motions.

It will be noted that the first-class motion requires the least amount of effort and time, whereas the fifth class is considered to be the least efficient. Therefore, the analyst should always endeavor to utilize the lowest practicable motion classification with which to properly perform the work. This will involve careful consideration of the location of tools and materials so that ideal motion patterns can be arranged.

Work that can be done by the feet should be arranged so that it is done simultaneously with work done by the hands.

Since the majority of work cycles are performed by the hands, it follows that it is economical to relieve the hands of work that can be done by the feet, if this work is being performed while the hands are occupied. Since the hands are more dexterous than the feet, it would be folly to have the feet perform elements while the hands were idle. Foot pedal arrangement allowing clamping, ejection of parts, feeding, etc., can often be arranged, thus freeing the hands for useful work and consequently reducing the cycle time (see Figure 7–2).

Fixed locations should be provided for all tools and materials so as to permit the best sequence and to eliminate or reduce the therbligs search, select, and find.

FIG. 7–2. Foot pedal arrangement on a Brown & Sharpe plain milling machine, used to start and stop machine operation, leaving operators' hands free to load and unload work.

In driving an automobile, we are all familiar with the shortness of time required to apply the foot brake. The reason is obvious; since the brake pedal is in a fixed location, no time is required to decide where the brake is located. The body responds instinctively and applies pressure to the area where the driver knows the foot pedal will be. If the location of the brake foot pedal varied from time to time, considerably more time would be needed to apply braking to the car. By providing fixed location for all tools and materials at the work station, the short hesitations required to search, select, and find the various objects needed to do the work will be eliminated or at least minimized (see Figure 7–3).

Courtesy: Westinghouse Electric Corp.

FIG. 7–3. Fixed locations for all materials and tools are provided in this work station thus minimizing search and select hesitations.

Gravity bins and drop delivery should be used to reduce reach and move times.

The time required to perform both of the transport therbligs, reach and move, is proportional to the distance that the hands must move in performing these elements. By utilizing gravity bins, components can be continuously brought to the normal working area, thus eliminating long reaches in order to get supplies of parts. Likewise, gravity chutes allow disposal of parts within the normal area, thus eliminating the necessity for long moves to dispose of the completed part or parts. Gravity chutes make possible a clean workplace area, as finished material will be carried away from the work area rather than stacked up all round the workplace (see Figure 7–4).

All materials and tools should be located within the normal area in both the vertical and horizontal plane.

The normal working area in the horizontal plane of the right hand includes the area generated by the arm below the elbow when moving in an arc pivoted at the elbow. This area will represent the most convenient

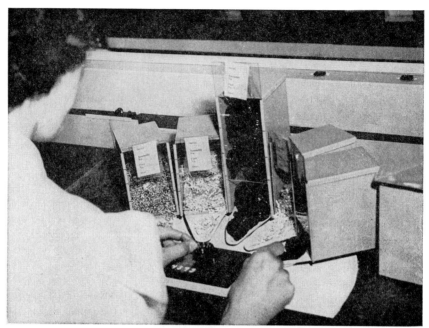

Courtesy: Alden Systems Co.

FIG. 7–4. Work station utilizing gravity bins and belt conveyor to reduce reach and move times. Note the conveyor in the background carrying other parts by this particular work station. Operator is feeding on to the conveyor from under the platform by merely dropping assembled parts on to feeder belt.

zone within which motions may be made by that hand with a normal expenditure of energy.

In a similar manner the normal area may be established by the left hand.

Since movements are made in the third dimension as well as in the horizontal plane, the normal working area applies to the vertical plane as well. The normal area relative to height for the right hand includes the area made by the lower arm in an upright position hinged at the elbow moving in an arc. In like manner there is a normal area for the left hand in a vertical plane (see Figures 7–5 and 7–6).

The maximum working area represents that portion of the workplace within which all tools and materials should be located and where work may be performed without excessive fatigue. This area is formed by drawing arcs with the arms fully extended and, as in the case of the normal working area, both the horizontal and vertical planes are considered.

In the design of both facilities and work stations, consideration should be given to such factors as arm reach, leg clearance, and body support as these human dimensions are important criteria in developing worker environment that is comfortable and efficient. The human dimensions

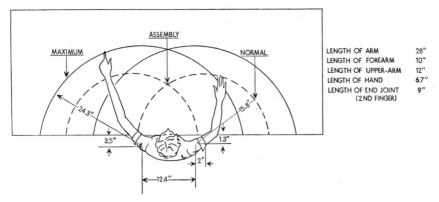

FIG. 7–5. Normal and maximum working areas in the horizontal plane for women. For men, multiply by 1.09.

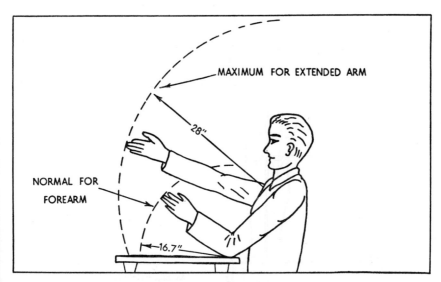

FIG. 7–6. Normal and maximum working areas in the vertical plane for women. For men, multiply by 1.09.

shown in Figures 7–7 and 7–8 should be used as a basis for the design of operation work stations.

Comfortable chair should be provided for the operator and the height so arranged that the work can be efficiently performed by the operator alternately standing and sitting.

The stool or chair used by the operator should receive careful attention in order to reduce operator fatigue. In general, the chair or bench seats should be broad, not too deep, with a contour slightly saddle-shaped and the front end chamfered. Wherever possible, backs should be provided for all chairs, and these should be designed so that they do not

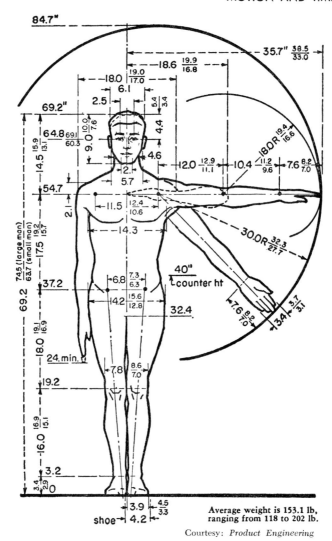

FIG. 7–7. Dimensions of the average adult male based on the 2½ to 97½ per cent range of measured subjects.

Courtesy: *Product Engineering*

interfere with movements of the arms. Chair manufacturers supply industrial chairs that are adjustable in height from the floor to the top edge of the seat. In recent years, both industrial and medical experts have collected data that in many instances prove that production costs have been lowered by using chairs and benches of proper height (see Figure 7–8).

If the height of the work station and chair is made so that the operator can alternately work in a standing and a sitting position, fatigue and job monotony will be substantially reduced. Monotony is definitely

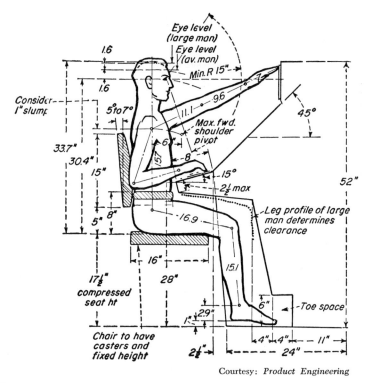

Courtesy: *Product Engineering*

FIG. 7–8. Seating is dependent on reach, vision, and work load on the operator. Dimensions shown are based on the small man, which will accommodate the reach limitations of 95 per cent of all men.

an important factor in producing fatigue, and with the present-day tendency toward specialization and resulting increases in fatigue accidents, everything possible should be done to reduce monotony.

In the event it is not practical to have the operator work alternately in a standing and sitting position, it has been found desirable to have a seat which can slightly tilt the body forward.

Proper illumination, ventilation, and temperature should be incorporated when possible.

As explained in Chapter 5, good, comfortable working conditions are fundamental for peak production and operator satisfaction. Defective illumination has long been recognized as being an important factor in causing operator fatigue, poor quality of product, and low production output. The National Safety Council in its Safe Practices Pamphlet No. 50, mentions that eyes are used in "serious" work about 70 per cent of the time and that failure to provide proper lighting will increase consumption of body energy (see Figure 7–9).

Ventilation and temperature are also important considerations in main-

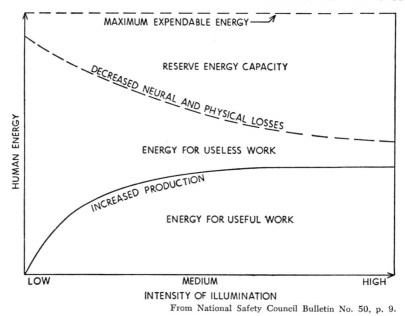

MAXIMUM EXPENDABLE ENERGY

RESERVE ENERGY CAPACITY

DECREASED NEURAL AND PHYSICAL LOSSES

ENERGY FOR USELESS WORK

INCREASED PRODUCTION

ENERGY FOR USEFUL WORK

HUMAN ENERGY

LOW   MEDIUM   HIGH

INTENSITY OF ILLUMINATION

From National Safety Council Bulletin No. 50, p. 9.

FIG. 7–9.   Better illumination releases energy for useful work.

taining good working conditions by controlling fatigue and accident causes. Laboratory data recorded in diversified industries are in agreement that atmospheric conditions exert an appreciable influence upon physical activity.

Members of the medical profession, industrialists, and psychologists have realized that colors are effective in stimulating or depressing. By having physical surroundings that relieve eyestrain and stimulate the worker by creating a more cheerful atmosphere, the industry will have fewer injuries and less absenteeism.

Visual requirements of the workplace should be considered so that eye fixation demands are minimized.

Certain visual requirements are characteristic of all work centers. Some equipment or controls may be scanned from nearby or remote points. Other areas will require more concentrated attention. By prepositioning those components requiring more concentrated observation, such as instruments and dials, not only will less eye fixation time be required but less eye fatigue on the part of the operator will result. Visual control areas are illustrated in Figure 7–10.

Rhythm is essential to the smooth and automatic performance of an operation, and the work should be arranged to permit an easy and natural rhythm wherever possible.

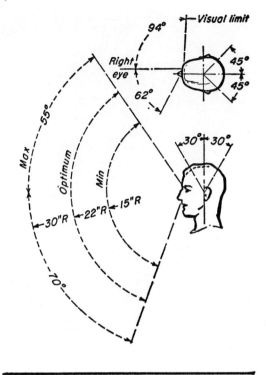

Courtesy: *Product Engineering*

FIG. 7–10. Effective visual areas for average employee.

If the sequence of basic motions performed can be arranged so there is a regular recurrence of like therbligs, or a regular alteration in like therbligs, the hands will instinctively work with a rhythmical effect. When work is performed with such a regularity or flow of movement, the operator appears to be working effortlessly yet invariably production is high and operator fatigue is low.

Multiple cuts should be taken whenever possible by combining two or more tools in one, or by arranging simultaneous cuts from both feeding devices if available (cross slide and hex turret).

Production planning in advance for the most efficient manufacture will include taking multiple cuts through combination tools and simultaneous cuts from different tools. Of course, the type of work to be processed and the number of parts to be produced will determine the desirability of combining cuts such as from the square turret and the hexagon turret. Figures 7–11 and 7–12 illustrate typical combined and multiple cuts that can be utilized in turret lathe work (see also Figure 7–13).

Courtesy: Warner & Swasey Co.

FIG. 7-11. Multiple and combined cut being performed on Warner & Swasey turret lathe. Two turning cuts are being taken while the part is being drilled from the hex turret.

All levers, handles, wheels, and other control devices should be readily accessible to the operator and should be designed so as to give the best possible mechanical advantage.

Many of our machine tools and other devices are mechanically perfect, yet are incapable of effective operation because the designer of the facility overlooked the various human factors in the operation of the equipment. Handwheels, cranks, and levers should be of such size and placed in such positions that operator manipulation can be done with greatest proficiency and with a minimum of fatigue.

Detailed studies have determined that for a given control location there is a definite point at which the size of the control and operator performance changes, so that performance at different control locations varies with the "36-in. height, horizontal axis, 0-degree position location which is commonly found on machine tools."[4]

Holding parts in position should be done by fixtures.

---

[4] Louis E. Davis, "Human Factors in Design of Manual Machine Controls," *Mechanical Engineering*, October, 1949.

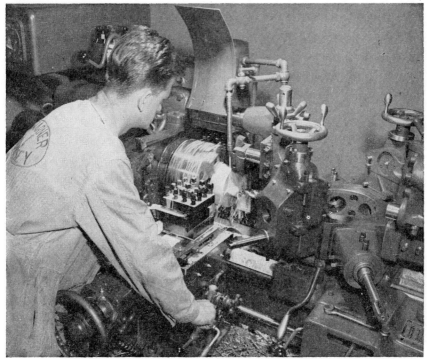

Courtesy: Warner & Swasey Co.

FIG. 7–12. A single turning cut from the cross slide combined with a drilling operation from the hex turret give a combined cut on this alloy steel part.

The hand is seldom an efficient holding device because, when it is occupied in holding the work, it cannot be free to do useful work. Parts to be held in position while being worked on should be supported by a fixture, thereby freeing the hands for productive motions. Fixtures not only save time in processing parts, but they permit better quality, in that the work can be held more accurately and firmly. Figure 7–14 illustrates a dual fixture for drilling two pieces simultaneously.

Investigate the possibility of powered or semiautomatic tools, such as power nut and screw drivers, speed wrenches, etc.

Power hand tools will not only perform work faster than manual tools but will do the work with considerably less operator fatigue. Greater uniformity of product can be expected when power hand tools are used. For example, a power nut driver will drive nuts consistently to a predetermined tightness in inch-pounds, whereas a manual nut driver cannot be expected to maintain constant driving pressure in view of operator fatigue.

Courtesy: Warner & Swasey Co.

FIG. 7–13. Two turning cuts being taken from the hex turret on a cast-iron workpiece. The turning tool holders are mounted in a multiple turning head which has an overhead pilot bar support for maximum rigidity.

Courtesy: Westinghouse Electric Corp.

FIG. 7–14. Dual drilling fixture allows drilling of two parts simultaneously.

PRACTICAL USE OF MOTION STUDY IN THE PLANNING STAGE

Motion Analysis As Applied in Planning

Production men in general agree that it is better to concentrate thinking about method improvement in the planning stage, rather than depend entirely on trying to correct manufacturing methods after they have been introduced. Insufficient volume may make it impossible to consider later many improvement proposals which might have been introduced in the planning stage with substantial saving over existing methods.

For example, let us take an operation that was done on a drill press in which a one-half inch hole was reamed to the tolerance of .500″/.502″. The activity of the job was estimated to be 100,000 pieces. The time study department established a standard of 8.33 hours per thousand to perform the reaming operation and the reaming fixture cost $500.00.

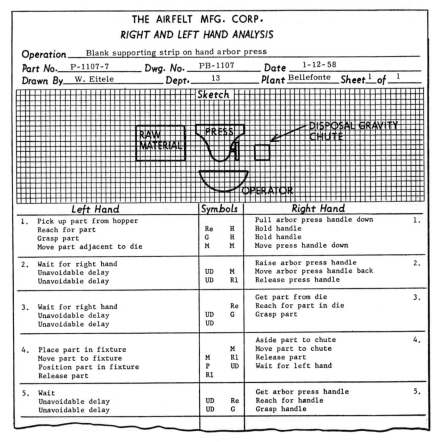

THE AIRFELT MFG. CORP.

RIGHT AND LEFT HAND ANALYSIS

Operation _____ Blank supporting strip on hand arbor press _____

Part No. __P-1107-7__ Dwg. No. __PB-1107__ Date __1-12-58__

Drawn By __W. Eitele__ Dept. __13__ Plant __Bellefonte__ Sheet __1__ of __1__

Sketch

RAW MATERIAL PRESS DISPOSAL GRAVITY CHUTE OPERATOR

Left Hand	Symbols		Right Hand	
1. Pick up part from hopper			Pull arbor press handle down	1.
Reach for part	Re	H	Hold handle	
Grasp part	G	H	Hold handle	
Move part adjacent to die	M	M	Move press handle down	
2. Wait for right hand			Raise arbor press handle	2.
Unavoidable delay	UD	M	Move arbor press handle back	
Unavoidable delay	UD	Rl	Release press handle	
3. Wait for right hand		Re	Get part from die	3.
Unavoidable delay	UD		Reach for part in die	
Unavoidable delay	UD	G	Grasp part	
4. Place part in fixture		M	Aside part to chute	4.
Move part to fixture	M	Rl	Move part to chute	
Position part in fixture	P	UD	Release part	
Release part	Rl		Wait for left hand	
5. Wait			Get arbor press handle	5.
Unavoidable delay	UD	Re	Reach for handle	
Unavoidable delay	UD	G	Grasp handle	

FIG. 7–15. Right- and left-hand analysis of a proposed method of a blanking operation.

Since a base rate of $1.80 per hour was in effect, the money rate per thousand pieces was $15.00.

Now let us assume that a methods analyst suggests broaching the inside diameter because his calculations reveal that the part can be broached at the rate of 5.00 hours per thousand. This would be a saving of 3.33 hours per thousand pieces, or a total saving of 333 hours. At our $1.80 base rate this would mean a direct labor savings of $599.40. However, it would not be practical to go ahead with this idea, as the tool cost for broaching is $700. Thus, the change would not be sound unless the labor savings can be increased to $700 so as to offset the cost of the new broaching tools.

Since the labor savings in a new broaching setup would be 3.33 × $1.80 per thousand, it can be calculated that 116,800 pieces would have to be ordered before the change in tooling would be justified.

$$\frac{\$700 \times 1000}{\$1.80 \times 3.33/M} = 116,800 \text{ pieces.}$$

However, if the broaching method had been used originally instead of the reaming procedure, it would have paid for itself in

$$\frac{\$700 - \$500}{\$1.80 \times 3.33/M} = 33,400 \text{ pieces.}$$

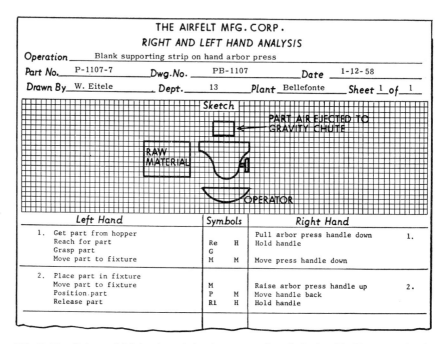

FIG. 7–16. Right- and left-hand analysis of a proposed method of a blanking operation in which unavoidable delays have been omitted.

With production requirements of 100,000 pieces, 3.33 × $1.80 × 66.6 thousands (difference between 100,000 and 33,400) = $398.00 in labor would have been saved over the present reaming method. Had a motion analysis been made in the planning stage this saving might have been realized.

FIG. 7–17. Components of upper jaw of pipe vise. Parts in order of assembly (left to right) are shown above, and parts assembled are shown below.

By keeping the laws of motion economy in mind, and breaking the proposed method into its basic divisions, it is possible to develop a right-hand, left-hand analysis prior to the starting of production. Then by assigning synthetic time values to the various elements of the operator process chart (see Chapter 10), the practicability of the proposed method can be determined. Let us see how this technique is practiced on a simple manufacturing job. The job involves:

1. A light blanking operation.
2. Low annual production requirements (200,000 pieces per year).
3. Competitive price.

With these requirements in mind, the methods analyst proposes performing the job on an arbor press with accompanying die to do the trimming. He then breaks the job down in the form of a right- and left-hand process chart as shown in Figure 7–15.

A review of this operator process chart reveals that several of the laws of motion economy have been violated. Motions of the right hand

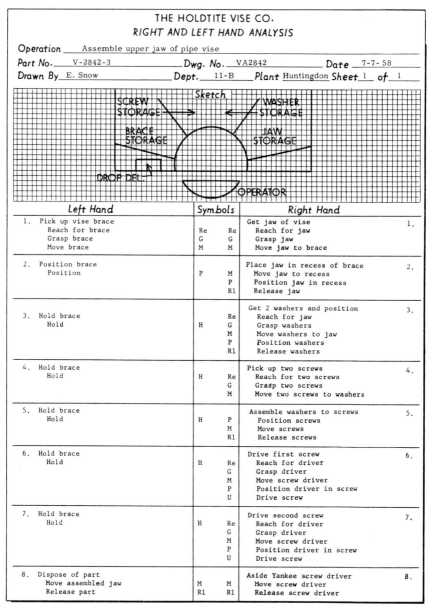

THE HOLDTITE VISE CO.
RIGHT AND LEFT HAND ANALYSIS

Operation _____ Assemble upper jaw of pipe vise _____
Part No. _____ V-2842-3 _____ Dwg. No. _____ VA2842 _____ Date _____ 7-7-58 _____
Drawn By _____ E. Snow _____ Dept. _____ 11-B _____ Plant Huntingdon Sheet 1 of 1

Sketch

SCREW STORAGE → ← WASHER STORAGE
BRACE STORAGE / JAW STORAGE
DROP DEL.
OPERATOR

Left Hand	Symbols		Right Hand
1. Pick up vise brace			Get jaw of vise 1.
Reach for brace	Re	Re	Reach for jaw
Grasp brace	G	G	Grasp jaw
Move brace	M	M	Move jaw to brace
2. Position brace			Place jaw in recess of brace 2.
Position	P	M	Move jaw to recess
		P	Position jaw in recess
		R1	Release jaw
3. Hold brace			Get 2 washers and position 3.
Hold	H	Re	Reach for jaw
		G	Grasp washers
		M	Move washers to jaw
		P	Position washers
		R1	Release washers
4. Hold brace			Pick up two screws 4.
Hold	H	Re	Reach for two screws
		G	Grasp two screws
		M	Move two screws to washers
5. Hold brace			Assemble washers to screws 5.
Hold	H	P	Position screws
		M	Move screws
		R1	Release screws
6. Hold brace			Drive first screw 6.
Hold	H	Re	Reach for driver
		G	Grasp driver
		M	Move screw driver
		P	Position driver in screw
		U	Drive screw
7. Hold brace			Drive second screw 7.
Hold	H	Re	Reach for driver
		G	Grasp driver
		M	Move screw driver
		P	Position driver in screw
		U	Drive screw
8. Dispose of part			Aside Yankee screw driver 8.
Move assembled jaw	M	M	Move screw driver
Release part	R1	R1	Release screw driver

FIG. 7–18. Right- and left-hand analysis of assembly of pipe vise jaw.

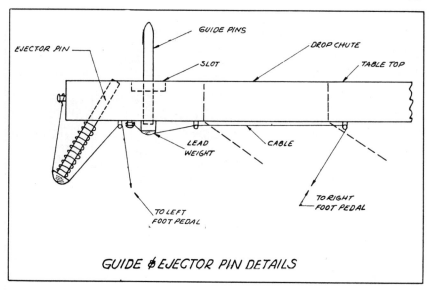

FIG. 7–19. Guide and ejector pin details for foot-operated mechanism.

and the left hand are not balanced, unavoidable delays occur in the pattern of the left hand, and both hands do not finish their work simultaneously.

Analysis of the poor setup discloses that the first wait of the left hand is during the period the right hand raises the handle of the arbor press. The left hand is then kept idle while the right hand removes the part from the die, and finally, is unavoidably delayed while the right hand reaches out to gain control of the arbor press handle.

It can also readily be seen that the right hand must grasp the arbor press handle every cycle as a result of relinquishing it earlier in the cycle in order to remove the finished part from the die. Therefore, if the operator did not have to remove the finished piece from the die, he would also be freed of the element "grasp arbor press handle." The improved method in the form of an operator process chart is shown in Figure 7–16.

If this method should be put in operation, we should have a balanced setup with considerably shorter cycle time. It is possible to develop a fixture to include leaf springs which will lift the part clear of the die on the return stroke of the arbor press. The piece can then be automatically ejected through the back of the press by an air blast actuated from the ram of the press.

This motion analysis in the planning stage allows the part to be blanked in the most economical manner.

Let us take another example and see how motion study in the planning stage helps determine the ideal method. The operation under study is the assembly of the components going into the upper jaw of a pipe vise. The parts involved are the jaw, brace, two lock washers, and two ma-

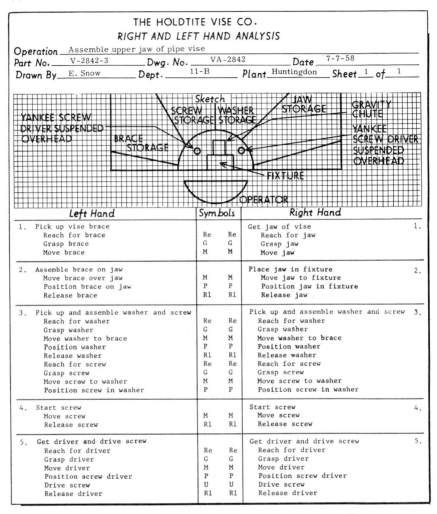

FIG. 7–20. Right- and left-hand analysis of proposed setup for assembly of pipe jaw vise.

chine screws (see Figure 7–17). The production schedule called for assembly of 10,000 of these units per year and the item must be priced to meet stiff competition.

Since the parts are all small and can be readily controlled with either hand, the method analyst may first consider hand assembly at a bench, with the operator seated and all parts fed to the normal work area by gravity bins. This method in the form of a right- and left-hand analysis would appear as shown in Figure 7–18.

A quick review of this method discloses that the left hand is ineffectively employed the majority of the cycle, since it is occupied by the therblig "hold" in five distinct areas. In order to alleviate this condition, the analyst considers making a fixture to hold the part. So as to eliminate

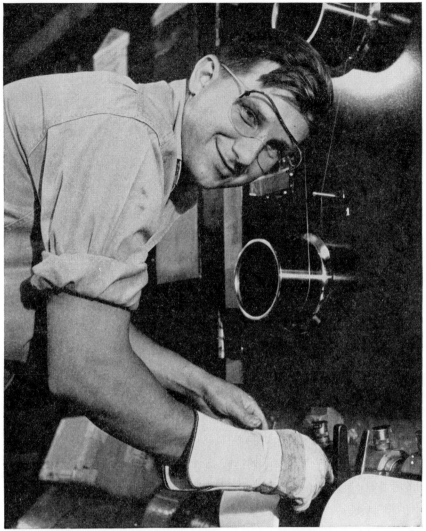

Courtesy: E. I. du Pont de Nemours & Co.

FIG. 7–21. Work station for doffing yarn.

the element "dispose of part," he introduces an ejector pin actuated by a foot pedal (see Figure 7–19). This ejects the part into an accompanying gravity chute. In order to dispose of the element "lay aside yankee screw driver," he suspends the tool overhead. So as to permit a balanced two-handed motion pattern throughout the cycle, an additional yankee screw driver is suspended overhead for the left hand. Thus both screws can be driven home simultaneously with the aid of self-aligning sleeves incorporated in the fixture. Through the use of fundamental motion data, it can be estimated that the improved method will increase the produc-

FIG. 7–22. Stroboscopic photograph showing motion pattern prior to motion planning on yarn doffing operation.

FIG. 7–23. Stroboscopic photograph showing motion pattern after motion planning on yarn doffing operation.

tivity by at least 50 per cent. A right- and left-hand analysis of this proposed method would appear as shown in Figure 7–20.

Figure 7–21 shows a work station for a "doffing yarn" operation. Figure 7–22 illustrates the motion pattern that the operator was following. The operation in this case was not planned and by means of stroboscopic photography, it can be seen that the operator was going through an elaborate body motion pattern. The planned method shown in Figure 7–23 reduced the number and difficulty of the motions so that the operator is less fatigued and his production is greatly improved.

The application of the laws of motion economy and an understanding of the therblig concept prove invaluable in establishing ideal methods in the planning stage, as well as improving existing methods.

TEXT QUESTIONS

1. When is micromotion study practical?
2. Define and give examples of the seventeen fundamental motions, or therbligs.
3. How may the basic motion search be eliminated from the work cycle?
4. What basic motion generally precedes reach?
5. What three variables affect the time for the basic motion move?
6. How does the analyst or observer determine when the operator is performing the element inspect?
7. Explain the difference between avoidable and unavoidable delays.
8. Why should fixed locations be provided at the work station for all tools and materials?
9. Which of the five classes of motion is the one most used by industrial workers?
10. Why is it desirable to have the feet working only when the hands are occupied?
11. Explain the significance of human dimensions.

GENERAL QUESTIONS

1. Which of the seventeen therbligs are classed as effective, and usually cannot be removed from the work cycle?
2. Take an operation out of your daily routine such as dressing, analyze it through the operator process chart, and try to improve the efficiency of your movements.
3. Explain why effective visual areas are reduced where concentrated attention will be required.

CHAPTER 8

Micromotion Study

THE COST OF CONDUCTING A MI-
cromotion study is approximately four times as great as the cost of conducting a visual motion study of the same operation. Consequently, it
is only when the activity of a specific job or class of work is high that it
is economically sound to utilize moving pictures for motion study. The
term "micromotion study" is used to signify the making of a detailed
motion study employing the motion-picture technique. Here each space
occupied by a single picture on the moving picture film, known as a
frame, is projected and studied independently, and then collectively
with successive frames.

The basic division-of-motion or therblig concept is usually more important in making a micromotion study than in conducting a visual motion study, in that a work assignment can more readily be broken down
into basic elements with the frame-by-frame analysis than when visual
motion studies are made. Since the object of the micromotion procedure
is to uncover every possible opportunity for improvement, down to the
performance of each therblig, it is fundamental that the analyst be able
to identify each basic division as performed.

Those laws of motion economy cited in Chapter 7 are equally valid in
micromotion study work. In fact, they should be expanded to include
the following corollaries:

A. Use of the human body
    1. Habits of best sequences of therbligs should be established.
    2. Any substantial variation in time required for a given therblig should
       be investigated and the cause determined.
    3. Hesitations should be carefully examined and analyzed so as to de-
       termine causes and then to eliminate them.

4. Cycles and portions of cycles completed in the least amount of time should be used as a goal to attain. Deviations from these minimum times should be studied in order to determine cause.

B. Arrangement and conditions of the workplace

1. Tools and materials should be located so as to allow the best possible sequence of therbligs, thus automatically building up rhythm in ballistic type movements that are faster, easier, and more accurate.

Preparing for the Micromotion Study

It is usually advisable to take motion pictures of the operation or operations to be studied in the laboratory provided for the purpose. This allows making the study without the interferences that would be encountered on the production floor, and permits taking adequate time so as to assure first-class pictures. Also, difficulty in providing such aids as adequate light, three-dimensional background (see Figure 8–1), and timing devices in the factory make taking of pictures in a laboratory more satisfactory.

Of course, at times it will be necessary to take the pictures outside of the laboratory, as for certain machine operations when it would be impractical to provide the facility in the laboratory. In fact, in the interest of economy, several industries today take all of their studies at the regular workplace in the factory. Satisfactory pictures can be made in this manner, but they will be assured if taken in the laboratory.

In making a micromotion study, it is wise to study either the best or, preferably, the best two operators. This procedure is quite different from time study where usually an average operator is selected for study (see Chapter 14). It is not always possible because the operation might be performed by only one person. In such instances, if past performance indicates that the individual is only a fair or a poor operator, then a competent, skilled, co-operative employee should be trained in the operation before the pictures are taken. Only first-class, proficient operators should be selected for filming. This is fundamental for a number of reasons: the proficient employee is usually a dexterous individual who will instinctively follow the laws of motion economy related to the use of the human body; this type of operator is usually co-operative and willing to be photographed; extra effort put forth by this operator will show greater results than when similar effort is employed by the mediocre person.

If the best two operators have been studied, analysis will indicate proficiency in different areas of the cycle for the two men. This may lead to greater improvement than if only one individual is studied.

The people who are being studied should be given at least a day's notice prior to the taking of the motion picture. This allows them to make any personal preparations they may wish and also permits them

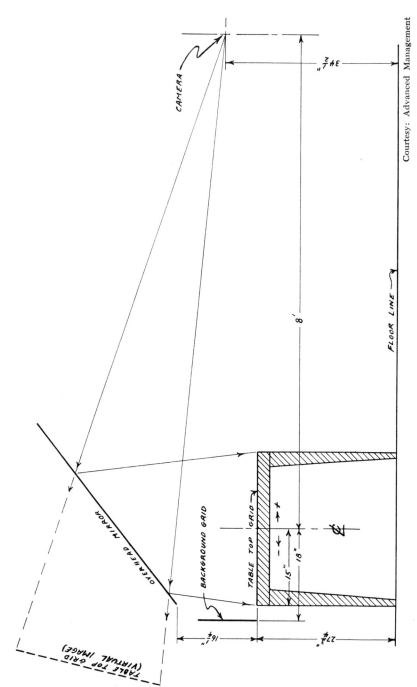

Courtesy: Advanced Management

FIG. 8–1. Schematic drawing of camera, overhead mirror, and workbench used for film analysis of operator movements.

to choose wearing apparel that will be conducive to making clear pictures.

In order to secure the co-operation of the foreman, it is essential that he be advised of the plans several days in advance. This is necessary so that he will be able to adjust his personnel in order to assure that his projected production schedules will be maintained. Interruptions brought about by film analysis work may cause a given section to lose several valuable man-hours, and if the foreman is not given advance notice of contemplated motion study work involving his section, he can hardly be expected to be co-operative.

Micromotion Study as a Training Aid

In addition to being used as a method improvement tool, micromotion study is finding increasing use as a training aid. The world of sports has used this tool for many years, for the purpose of developing timing of movement, rhythm, and smoothness of performance in various athletes. Motion pictures are made of outstanding performers in a given sport, and then the pictures are enlarged several times and projected on the screen so as to facilitate detailed analysis of their motions. Less proficient performers are then able to pattern their efforts after the experts.

Industry is finding that it can attain the same results accomplished in the area of athletics. By filming highly skilled workmen and showing the pictures in slow motion and highly enlarged, it is possible to train new employees in a minimum of time to follow the ideal motion-method pattern.

One Pennsylvania concern engaged in the manufacture of loose-leaf notebooks, writing paper, envelopes, tablets, and similar paper items continually takes motion pictures for training purposes, not only in its own plant but in affiliated plants. By continually exchanging motion pictures taken at the different plants, they can take advantage of method improvements introduced throughout the corporation, and they are able to train their employees in following the new method in a minimum of time.

Management should take full advantage of the industrial movies, once a micromotion program is launched. By showing all pictures taken of the various operations to the operators involved and to their fellow workers, immeasurable goodwill and individual interest are established throughout the organization. Once operators understand the usefulness and need of micromotion study, their assistance can be enlisted in the working out of improved methods.

Micromotion Equipment

In order to be able to do an acceptable job in micromotion study, it will be necessary to budget a minimum of $1,500 for camera, projection equipment, and the other facilities necessary to carry out a complete program. This figure is only a rough approximation based on current prices and can fluctuate appreciably in either direction as market conditions change.

Today, industrial pictures are almost altogether confined to 16mm. and this size equipment will prove to be quite satisfactory. It offers an excellent alternative to the high-cost 35mm. equipment and the lack of detail experienced with 8mm. facilities.

The Motion-Picture Camera

The most important piece of equipment in micromotion work is the camera. Several acceptable cameras are on the market today, each having certain desirable features. Some cameras are equipped with spring drive, others with electric motor drive, and some provide both of these drives in the same camera. Straight spring-driven cameras are on the average about 30 per cent lower in cost than constant speed, motor-driven cameras, and offer the additional advantage of not requiring a nearby power source. In general, the film capacity of the spring-driven camera is as large or larger than that of its motor-driven companion.

The principal disadvantage of the spring-driven camera is that rewinding is a periodic necessity. The operator may forget to do this and have to stop and rewind at a critical point in the job being studied. A decade ago these cameras sometimes failed to maintain an even speed, but the better spring-driven cameras on the market today run at a speed sufficiently constant to offer no problem in this respect.

Electric, synchronous, motor-driven cameras assure constant speed exposure, and thus it is not necessary to include a microchronometer or other timing device in the background of the pictures being taken.

FIG. 8–2. Eastman Cine-Kodak Special II camera equipped with 200-foot magazine, standard Kodak Cine Ektar f/1.4 lens and accessory Kodak Cine Ektar 102mm. f/2.7 (long-focus) lens.

FIG. 8–3.   Eastman Cine-
Kodak Special II camera.

Standard models are available which allow speeds of either 1 frame per second, 10 frames per second, or 1,000 frames per minute. The latter, being the most popular for motion study work, is slightly faster than the normal camera speed of 960 frames per minute (see Figures 8–2 and 8–3).

The Lens

In selecting a camera, one must consider the matter of "picture-making scope."[1] This depends almost entirely on the lens and the shutter.

The larger a lens is in relation to its focal length, which is the distance from the lens to the film, the more light will be admitted during a given period, and the more light per interval, the greater the scope given to the camera.

Often we hear the term "speed" referred to when describing the lens of the camera. By "speed" is meant the comparison of the diameter to the focal length of the lens. Thus, an $f/16$ lens is one whose diameter is one sixteenth of its focal length. Likewise, an $f/3.5$ lens is one in which the diameter is $1/3.5$ of its focal length. From this, it can readily be seen that the larger the f number, the slower the lens and the smaller the f number, the faster the lens. Actually the f number of a lens is determined by the ratio of the focal length and the aperture (diameter of the largest diaphragm opening) at which the lens will be most effective.

The faster a lens, the greater its cost. In order to be assured of good pictures throughout a plant, an $f/1.9$ lens should be provided. This lens will give the versatility needed for almost all industrial pictures. To compare the speeds of two lenses, keep in mind that the speeds will vary

[1] *How to Make Good Pictures,* Eastman Kodak Company, Rochester, N.Y.

inversely as the square of their f numbers. Thus an $f/4$ lens would be sixteen times as fast as an $f/16$ lens (see Figure 8–4).

To be assured of getting good pictures in all situations, three lenses should be provided: one of standard focal length with a field width of

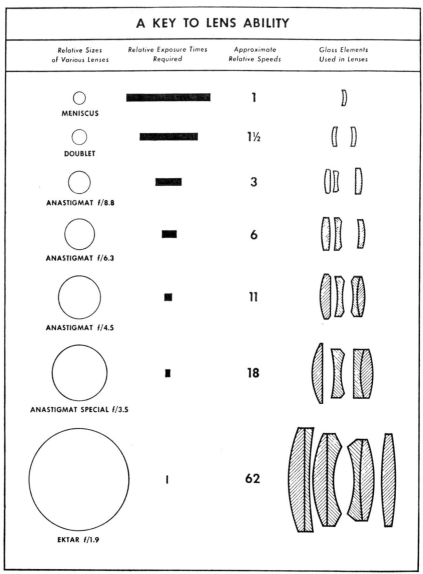

Courtesy: Eastman Kodak Co.

FIG. 8–4. The larger the relative size of the lens, the greater is its speed, or ability to collect light and transmit it to the film—and the shorter the exposure needed under any given light conditions. Notice, also, that as size and ability increase, the lens in general becomes more complex, hence more expensive to make.

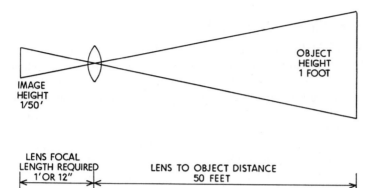

LENS FOCAL
LENGTH REQUIRED   LENS TO OBJECT DISTANCE
|← 1' OR 12" →|←   50 FEET   →|

Courtesy: Eastman Kodak Co.

FIG. 8–5. Relationship of focal length of lens to object size and distance and image size.

approximately 10 feet at a 25-foot distance; a wide-angle lens giving a 15-foot field width at a 25-foot distance; and a long-focus lens with a field width of about three feet at a 25-foot distance (see Figure 8–5).

Often it is not possible to move the camera equipped with only standard lens far enough away from the scene to secure all of the details required. The size of the room or work area may be such that it limits positioning the camera. In cases like this, a wide-angle lens is necessary to broaden and heighten the field of view, so that analysis can be made of the complete work station and all of the operator's movements.

The long-focus lens is employed when it becomes desirable to obtain greater detail, through larger images, than is possible with the standard lens. This situation may frequently arise when studying the finger motions of the operator performing a delicate manipulative operation. In such situations, it would be disturbing to the operator to move the camera as close as would be necessary if only a standard lens were available.

It is well to remember that the wide-angle lens will minimize camera movement, and rock-steady pictures can readily be taken by holding the camera against the head. However, when the long-focus or telephoto lens is put into use, camera movements will be accentuated. Therefore, a tripod must be used in order to get steady pictures when filming with this lens.

The Shutter

It is important that shutter speeds do not vary: all the good effects of a fine lens can be nullified through lack of control of the shutter. The camera purchased must be of such quality that shutter speeds can be depended upon.

Black-and-White versus Color Film

There is usually the consideration of whether or not to use color film. The obvious advantage of color film is its universal appeal when projected on the screen. If the films are shown to members of the production floor for industrial relations purposes, the extra cost of colored film is well justified. Colored film generally costs about one third more than black-and-white reversible film.

To obtain good pictures using colored film requires greater care because lighting is considerably more critical. With the fast lenses and high-speed films available, excellent black-and-white movies can be made with regular industrial lighting fixtures. However, if colored film is used, it is necessary to introduce photographic flood or reflector-type flood lamps. In addition to the high illumination level needed for proper exposure of colored film, it is important that the light be sufficiently dispersed so that all colors are uniformly lighted. This requirement should be met, since contrast in colored photography is provided by differences between colors.

Since less care relative to lighting need be exercised, and the film costs less, it is wise to begin a motion study program by taking black-and-white pictures. As further use of the pictures becomes advisable and experience is gained, it may be well to use colored film.

Light Meter

Even though a broad latitude is given in XX reversible film, judgment should not be relied upon to determine the intensity of the light being cast upon the subject that is to be photographed. A light meter is the only tool that assures an accurate recording of the light intensity. Since the light that strikes the film in the camera is reflected light, it is necessary that this light be measured rather than incident light, which is the light cast upon the subject.

It must be remembered that the exposure should be constant for the film being used. Since exposure equals light times time, it is essential that the quantity of light be known. If the quantity of light is small, the time will be great; conversely, if the amount of light is great, the time will be short.

A photoelectric cell exposure meter is shown in Figure 8–6. A light reading is made by aiming the meter toward the scene and pointing the instrument downward. It is important that the meter is not pointed toward a floodlight or, for outdoor pictures, toward the sky. If this is done, an inflated reading will result in improper setting of the f-stop number and consequent underexposure of the film. Reflected brightness from the scene energizes the light-sensitive photoelectric cell, and intensity is read on the scale in candles per square foot.

Courtesy: Weston Electrical Instrument Corp.

FIG. 8–6. Exposure meter for measuring intensity of reflected light.

Tripod

If the camera is carefully supported against the head, it is possible to get fairly steady pictures. However, more satisfactory pictures will result if the camera is rigidly supported during the picture-taking process.

Rather than construct a homemade tripod to support the camera, it is advisable to purchase one that gives versatility as well as assures rock-steady pictures. The head of the tripod illustrated in Figure 8–2 can be rotated on both a horizontal and vertical axis and when required can be locked in any given position for multiple exposure filming. The legs are adjustable so that pictures can be taken while supporting the camera at heights ranging from 2½ to 5 feet.

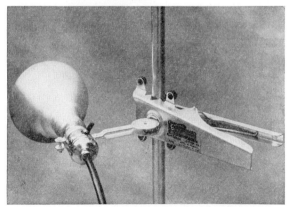

Courtesy: S.O.S. Cinema Supply Corp.

FIG. 8–7. Convenient method of holding floodlight reflector or other accessory. Can be clamped on table or stand and allows positioning of light at any angle.

Floodlights

With the high-speed films and fast lenses available today, black-and-white pictures can be made satisfactorily in a good share of the factory without the aid of supplementary lighting. There will, however, be cases where it may be desirable to take pictures in areas away from windows and light fixtures; then supplementary lighting will be needed in order to assure good pictures.

When additional light is called for, two floodlights will take care of the job. One should be placed close to either side of the camera, while the second should be located so that a 45-degree angle is made between the floodlight and the axis running through the camera and the subject. Figure 8–7 illustrates a photographic flood lamp and reflector equipped with a ball-and-swivel socket to allow positioning at any angle.

Courtesy: Lafayette Instrument Co.

FIG. 8–8. Sixteen millimeter projector equipped with automatic indexer. Designed for film analysis, this projector will index one frame at a time with each press on control button.

Projection Equipment

Many styles and makes of projection equipment are available today and care should be exercised in selecting a projector that will allow:

1. Counting frames.
2. Hand cranking as well as power drive.
3. Variable speed projecting.
4. Clear pictures.

If the projector is equipped with a frame counter, it will save the analyst the laborious, monotonous operation of counting frames while analyzing elemental motions.

The hand-crank attachment is necessary in order to move the film one frame at a time either backward or forward, depending on whether a clockwise or counterclockwise direction is used.

Variable speed is a characteristic which makes the projector more versatile. When this feature is incorporated in the projector, it will be useful for training operators in following the correct method. Also, it will be helpful in training time study men to performance rate or level (see Chapter 15). Figure 8–8 illustrates a 16mm. projector that gives

Courtesy: Lafayette Instrument Co.

FIG. 8–9. Microchronometer.

all the fundamental characteristics required to do a good job of projecting for both motion study and micromotion study work.

Microchronometer

Frank Gilbreth designed a fast-moving, spring-driven clock which recorded time to .0005 minutes. He called his clock a microchronometer and used it for determining elapsed elemental times when viewing his films taken with a hand-cranked camera.

The microchronometer shown in Figure 8–9 is driven by a synchronous motor, thus assuring constant speed. There are 100 divisions on the face of the clock, each having a value of .0005 minutes. The large sweep hand makes a complete revolution in three seconds, while the smaller hand takes 30 seconds to circle the dial.

By placing the microchronometer within the viewing area, the analyst can determine the elapsed time from one frame to the next. It also serves to identify specific cycles or points within a cycle.

Splicer and Viewer

Once the pictures have been taken and developed, they will need to be reviewed for specific titling, removal of certain substandard parts, adjustment of sequence, and so forth. A combination splicer, viewer, and rewinder, as illustrated in Figure 8–10, has been designed to aid in performing the editing function. As the film is passed through the viewer, it

Courtesy: Craig, Inc.

FIG. 8–10. Combination splicer, viewer, and rewinder makes a convenient tool to perform the editing function.

can be decided where the cut should be made. After removal of the censored film, the fixture permits immediate splicing and continued inspection of the film.

Optical Screen

In the analysis of the films, it is not always convenient to set up a screen and then view in darkness or semidarkness the films projected some distance away. In order to allow the analyst to view films at a desk or table and under normal daylight conditions, an optical screen, as illustrated in Figure 8–11, is available. This unit has a recessed area for placing the projector, and the pictures are shown against a mirror inside the enclosed cabinet and placed at an angle of about 45 degrees to the lens of the projector. The mirror then reflects the image to an opal glass pane which is located in the unit directly in front of the analyst. This arrangement permits viewing the pictures at extremely close range so that all details of each frame are clearly observed. Since the pictures are quite sharp even in bright daylight, the analyst can record and plot his data as he goes along without the inconvenience of working in darkness.

FIG. 8–11. Observer is analyzing a film under normal daylight conditions. Note clarity of image on optical screen.

Storage of Films

Damage to films is a result of use or misuse, rather than storage. In the United States, the storage of films represents no major problem, as temperatures and humidities in this country do not deviate greatly from the most desirable storage conditions for films, which is around 40 per cent relative humidity at about 75° F. If stored films begin to show mold growth and fungus, then it is certain that the humidity is too high, and steps should be taken to reduce it. On the other hand, if the films become brittle after being stored a short while, it will be necessary to raise the humidity of the air in the storage area to the proper level.

The 16mm. films available today are produced on a safety base and present no particularly dangerous fire hazard. In fact, the hazard induced is no more severe than that of any newsprint paper stored in the same quantity and form.

Ideally, films should be placed in cans and stored on edge in metal cabinets. The cabinets should not be located in basements or top building floors, as basements invariably are too damp and top floors frequently become too hot in summer. In locating the cabinets, make sure that they are not placed up against a source of heat such as a radiator or steampipe.

Many metal storage cabinets available today allow controlled humidification. When the humidity drops below 25 per cent, the proper amount of moisture can be added and the air circulated by mechanical humidifiers.

Summary

In summary, the following equipment is recommended in order to carry on a first-rate program of micromotion study and achieve resulting labor relation benefits.

1. One motion picture camera with film capacity of 100 feet.
2. One $f/1.9$ lens.
3. One wide-angle lens.
4. One telescopic lens.
5. One tripod with head that can be rotated on both a horizontal and vertical axis.
6. One exposure meter.
7. Two photoflood lamps with swivel-type reflectors.
8. One projector with hand-crank and frame counter attachment adapted for showing films at normal speed to audiences.
9. One portable screen.
10. One optical screen.
11. One titling kit.
12. One splicer and viewer.
13. One steel cabinet for film storage.
14. One microchronometer.

TEXT QUESTIONS

1. How does micromotion study differ from motion study?
2. For micromotion study, what additional considerations should be given to "use of human body" and "arrangement and conditions of workplace"?
3. What advantage is there in taking micromotion pictures in the laboratory provided for that purpose as compared to the production floor?
4. Why is the best operator usually selected in the micromotion procedure?
5. What consideration should be given the foreman relative to taking micromotion pictures in his department?
6. How can micromotion study be helpful in training?
7. What types of cameras have been used for micromotion study? What are the advantages and disadvantages of each?
8. Why are the lens and shutter important in micromotion photography?
9. Why isn't color film used more often in micromotion study? Summarize the advantages of color film.
10. Why is a light meter necessary in micromotion photography?
11. What "extra" devices should be included with a projector so as to make it ideal for film analysis work?
12. Where should the microchronometer be placed during the picture taking process?
13. What is an optical screen? What are the advantages of using one?
14. How does humidity affect stored films?
15. What is meant by the "speed" of the lens?
16. How fast would an $f/1.8$ lens be as compared to an $f/5.6$ lens?
17. Would an $f/16$ lens be considered a fast lens? Why?

GENERAL QUESTIONS

1. Make a sketch of your desk or work station and show arrangement and conditions that would agree with the laws of motion economy and their corollaries.
2. Interview at least two factory workmen and get their reaction to micromotion study through the film analysis technique.
3. What activity within an industrial organization other than methods analysis might include the use of micromotion equipment? How?
4. Discuss the relative merits of the telephoto and the wide-angle lens.

CHAPTER 9

Taking Motion Pictures for Micromotion Study and Film Analysis

IN GENERAL, THE FUNDAMENTAL steps in making a micromotion study, in order of their chronological sequence, are:

1. Take moving pictures of two of the most superior operators.
2. Analyze the film on a frame-by-frame basis, plotting the results on a simo chart (simultaneous motion chart).
3. Consider the laws of motion economy and their corollaries and create an improved method.
4. Teach and standardize the new method.
5. Take moving pictures of the new method.

Taking the Moving Pictures

Several factors should be checked before taking moving pictures on the production floor or in the laboratory. First, be sure that the selected operators have had a reasonable advance notice that pictures are to be taken. This is important so that they can be properly groomed and attired. It is also necessary to be sure that clearance has been obtained from the departmental foreman for the use of his operators. In some plants, it is necessary to obtain clearance from the union before proceeding with the picture taking. Even if this is not required, it is always wise, in the interests of healthy labor relations, to keep the union officers completely informed as to the intent relative to all phases of the moving-picture procedure. This is important since some plants have misused the data developed by the micromotion technique to the detriment of organized labor, and thus have caused suspicion and resentment toward the filming technique. Every effort should be made to avoid creating the same reaction to the micromotion procedure that developed toward the stop watch during the 1920's.

Then make sure that there is an adequate inventory of material so that it will not be necessary to replenish various supplies during the picture taking process. The camera should be carefully checked to ascertain that it is in good working order and that the lens is clean. After this, the cameraman should be ready to place the camera in the most advantageous position for taking pictures.

As has been pointed out, it is possible to get fairly steady pictures by holding the camera in the hand while supported against the head; however, it is advisable to use a good, sturdy tripod. The camera should be placed as close to the work area as conveniently possible so as to give clear detail of the most remote areas of the work station within which the operator performs. When the camera is placed at a sufficient height the operator motions in the horizontal plane will tend to be perpendicular to the line of sight and, consequently, will be easily analyzed upon projection of the developed film. When pictures are filmed in the laboratory, a mirror can be placed close to the work station at an angle of about 45 degrees. This will give a top view as well as front view when pictures are taken with the line of sight parallel to the plane of the work station (see Figure 9–1).

Courtesy: Advanced Management

FIG. 9–1. Three-dimensional view of operator at work station allows all motions to be in clear view for analysis purposes.

By placing a grid background behind the operator and perpendicular to the work station, and incorporating a similar cross section with two-inch scribed squares on the work area, it will be possible for the micromotion analyst to record true distances of the elemental therbligs when analyzing the film. Depending on the position of the grids and the position of the hand relative to the grid, grid distances will have to be corrected in order to obtain true distances. The correction factor may be determined by ordinary triangulation.

Upon completing the arrangement of the scene, loading the camera, and checking the illumination with the exposure meter, the analyst

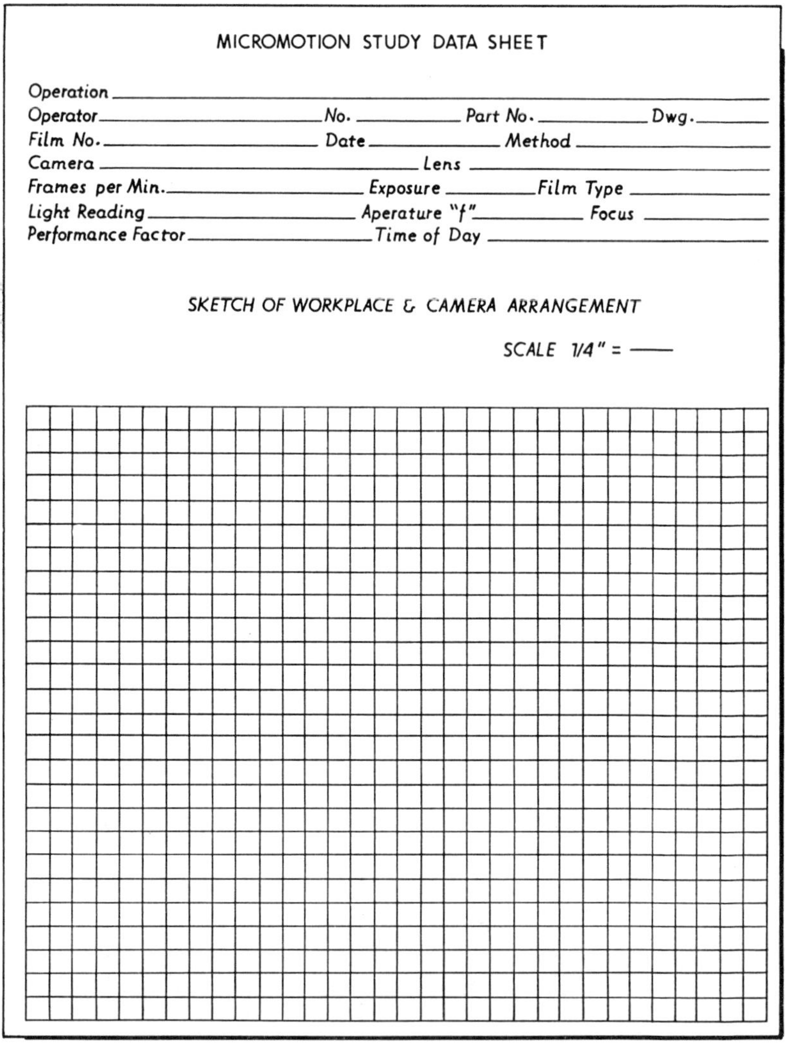

MICROMOTION STUDY DATA SHEET

Operation _____

Operator_____ No. _____ Part No._____ Dwg._____

Film No. _____ Date _____ Method _____

Camera _____ Lens _____

Frames per Min._____ Exposure _____Film Type _____

Light Reading_____ Aperature "f"_____ Focus _____

Performance Factor_____Time of Day _____

SKETCH OF WORKPLACE & CAMERA ARRANGEMENT

SCALE 1/4" = ——

FIG. 9–2. Micromotion study data sheet.

should set the lens to the correct opening as determined by the exposure meter for the emulsion speed of the film being used. Next, the distance between the subject and the film plane should be measured and the lens focused while precision-framing the subject. Pertinent information relative to the various camera adjustments should then be recorded on the micromotion study data sheet (see Figure 9–2).

After the above has been done, the camera film meter should be set to zero so that it will be possible to detect at all times the number of feet of exposed film and the remaining feet of unexposed film in the camera. This procedure is not necessary on some modern cameras, as reloading automatically sets the dial at zero feet of exposed film. At this point make sure that the speed required has been established and that the camera has been wound. (This of course is not necessary in electric-driven cameras.) About 35 feet of film at normal speed of 16 frames per second can be exposed before it is necessary to rewind the camera. Modern cameras have a warning bell that sounds when they are nearly run down. After the bell rings, about three additional feet of film can be exposed without fear of variation in the film exposure speed.

Upon completion of several practice cycles so as to relieve the operator of any nervousness he may have developed while being "put under the spotlight," he is requested to give his best performance, and then the film is exposed. Several cycles, depending on their duration, should be taken for analysis. Often, the first cycle is unsatisfactory, as the operator may develop a case of nerves when he hears the camera begin to operate. This reaction is usually short in duration, and he will soon acquire his normal feel for the work. Usually, operators enjoy being photographed, and little difficulty is encountered in getting excellent co-operation from them.

Analyzing the Film

Before analyzing the film, the analyst should run the pictures through several times in order to determine the cycle that represents the best performance. If the projector is equipped with a frame counter, this can readily be done by noting the transpired frames of each cycle. If a microchronometer was included in the scene, then it is a simple matter to observe the "winks" required to perform the cycle from the projected pictures. The shortest cycle usually is the best one to study.

Once the cycle that is to be studied is determined, the analyst can begin the frame-by-frame analysis procedure. Although the study can be made at any point in the cycle, it is customary to begin the analysis at the frame after "release of finished part" of the previous cycle. Thus, the first basic operation employed in most instances would be reach, in order to pick up a part or tool so as to begin production on the cycle being studied.

Once the starting point of the cycle has been determined, then the analyst should set the frame counter to zero so as to facilitate recording elapsed elemental times.

After the therblig being employed by the operator is noted, the film should be advanced a frame at a time until termination of the basic division. The number of frames exposed is then read off the frame counter and recorded on the micromotion data sheet.

Reach and move motions are considered as beginning at the frame preceding the frame in which noticeable movement occurs, and as ending in the frame where noticeable motion ceases. In motions where only minor movements occur, such as grasp, release, and position, the beginning point is considered to be the frame in which the preceding motion ended, and the ending point is the frame preceding the one in which the following motion showed noticeable movement.

While reviewing the film, the analyst carefully observes the motion class being used while performing the basic division, and records this information on his data sheet. At all times, the analyst must have an open and probing mind so as to determine the possibilities of either eliminating or improving each basic division.

After briefly describing the basic division in the space provided (as "move 12 inches for fixture" in Figure 9–3), the analyst draws a horizontal line across the portion of the paper representing the body member being studied. For the most part, only the arms and hands of the operator are studied, although sometimes it is desirable to analyze foot motions as well as the body motions.

The motion symbol should be recorded in the space provided, and in combined motions, symbols of the elements occurring simultaneously should be noted. Thus, a preposition may occur during a move, such as when the hand aligns a bolt while transporting it. In this case, the element description would be "Move bolt —— inches," and the symbols recorded would be "P.P. and M."

In the motion class columns, it is helpful to differentiate the productive elements from the nonproductive elements. This is usually done through color; thus, the elements reach, grasp, move, use, and assemble would be shown as solid black, and the remainder of the therbligs would be shown in red or by crosshatching if the charts are to be duplicated. Delay times are signified as Class 1 motions in red. All other therbligs are identified on the chart by the motion class utilized in performing the operation.

The time scale selected should provide enough room to identify clearly the shortest basic divisions so as to give a neat-appearing chart that can be easily studied and diagnosed for improvement. Release is the shortest of all the therbligs, taking but one frame at normal camera speed. Thus, if each division of the time scale shown in Figure 9–4 should be equated to .002 of a minute or four "winks," a neat-appearing chart would result.

After the first basic division of one hand has been studied, analyzed,

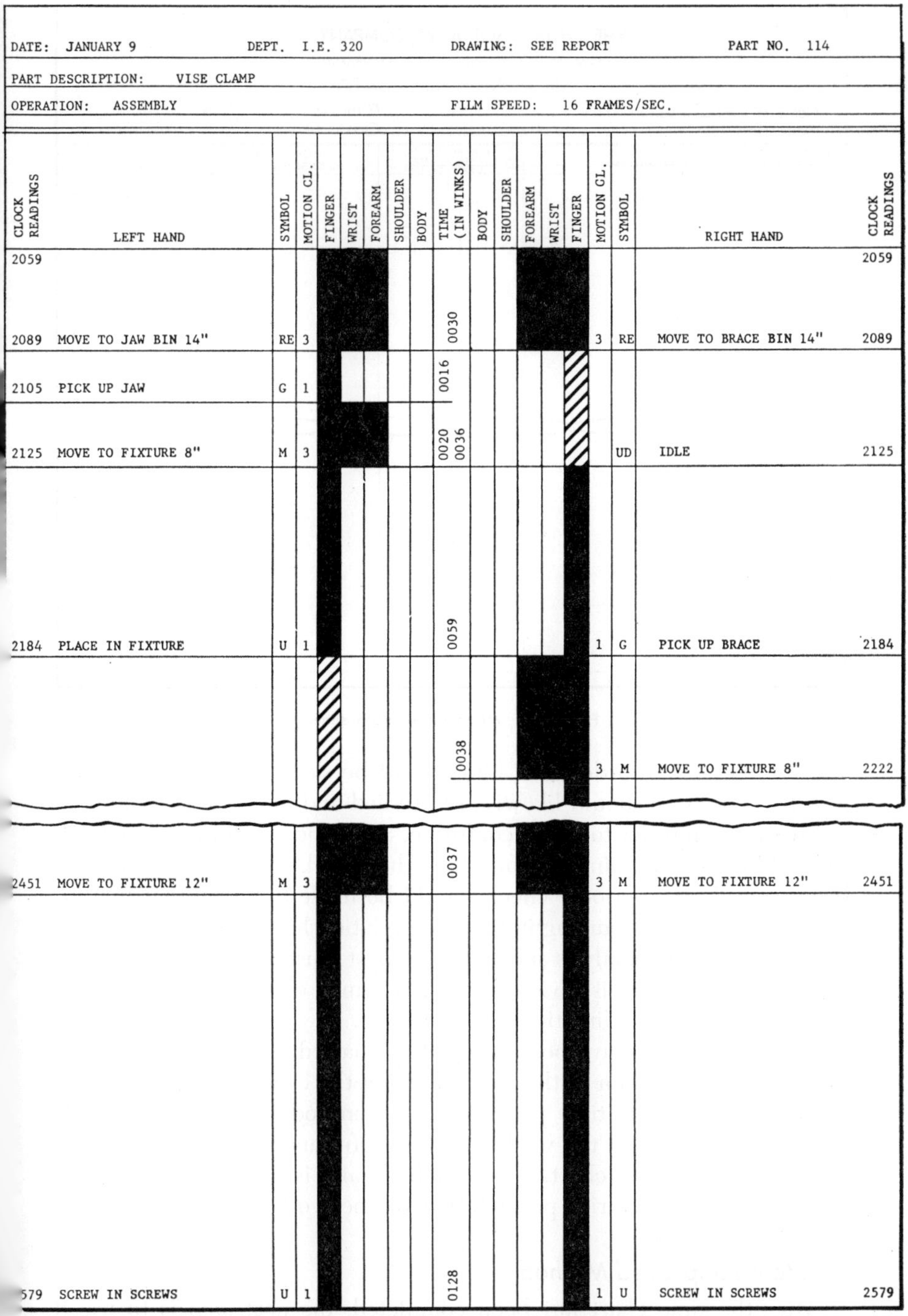

DATE: JANUARY 9   DEPT. I.E. 320   DRAWING: SEE REPORT   PART NO. 114

PART DESCRIPTION: VISE CLAMP

OPERATION: ASSEMBLY   FILM SPEED: 16 FRAMES/SEC.

CLOCK READINGS	LEFT HAND	SYMBOL	MOTION CL.	FINGER	WRIST	FOREARM	SHOULDER	BODY	TIME (IN WINKS)	BODY	SHOULDER	FOREARM	WRIST	FINGER	MOTION CL.	SYMBOL	RIGHT HAND	CLOCK READINGS
2059																		2059
2089	MOVE TO JAW BIN 14"	RE	3						0030						3	RE	MOVE TO BRACE BIN 14"	2089
2105	PICK UP JAW	G	1						0016									2105
2125	MOVE TO FIXTURE 8"	M	3						0020 0036							UD	IDLE	2125
2184	PLACE IN FIXTURE	U	1						0059						1	G	PICK UP BRACE	2184
									0038						3	M	MOVE TO FIXTURE 8"	2222
2451	MOVE TO FIXTURE 12"	M	3						0037						3	M	MOVE TO FIXTURE 12"	2451
2579	SCREW IN SCREWS	U	1						0128						1	U	SCREW IN SCREWS	2579

FIG. 9–3. Film analysis of vise clamp assembly.

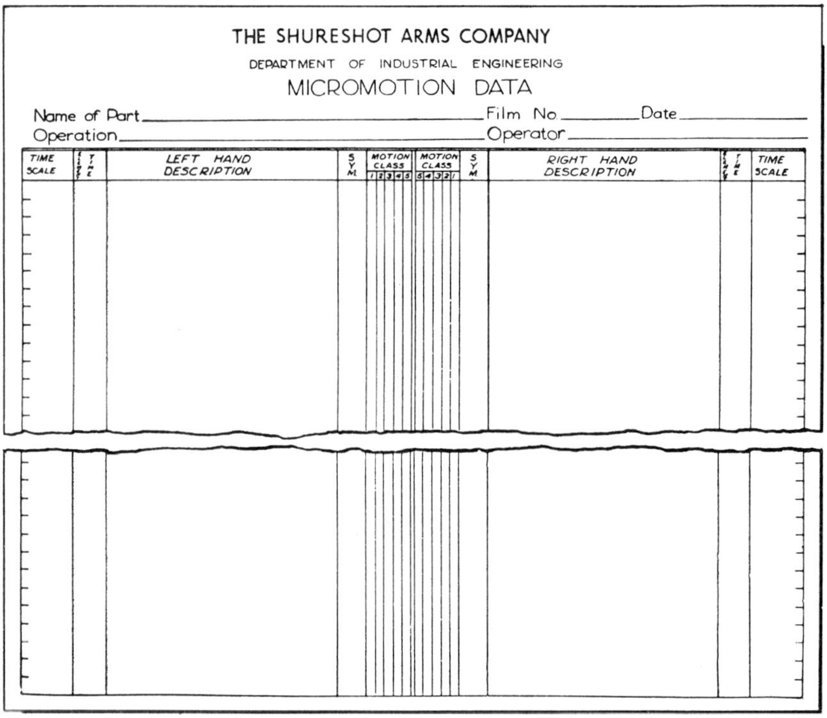

THE SHURESHOT ARMS COMPANY

DEPARTMENT OF INDUSTRIAL ENGINEERING

MICROMOTION DATA

Name of Part_____ Film No_____ Date_____
Operation_____ Operator_____

TIME SCALE	$\begin{smallmatrix}T\\T\end{smallmatrix}$	LEFT HAND DESCRIPTION	S Y M	MOTION CLASS 1 2 3 4 5	MOTION CLASS 5 4 3 2 1	S Y M	RIGHT HAND DESCRIPTION	$\begin{smallmatrix}T\\T\end{smallmatrix}$	TIME SCALE

FIG. 9–4. Micromotion data sheet.

and the method recorded, the film should be slowly advanced, and the next basic division should likewise be studied and so on until completion of the cycle. In order to avoid confusion, one hand should be completely studied before beginning to study the other hand. As the second hand is being considered, periodic check should be made to verify that the motions recorded are occurring in the same relationship with the other hand as indicated in the analysis sheet. The analyst must remember that when the projected picture is reviewed the left arm is on the right side of the picture. In fact, all directions are reversed.

After both hands have been completely charted, a summary should be included at the bottom of the chart showing the cycle time, pieces made per cycle, production time per cycle, and nonproduction time per cycle. Sometimes a sketch of the workplace is helpful and this can be included at the bottom of the chart. The sketch usually is not necessary, as the film will give a pictorial presentation of the work area.

Create an Improved Method

After the simo chart has been completed, the next step is to use it. The nonproductive sections of the chart represent a good place to start. These sections will include the therbligs hold, search, select, position, preposition, inspect, and plan, and all the delays. The more of these that can be eliminated, the better will be the proposed method. However, the analysis should not be confined to the red sections of the chart, as possibilities for improvement exist in the productive portions as well. For example, the productive element "reach 24" can be improved by reducing the distance and, consequently, lowering the motion class.

A micromotion check list is helpful for the analyst so that he does not forget to consider all the feasible possibilities for improvement. Table VII illustrates a check list that covers most of the considerations that

TABLE VII

CHECK LIST FOR SIMO CHART

---

1. Are both hands beginning their therbligs simultaneously?
2. Are both hands ending their therbligs at the same time?
3. Can delay or idle times be removed from the cycle?
4. Is the motion pattern of the arms symmetrical?
5. Are motions made radially from the body in opposite directions?
6. Can a fixture be incorporated so as to eliminate hold?
7. Are all materials and tools within the normal work area in both the horizontal and vertical planes?
8. Are motions confined to lowest possible classifications?
9. Are tools and materials located so as to permit best sequence of motions?
10. Can foot-operated mechanisms be advantageously introduced?
11. Have gravity chutes and drop delivery been provided for?
12. Are all tools prepositioned in a manner to minimize grasp time and reduce the search and select therbligs?
13. Has an automatic ejector been incorporated in the fixture?
14. Can position times be reduced by providing "pilots" or some other device for mating parts?

---

apply to the laws of motion economy and their corollaries.

Figure 9–5 illustrates a completed simo chart of the assembly of a variable resistor. This chart was constructed after a new fixture was developed to facilitate assembly and represents a method considerably improved over the original method of assembly. Yet an analysis of this chart will disclose several areas for further improvement. The right- and left-hand movements are not balanced in many parts of the cycle, and there are ten ineffective motions performed by the left hand and eleven ineffective motions executed by the right hand. Several of the moves and reaches appear to be unduly long, suggesting shortening of distances at the work station layout.

The micromotion technique should be used to uncover every inefficiency regardless of its apparent insignificance. Sufficient numbers of minute improvements in total will result in an appreciable annual savings.

MICROMOTION DATA

NAME OF PART. VARISTOR   NO. 30 A   FILM NO. 5209

OPERATION. ASSEMBLY OF VARISTOR   OPERATOR. MAYHEW

TIME SCALE	E.T.		LEFT-HAND DESCRIPTION		MOTION CLASS					MOTION CLASS						RIGHT-HAND DESCRIPTION	NO.	WINKS	TIME SCALE
					1	2	3	4	5	5	4	3	2	1					
0163 0170	WINKS 7	NO 1	MOVING TOWARD BINS	RE											RL	RELEASE ASSEMBLY	NO.	WINKS	0163
0182	12	2	GRASP SPRING WASHER	G											RE	MOVE TO BIN	1	10	0173
															G	GRASP BOLT	2	9	0182
0201	18	3	MOVE TO FIXTURE	M											M	MOVE TO FIXTURE POSITION BOLT	3	19	0201
0250	49	4	WAIT FOR LEFT HAND	UD											P		4	49	0250
0254	4	5	POSITION WASHER	P											RL	RELEASE BOLT	5	4	0254
0272	18	6	PLACE ON BOLT	A											UD	WAIT FOR LEFT HAND	6	19	0273
0276	4	7	RELEASE WASHER	RL															
0295	19	8	MOVE TO BINS	RE											RE	MOVE TO BIN	7	18	0291
															G	GRASP BRASS WASHER	8	11	0302
0310	15	9	GRASP TUBE	G															
0340	30	10	MOVE TO FIXTURE	M															
0343	3	11	POSITION	P											M	MOVE TO FIXTURE	9	43	0345
0349	6	12	PLACE TUBE ON BOLT	A											P	POSITION WASHER	10	4	0349
0354		13	HOLD	H															
0356	2	14	RELEASE TUBE	RL															
			MOVE TO BIN AND	RE											A	PLACE WASHER ON BOLT	11	30	0379
0385	29	15	GRASP FIBER WASHER	G											RL	RELEASE WASHER	12	2	0381
0402	17	16	MOVE TO FIXTURE	M											RE	MOVE TO BIN	13	19	0400
															G	GRASP CONTACT	14	6	0406
															M	MOVE TO FIXTURE	42	21	1122
															P	POSITION DRIVER	43	5	1127
1184	100	40	HOLD POSITIONER UP	H											U	TIGHTEN NUT	44	57	1184
1186	2	41	RELEASE POSITIONER	RL											RL	RELEASE DRIVER	45	2	1186
															RE	MOVE TO FIXTURE	46	11	1197
															G	GRASP ASSEMBLY	47	4	1201
1205	19	42	MOVE TO BINS	RE											M	MOVE TOWARD BINS	48	11	1212

TIME PER PIECE

1049 WINKS

OR

0.5245 MIN.

R. E. Call

FIG. 9–5. Simo chart assembly of variable resistor.

Teach and Standardize the New Method

In order to be assured that full benefits are realized from the micromotion study, it is important that the improved method be put into practice as soon as possible and that it be followed in exact detail by all

operators to whom it applies. Verbal explanations as to the motion pattern
to be followed are usually inadequate: both time and effort will be
saved if an instruction chart is completed giving specific information as
to the "how" of the improved method.

The typical micromotion instruction sheet, in form, is similar to the
operator process chart discussed in Chapter 6. A layout of the work area
drawn to scale heads the instruction sheet and following this is shown
the motion sequence of both the right hand and the left hand. These
elements appear in relationship to each other. Special tools such as form
cutters, gages, jigs, and fixtures are identified after the element in which
they are used. Also, speeds, feeds, depth of cut, and other pertinent manufacturing information will be shown. Usually, a time summary will ac-
company the instruction sheet, so that the operator will be able to
measure his performance against standard while being trained in the
new method. A typical instruction sheet appears in Figure 9–6.

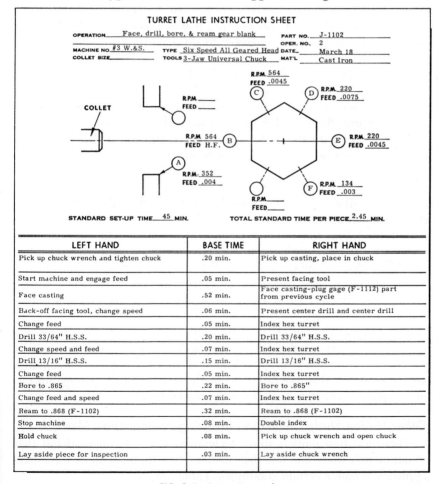

TURRET LATHE INSTRUCTION SHEET

OPERATION __Face, drill, bore, & ream gear blank__   PART NO. __J-1102__
                                                       OPER. NO. __2__
MACHINE NO. __#3 W.&S.__   TYPE __Six Speed All Geared Head__ DATE __March 18__
COLLET SIZE _____   TOOLS __3-Jaw Universal Chuck__   MAT'L __Cast Iron__

STANDARD SET-UP TIME __45__ MIN.   TOTAL STANDARD TIME PER PIECE __2.45__ MIN.

LEFT HAND	BASE TIME	RIGHT HAND
Pick up chuck wrench and tighten chuck	.20 min.	Pick up casting, place in chuck
Start machine and engage feed	.05 min.	Present facing tool
Face casting	.52 min.	Face casting-plug gage (F-1112) part from previous cycle
Back-off facing tool, change speed	.06 min.	Present center drill and center drill
Change feed	.05 min.	Index hex turret
Drill 33/64" H.S.S.	.20 min.	Drill 33/64" H.S.S.
Change speed and feed	.07 min.	Index hex turret
Drill 13/16" H.S.S.	.15 min.	Drill 13/16" H.S.S.
Change feed	.05 min.	Index hex turret
Bore to .865	.22 min.	Bore to .865"
Change feed and speed	.07 min.	Index hex turret
Ream to .868 (F-1102)	.32 min.	Ream to .868 (F-1102)
Stop machine	.08 min.	Double index
Hold chuck	.08 min.	Pick up chuck wrench and open chuck
Lay aside piece for inspection	.03 min.	Lay aside chuck wrench

FIG. 9–6. Instruction card.

It is important that the foreman or line supervisor be well versed in the proposed method so that he will be able to give assistance in training the workmen. Usually, instruction sheets are run off in ditto or some other rapid duplicating process so that copies can be filed in the methods section, time study section, and foremen's office, as well as given to each operator performing the operation. A hanger for the instruction sheet should be provided at the operator's work station so that it can readily be referred to at all times during the operating cycle. If a clear plastic envelope is provided to hold the instruction sheet, it will remain readable for a considerably longer period of time.

The foreman, with the methods engineer, should periodically check each operation on the production floor to be sure that the new method is being followed, and to answer any question that may come up relative to the new procedure. Installation and follow-up are two very important phases in micromotion methods improvement. Often it is difficult for the average operator to justify the new method because the changes may appear so insignificant. Consequently, it will be necessary for both the foreman and the methods engineer to do a real job of selling the improved system.

Unless periodic checks are made for at least several weeks, operators may go back to their old way of doing the job and disregard completely the new technique. One of the added benefits of the written instruction sheet is getting the operator to conform to the established instructions.

As soon as one of the better operators has become skilled in the new method, moving pictures can be taken and a simo chart constructed to illustrate the improvements resulting from the study. The same operators selected in making pictures of the unimproved method should be used. This will give a better comparison for evaluating the savings than if different operators were used in the final pictures. Once the new pictures have been taken, they should be used as a training tool for all other operators performing the same operation. Seeing how the operation should be done is much more helpful than reading or hearing how it should be done. The psychological impact of seeing a fellow worker perform the new method is a force in breaking down the inherent human resistance to change.

The completed simo chart of the improved method when compared to the one drawn of the old method will clearly present the savings. Figure 9–7 illustrates a proposed method after a complete micromotion study. Note that this tool not only shows the amount of savings but vividly explains how these results were made possible.

Other Motion Study Techniques Involving Photographic Methods

There are two motion study techniques that give more detail than visual motion study and less than micromotion study. Both of these have application under certain conditions. These are:

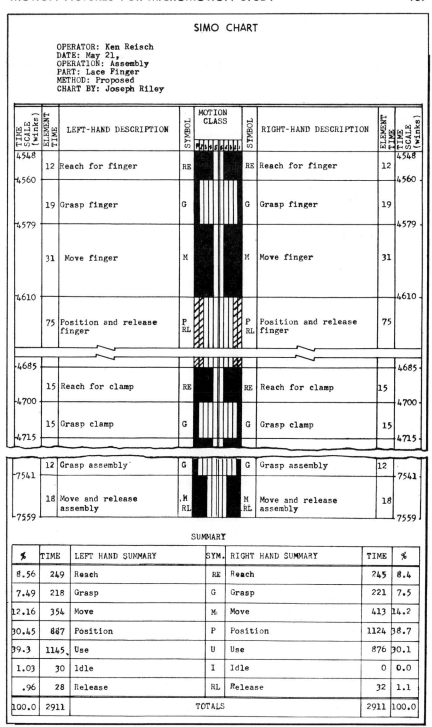

SIMO CHART

OPERATOR: Ken Reisch
DATE: May 21,
OPERATION: Assembly
PART: Lace Finger
METHOD: Proposed
CHART BY: Joseph Riley

TIME SCALE (winks)	ELEMENT TIME	LEFT-HAND DESCRIPTION	SYMBOL	MOTION CLASS	SYMBOL	RIGHT-HAND DESCRIPTION	ELEMENT TIME	TIME SCALE (winks)
4548	12	Reach for finger	RE		RE	Reach for finger	12	4548
4560	19	Grasp finger	G		G	Grasp finger	19	4560
4579	31	Move finger	M		M	Move finger	31	4579
4610	75	Position and release finger	P RL		P RL	Position and release finger	75	4610
4685	15	Reach for clamp	RE		RE	Reach for clamp	15	4685
4700	15	Grasp clamp	G		G	Grasp clamp	15	4700
4715								4715
7541	12	Grasp assembly	G		G	Grasp assembly	12	7541
7559	18	Move and release assembly	,M RL		M RL	Move and release assembly	18	7559

SUMMARY

%	TIME	LEFT HAND SUMMARY	SYM.	RIGHT HAND SUMMARY	TIME	%
8.56	249	Reach	RE	Reach	245	8.4
7.49	218	Grasp	G	Grasp	221	7.5
12.16	354	Move	M:	Move	413	14.2
30.45	887	Position	P	Position	1124	38.7
39.3	1145	Use	U	Use	876	30.1
1.03	30	Idle	I	Idle	0	0.0
.96	28	Release	RL	Release	32	1.1
100.0	2911	TOTALS			2911	100.0

FIG. 9–7. Simo chart of improved method for the assembly of lace finger in textile machinery.

1. Memomotion study.
2. Cycle graphic and chronocycle graphic study.

Memomotion study is a moving picture technique developed by Marvin Mundel for analyzing the principal movements in an operation. When using the camera for "Memomotion" study, the analyst exposes the film at 50, 60, or 100 frames per minute. The speed of 100 frames per minute allows the timing of any element with the same precision as the decimal minute stop watch (see Chapter 13). Moreover, "Memomotion" gives a permanent record of the motion pattern being used and the method employed, thus permitting a more complete and detailed analysis than the procedure described under visual motion study. Memomotion study is particularly applicable for studying interrelated events where the activity does not justify a micromotion study. Consequently, on operations where crew activities are employed, the technique is much more thorough and accurate than the visual type of study (Figure 9–8).

On long cycle studies where the cost of a micromotion study would be prohibitive, the memomotion technique finds application since less film is used and, consequently, the amount of film to be analyzed is reduced. The speed of one frame per second, the most popular in memomotion study movies, uses just one sixteenth the amount of film that would be utilized if the job were taken at normal speed. For example, to study a three-minute cycle job would require exposing only 4.5 feet of film.

$$\frac{3 \text{ min.} \times 60 \text{ frames/min.}}{40 \text{ frames/foot}} = 4.5 \text{ feet.}$$

The motion picture camera and other equipment described in Chapter 8 will be completely suitable for memomotion study work. However, it will be necessary to add to this a special 3- or 4-speed drive, costing between $250 and $350, which must be attached to the standard camera.

A cyclegraph is a photographic record of a body motion. "Still" film is used, but a light is attached to the body member, so that the path of the motion is revealed when the picture is developed.

A chronocyclegraph is similar to the cyclegraph, except that speed as well as path of the motion is determined from the resulting photograph. In the chronocyclegraph, the light attached to the body member flickers. Speed is determined by the length of the alternate streaks of light and dark voids. Consequently, it is possible for the analyst to determine hesitations that may develop because of some obstacle in the existing motion pattern. Likewise, the influence on time of directional change can be determined. It is also possible to determine if rhythm is being developed by taking a series of chronocyclegraphs of different cycles and noting the similarity in the movement paths.

The practical uses of the cyclegraph and chronocyclegraph are con-

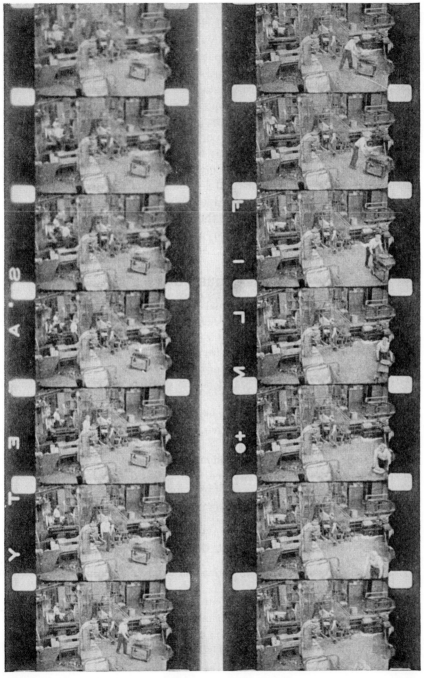

FIG. 9–8. Portion of memomotion study of four men operating hydraulic extrusion press. Film exposed at rate of one frame per second.

fined to operations of short cycle and those requiring skill. For such work, this type of study is particularly helpful in operator training.

It is especially helpful in those work areas where no fixtures or tool stations exist to direct the motion pattern. For example, in the operation of wrapping lilt fixative and turban, or folding a garment, or making a bed no definite motion pattern is established by equipment to shape the movements of the hands. The chronocyclegraph will provide a record of the ideal motion pattern for the trainee to follow.

It can be appreciated that, on complex motion patterns, the chronocyclegraph is a helpful supplement to the right- and left-hand process chart. With the chronocyclegraph giving a pictorial presentation of the motion pattern and the right- and left-hand chart a description of the motion pattern, a complete record is obtained.

Both the chronocyclegraph and the cyclegraph were originally developed by Gilbreth, but they have not been used extensively in this country.

TEXT QUESTIONS

1. What are the important steps in making a micromotion study?
2. What precautionary procedures should be observed before beginning the actual filming?
3. How does the simo chart differ from the operator process chart?
4. Which motions are classified as ineffective on the simo chart?
5. What class of motion is signified on the simo chart when plotting any of the delays?
6. What is the purpose of the micromotion instruction sheet?
7. In film analysis, why is it not advisable to analyze both hands simultaneously?
8. What advantages does memomotion study have over micromotion study?
9. How much film would be required to study a cycle 13.5 minutes in duration using a memomotion speed of 50 frames per minute?
10. What advantages does the chronocyclegraphic study have over the cyclegraphic study?

GENERAL QUESTIONS

1. Why do some unions require permission before moving pictures are taken on the production floor?
2. In general, what is the operators' attitude relative to being filmed?
3. How can industrial relations be improved with the micromotion procedure?
4. Investigate the work done by Anne Shaw of England in conjunction with chronocyclegraphic studies.

CHAPTER 10

Synthetic Basic Motion Times

By analyzing an operation's basic divisions of accomplishment from the standpoint of the fundamental laws of motion economy, it is possible to perform the work more easily and speedily. Breaking a job down into its basic components highlights the ineffective motions and permits their elimination or improvement. However, up to this point, the element of time has not been mentioned. Because of the extremely short duration of therbligs, until recent years it was virtually impossible to measure their magnitude accurately. For example, the basic division "release" is performed in less than one frame of normal camera speed ($\frac{1}{16}$ second). Until the advent of the high-speed camera, the terminal points of release could not be precisely identified.

The potential uses of valid time values for the basic divisions of accomplishment are apparent. With this additional information, it is possible to evaluate alternative motion patterns and eventually establish the completely ideal method. Time standards can be achieved by merely itemizing the basic divisions comprising an operation, assigning the appropriate time values, and then summing up the individual times. This would allow establishing consistent, accurate standards without complete dependence on the stop watch.

Since the time of Taylor, management has realized the desirability of having the elements of time assigned to the various basic divisions of accomplishment.

One of the earliest men to investigate this area was W. G. Holmes. He tabulated values based on the measurement of the various body members, including the finger, hand, foot, and arm, in a Time of Movements Chart.[1] Representative times established by Holmes are:

---

[1] W. G. Holmes, *Applied Time and Motion Study* (New York: Ronald Press Co., 1938), p. 244.

1. Hand with hinge movement at the wrist .0022 minute when moved 0 to 2 inches.
2. Arm with angular movement at the shoulder .0060 minute when moved 30 degrees.
3. Nerve reaction, eye to brain or reverse .0003 minute.

Actually, Holmes has taken his analysis to such a point that it is difficult and cumbersome to handle. He has provided times for nerve reactions from the eye to the brain, the knee to the brain, and the foot to the brain; also, times for mental process and mind decision such as time to hear or smell, or realize contact.

R. M. Barnes has advocated a technique similar to Holmes' in the development of basic motion data. Barnes states: "There is a trend toward the use of standard time values for therbligs or combination of therbligs and under certain conditions such time values may be more useful than the time values for longer elements obtained from stop watch time studies."[2]

Barnes' analysis was further developed by Harold Engstrom at the General Electric Company in Bridgeport, Connecticut. Engstrom described his technique as follows:[3]

1. Analyze certain classes of work such as light bench assembly work or machine operation. The standards developed must be confined to particular classes of work and no attempt made to embrace the entire gamut of industrial operations.
2. The jobs are then time studied to determine the basic elements of which they are comprised.
3. These time studied jobs are then photographed by means of a measurement camera for the purpose of micromotion analysis.
4. The evaluations of the effort of the worker are then made.
5. From the motion pictures previously taken, make combinations of therbligs into two major classifications, such as Get, which consists of Transport Empty and Grasp; Place, which consists of Transport Loaded, Preposition, Position, and Release Load. Dispose should be treated as Place.
6. These data are then tabulated.

It has never been a question of need but a question of how can the job of determining time values for the various basic divisions be done practically. In recent years, considerable progress has been made in the assignment of time values to basic elements of work. These time values are referred to as synthetic basic motion times.

Definition of Synthetic Basic Motion Times

Synthetic basic motion times are a collection of valid time standards assigned to fundamental motions and groups of motions that cannot be

---

[2] Ralph M. Barnes, *Motion and Time Study* (3rd ed.; New York: John Wiley & Sons, Inc., 1949), p. 439.

[3] *Proceedings, National Time and Motion Study Clinic, 1940*, pp. 45–46.

precisely evaluated with ordinary stop-watch time study procedure. They are the result of studying a large sample of diversified operations with a timing device such as the motion-picture camera that is capable of measuring very short elements. The time values are synthetic in that they are often the result of logical combinations of therbligs. For example, a series of time values may be established for different categories of grasp. Within the grasp time may be included the therbligs search, select, and grasp. The time values are basic in that further refinement is not only difficult but impractical. Thus, we have the term *synthetic basic motion times.*

Necessity of Synthetic Basic Motion Times

Since 1945, there has been a growing interest in the use of synthetic basic motion times as a modern method of establishing rates quickly and often accurately without the use of the stop watch or other time recording device. In view of this, it is recommended that the student reread Chapter 10 after completing Chapter 18 on Standard Data. A by-product of synthesized time standards that probably has been as useful, if not more so, than the time standard itself, is a development of method consciousness to a refined degree in all parties associated with the establishment of standards using synthetic values. For this reason, the author believes that the entire subject of synthetic basic motion times should be meshed or integrated with the motion and micromotion techniques, even though it is also very closely allied to the work measurement phase.

Even with the laws of motion economy and basic division of accomplishment concept clearly established, the methods analyst without reliable time values of the basic divisions has only a portion of the facts necessary to engineer a method prior to beginning actual production. If he did not have time values of the basic divisions, how could he be sure that his proposed method was the best? With reliable motion times, he would be able to evaluate his proposed methods in terms of the average or normal worker, who would eventually be the recipient of his ideas. It is apparent that the method used determines time to do a task, and it follows that if time values for all forms of activity were available, then the most favorable methods could be determined in advance.

Today, the practicing methods analyst has several sources of established synthetic values from which he can obtain information that may be helpful in his work.

Work-Factor

The Work-Factor Company is one of the pioneer concerns in the field of establishing standards synthetically with motion-time values. Work-Factor data were made available in 1938, after a period of four years of gathering values by the micromotion technique, stop-watch procedures, and the use of a "specially constructed photoelectric time machine."[4]

Work-Factor recognizes the following variables which influence the time required to perform a task:

1. The body member making the motion, such as arm, forearm, finger-hand, foot.
2. The distance moved (measured in inches).
3. The weight carried (measured in pounds).
4. The manual control required (care, directional control or steering to a target, changing direction, stopping at a definite location).

Through analysis of films, Work-Factor concluded, as the Gilbreths did many years earlier, that finger motions can be performed more rapidly than arm motions, and arm motions are made in shorter periods of time than body motions.

All proponents of fundamental motion data techniques have recognized the element of distance in making reaches and moves and, in fact, all motions. The longer the distance the more time is required, of course. Work-Factor has tabularized values for finger and hand movements from one inch up to four inches, and for arm movements from one inch to forty inches. Weight or resistance will influence time according to the magnitude of the part being moved.

Manual control is influenced by (1) care or precaution, (2) directional control, (3) change of direction, and (4) definite stop. The presence of any one of these difficulties is referred to as a Work-Factor and the more Work-Factors involved in a motion of a given distance, the greater the time value.

A Work-Factor has been defined as the index of additional time required over and above the basic time.

Care or precaution is evident during motions involving possible damage or injury, such as moving a full vessel of acid or handling a thin piece of glass.

Directional control is apparent when a motion is employed to direct or steer a body member or part being transported through a limited clearance or toward a small target.

Change of direction, as the name implies, is the manual control brought about by changing the direction of a motion, as in moving around a part or obstacle. For example, to move a nut in back of a panel would require a change in direction once the moving hand reached the front of the panel.

Definite stop is the manual control brought about when the operator, through his muscular co-ordination, stops a motion at a predetermined place.

---

[4] Work-Factor Bulletin No. 101, *Information About the Work-Factor System of Labor Measurement.*

TABLE VIII

Distance Moved, Inches	Basic	Work-Factors			
		1	2	3	4
(A) Arm—Measured at Knuckles					
1......	.0018	.0026	.0034	.0040	.0046
2......	.0020	.0029	.0037	.0044	.0050
3......	.0022	.0032	.0041	.0050	.0057
4......	.0026	.0038	.0048	.0058	.0066
5......	.0029	.0043	.0055	.0065	.0075
6......	.0032	.0047	.0060	.0072	.0083
7......	.0035	.0051	.0065	.0078	.0090
8......	.0038	.0054	.0070	.0084	.0096
9......	.0040	.0058	.0074	.0089	.0102
10......	.0042	.0061	.0078	.0093	.0107
11......	.0044	.0063	.0081	.0098	.0112
12......	.0046	.0065	.0085	.0102	.0117
13......	.0047	.0067	.0088	.0105	.0121
14......	.0049	.0069	.0090	.0109	.0125
15......	.0051	.0071	.0092	.0113	.0129
16......	.0052	.0073	.0094	.0115	.0133
17......	.0054	.0075	.0096	.0118	.0137
18......	.0055	.0076	.0098	.0120	.0140
19......	.0056	.0078	.0100	.0122	.0142
20......	.0058	.0080	.0102	.0124	.0144
22......	.0061	.0083	.0106	.0128	.0148
24......	.0063	.0086	.0109	.0131	.0152
26......	.0066	.0090	.0113	.0135	.0158
28......	.0068	.0093	.0116	.0139	.0159
30......	.0070	.0096	.0119	.0142	.0163
35......	.0076	.0103	.0128	.0151	.0171
40......	.0081	.0109	.0135	.0159	.0179
Weight M	2	7	13	20	....
(pounds) F	1	3½	6½	10	....

Table VIII illustrates the Work-Factor "Moving" Time Table with values given in .0001 minutes. Basic time values are shown as well as values for motions involving 1, 2, 3, and 4 Work-Factors. In addition to the Work-Factor Motion Time Table, the Work-Factor Company also has tables which provide methods of analysis and time values for the elements of grasp, preposition and assemble. These values are in terms of select time, which has been defined as "that time required for the average, experienced operator, working with good skill and good effort (commensurate with good health and physical and mental well-being) to perform an operation on one unit or piece." In order to determine the standard time, the analyst must add an allowance to the Work-Factor values, since the select time includes no allowance for personal needs, fatigue, unavoidable delays, or incentive allowance. A typical break-down study of a draw operation on a Bliss double action 240-ton press is shown in Figure 10–1.

OPERATION NAME   Oldsmobile Case: 1st Draw Operation (2 Pin Die)   WORK FACTOR ANALYST
                                                                                        H. B. Amster
EQUIPMENT   Mach #1031: Bliss Double Action Draw Press 240 Tons   72.5 RPM

MATERIAL   CR Steel: Tmk = .050 = .003" Dia = 19.25"   Wt = 4.04 lbs.   SHEET 1 OF 1

NO.	LEFT HAND Elemental Description	Motion Analysis	Elem. Time	Cumulative Time (L)	Cumulative Time (R)	Elem. Time	Motion Analysis	RIGHT HAND Elemental Description	Mach.
1	Reach for blank	A20D	0080	0080	0080	0080	A20D	Reach for blank	
2	Grasp blank	F1W	0023	0103	0103	0023	F1W	Grasp blank	
3	Carry blank to die	A40WSD	0159	0262	0262	0159	A40WSD	Carry blank to die	
4	Release & clear fingers	F3W	0028	0290	0290	0028	F3W	Release & clear fingers	
5	Place fingers on blank	F3D	0028	0318	0399	0109	A40D	Reach for trip lever	
6	Push blank against pins	A2P	0029	0347	0415	0016	F1	Grasp lever (No W Req'd)	
7	Withdraw hand (A10) & wait		0146	0493	0493	0078	A10WW	Pull lever to trip press (10 lbs.)	
8	Move hand to hold blank (turn Simo	A30D	0096	0589	0589	0096	A30D	Reach for oil rag (turn 90°-Simo)	
9	Press down to hold blank	A1W	0026	0615	0606	0017	F2	Grasp rag	
10	Hold Blank at center	---	----		0691	0085	A12UD	Carry rag & dip in oil pan	
11	" " " "	---	----		0723	0032	A6	Raise from oil pan	
12	" " " "	---	----		0749	0026	A4	Shake (squeeze Simo)	
13	" " " "	---	----		0804	0055	A18	Carry rag to stack of blanks	
14	" " " "	---	----	0913	0913	0109	A40U	Apply oil (circular motion)	
15	Release blank	A1W	0026	0939	0955	0042	A10	Raise rag from blank	
16	Withdraw hand from blank	A16	0052	0991	0997	0042	A10	Strike to dislodge blank	
17	Approach blank	A3D	0032	1023	1048	0051	A15	Withdraw rag to side	
18	Grasp blank	F1W	0023	1046		----	---	Hold rag	
19	Turn blank over (release Simo)	2A14W	0138	1184		----	---	" "	
20	Move hand to blank center	A13D	0067	1251		----	---	" "	
21	Press down to hold blank	A1W	0026	1277	1277	0055	A18	Carry rag to blank	
22	Hold blank at center	---	----		1386	0109	A40U	Apply oil (circular motion)	
23	Release blank	A1W	0026	1412	1437	0051	A15	Toss rag near pan	
24	Hand idle (turn 90° Simo)	---	----		1517	0080	A20D	Reach for trip lever (turn Simo)	
25	" "	---	----		1533	0016	F1	Grasp handle (No W req'd)	
26	" "	---	----		1781	0248		Wait (.0493 + .1380 - .1533 - .0092 = .0248)	
27	Move hand to piece on punch	A20D	0080	1873	1873	0092	A15WW	Push lever to stop press (10 lbs.)	
28	Catch piece on palm	React	0020	1893	1896	0023	F1W	Release handle	
29	Carry piece to chute (balance)	A40WPD	0159	2052		----	---	Hand idle	
30	Toss to chute or stack	A5W	0043	2095		----	---	" "	
31	Turn to worktable	120°	0100	2195	2195	0100	120°	Turn to worktable	

(Mach. column note, vertical: Mach. Cycle = 0.1380 min.)

FIG. 10–1.

The symbols used in this analysis carry the following meaning:

W—weight   A—arm
S—steering   L—leg
P—precaution   T—trunk
U—change direction   F—finger
D—definite stop   FT—foot
                             FS—forearm swivel

In making a Work-Factor study, the analyst first lists all motions made by both hands necessary to perform the task; then he identifies each motion in terms of the distance moved, body member used, and Work-Factors involved. He then selects from the table of values the appropriate figure for each of the basic motions and summarizes these to obtain the total time required by the normal operator to perform the task.

To this total time percentage allowances for personal delays, fatigue, and unavoidable delays must be added in order to determine the allowed time.

Methods-Time Measurement

In 1948, the text *Methods-Time Measurement* was published, giving time values for the fundamental motions of reach, move, turn, grasp, position, disengage, and release.[5] The authors have defined M.T.M. as "a procedure which analyzes any manual operation or method into the basic motions required to perform it, and assigns to each motion a pre-determined time standard which is determined by the nature of the motion and the conditions under which it is made."[6]

The M.T.M. data, as in the case of Work-Factor, are the result of frame-by-frame analysis of motion-picture films involving a diversified area of work. The data taken from the various films were "leveled" (adjusted to the time that would be required by the normal operator) by the Westinghouse technique. This method of performance rating is described in Chapter 15 of this text. The data were then tabulated and analyzed in an effort to determine the degree of difficulty caused by variable characteristics. For example, it was found that not only distance but also the type of reach affected reach time. Further analysis seemed to indicate that there were five distinct cases of reach, each requiring different time allotments to perform for a given distance. These are:

1. Reach to object in fixed location, or to object in other hand, or on which other hand rests.
2. Reach to single object in location which may vary slightly from cycle to cycle.
3. Reach to object jumbled with other objects so that search and select occur.
4. Reach to a very small object or where accurate grasp is required.
5. Reach to indefinite location to get hand in position for body balance, or next motion, or out of way.[7]

Also, move time was influenced not only by distance and weight of the object being moved, but by the specific type of move. Three cases of move were found to exist. These are:

1. Move object to other hand or against stop.
2. Move object to approximate or indefinite location.
3. Move object to exact location.[8]

Table IX summarizes M.T.M. values that have been developed to date. It will be noted that the time values of the therblig grasp vary from 2.0 T.M.U.'s to 12.9 T.M.U.'s (1 T.M.U. equals .00001 hr.) depending on the classification of the grasp. Likewise, there are two cases of release and eighteen cases of position which influence time.

The steps followed in applying M.T.M. technique are similar to those for Work-Factor. First, the analyst summarizes all motions required to perform the job properly for both the left hand and the right hand. Then

[5] H. B. Maynard, G. J. Stegemerten, J. L. Schwab, *Methods-Time Measurement* (New York: McGraw-Hill Co., Inc., 1948).

[6] *Ibid.*

[7] *Ibid.*

[8] *Ibid.*

T.M.U. = see pp 199

TABLE IX

TABLE I—REACH—R

Distance Moved Inches	Time TMU				Hand In Motion		CASE AND DESCRIPTION
	A	B	C or D	E	A	B	
¾ or less	2.0	2.0	2.0	2.0	1.6	1.6	A Reach to object in fixed location, or to object in other hand or on which other hand rests.
1	2.5	2.5	3.6	2.4	2.3	2.3	
2	4.0	4.0	5.9	3.8	3.5	2.7	
3	5.3	5.3	7.3	5.3	4.5	3.6	B Reach to single object in location which may vary slightly from cycle to cycle.
4	6.1	6.4	8.4	6.8	4.9	4.3	
5	6.5	7.8	9.4	7.4	5.3	5.0	
6	7.0	8.6	10.1	8.0	5.7	5.7	
7	7.4	9.3	10.8	8.7	6.1	6.5	
8	7.9	10.1	11.5	9.3	6.5	7.2	C Reach to object jumbled with other objects in a group so that search and select occur.
9	8.3	10.8	12.2	6.9	6.9	7.9	
10	8.7	11.5	12.9	10.5	7.3	8.6	
12	9.6	12.9	14.2	11.8	8.1	10.1	
14	10.5	14.4	15.6	13.0	8.9	11.5	D Reach to a very small object or where accurate grasp is required.
16	11.4	15.8	17.0	14.2	9.7	12.9	
18	12.3	17.2	18.4	15.5	10.5	14.4	
20	13.1	18.6	19.8	16.7	11.3	15.8	
22	14.0	20.1	21.2	18.0	12.1	17.3	E Reach to indefinite location to get hand in position for body balance or next motion or out of way.
24	14.9	21.5	22.5	19.2	12.9	18.8	
26	15.8	22.9	23.9	20.4	13.7	20.2	
28	16.7	24.4	25.3	21.7	14.5	21.7	
30	17.5	25.8	26.7	22.9	15.3	23.2	

TABLE II—MOVE—M

Distance Moved Inches	Time TMU			Hand In Motion B	Wt. Allowance			CASE AND DESCRIPTION
	A	B	C		Wt. (lb.) Up to	Factor	Constant TMU	
¾ or less	2.0	2.0	2.0	1.7	2.5	0	0	
1	2.5	2.9	3.4	2.3				
2	3.6	4.6	5.2	2.9	7.5	1.06	2.2	A Move object to other hand or against stop.
3	4.9	5.7	6.7	3.6				
4	6.1	6.9	8.0	4.3	12.5	1.11	3.9	
5	7.3	8.0	9.2	5.0				
6	8.1	8.9	10.3	5.7	17.5	1.17	5.6	
7	8.9	9.7	11.1	6.5				
8	9.7	10.6	11.8	7.2				
9	10.5	11.5	12.7	7.9	22.5	1.22	7.4	B Move object to approximate or indefinite location.
10	11.3	12.2	13.5	8.6				
12	12.9	13.4	15.2	10.0	27.5	1.28	9.1	
14	14.4	14.6	16.9	11.4				
16	16.0	15.8	18.7	12.8	32.5	1.33	10.8	
18	17.6	17.0	20.4	14.2				
20	19.2	18.2	22.1	15.6				
22	20.8	19.4	23.8	17.0	37.5	1.39	12.5	
24	22.4	20.6	25.5	18.4				C Move object to exact location.
26	24.0	21.8	27.3	19.8	42.5	1.44	14.3	
28	25.5	23.1	29.0	21.2				
30	27.1	24.3	30.7	22.7	47.5	1.50	16.0	

TABLE III—TURN AND APPLY PRESSURE—T AND AP

Weight	Time TMU for Degrees Turned										
	30°	45°	60°	75°	90°	105°	120°	135°	150°	165°	180°
Small— 0 to 2 Pounds	2.8	3.5	4.1	4.8	5.4	6.1	6.8	7.4	8.1	8.7	9.4
Medium—2.1 to 10 Pounds	4.4	5.5	6.5	7.5	8.5	9.6	10.6	11.6	12.7	13.7	14.8
Large— 10.1 to 35 Pounds	8.4	10.5	12.3	14.4	16.2	18.3	20.4	22.2	24.3	26.1	28.2

APPLY PRESSURE CASE 1—16.2 TMU.   APPLY PRESSURE CASE 2—10.6 TMU.

Courtesy: M.T.M. Association

TABLE IV—GRASP—G

Case	Time TMU	DESCRIPTION
1A	2.0	**Pick Up Grasp**—Small, medium or large object by itself, easily grasped.
1B	3.5	Very small object or object lying close against a flat surface.
1C1	7.3	Interference with grasp on bottom and one side of nearly cylindrical object. Diameter larger than ½″.
1C2	8.7	Interference with grasp on bottom and one side of nearly cylindrical object. Diameter ¼″ to ½″.
1C3	10.8	Interference with grasp on bottom and one side of nearly cylindrical object. Diameter less than ¼″.
2	5.6	**Regrasp.**
3	5.6	**Transfer Grasp.**
4A	7.3	Object jumbled with other objects so search and select occur. Larger than 1″ x 1″ x 1″.
4B	9.1	Object jumbled with other objects so search and select occur. ¼″ x ¼″ x ⅛″ to 1″ x 1″ x 1″.
4C	12.9	Object jumbled with other objects so search and select occur. Smaller than ¼″ x ¼″ x ⅛″.
5	0	Contact, sliding or hook grasp.

TABLE V—POSITION*—P

CLASS OF FIT		Symmetry	Easy To Handle	Difficult To Handle
1—Loose	No pressure required	S	5.6	11.2
		SS	9.1	14.7
		NS	10.4	16.0
2—Close	Light pressure required	S	16.2	21.8
		SS	19.7	25.3
		NS	21.0	26.6
3—Exact	Heavy pressure required.	S	43.0	48.6
		SS	46.5	52.1
		NS	47.8	53.4

*Distance moved to engage—1″ or less.

TABLE VI—RELEASE—RL

Case	Time TMU	DESCRIPTION
1	2.0	Normal release performed by opening fingers as independent motion.
2	0	Contact Release.

TABLE VII—DISENGAGE—D

CLASS OF FIT	Easy to Handle	Difficult to Handle
1—Loose—Very slight effort, blends with subsequent move.	4.0	5.7
2—Close — Normal effort, slight recoil.	7.5	11.8
3—Tight — Considerable effort, hand recoils markedly.	22.9	34.7

TABLE VIII—EYE TRAVEL TIME AND EYE FOCUS—ET AND EF

Eye Travel Time $= 15.2 \times \dfrac{T}{D}$ TMU, with a maximum value of 20 TMU.

where T = the distance between points from and to which the eye travels.
D = the perpendicular distance from the eye to the line of travel T.

Eye Focus Time = 7.3 TMU.

TABLE IX—BODY, LEG, AND FOOT MOTIONS

DESCRIPTION	SYMBOL	DISTANCE	TIME TMU
Foot Motion—Hinged at Ankle.	FM	Up to 4″	8.5
With heavy pressure.	FMP		19.1
Leg or Foreleg Motion.	LM —	Up to 6″	7.1
		Each add'l. inch	1.2
Sidestep—Case 1—Complete when lead-ing leg contacts floor.	SS-C1	Less than 12″	Use REACH or MOVE Time
		12″	17.0
		Each add'l. inch	.6
Case 2—Lagging leg must contact floor before next motion can be made.	SS-C2	12″	34.1
		Each add'l. inch	1.1
Bend, Stoop, or Kneel on One Knee.	B,S,KOK		29.0
Arise.	AB,AS,AKOK		31.9
Kneel on Floor—Both Knees.	KBK		69.4
Arise.	AKBK		76.7
Sit.	SIT		34.7
Stand from Sitting Position.	STD		43.4
Turn Body 45 to 90 degrees—			
Case 1—Complete when leading leg contacts floor.	TBC1		18.6
Case 2—Lagging leg must contact floor before next motion can be made.	TBC2		37.2
Walk.	W-FT.	Per Foot	5.3
Walk.	W-P	Per Pace	15.0

TABLE X—SIMULTANEOUS MOTIONS

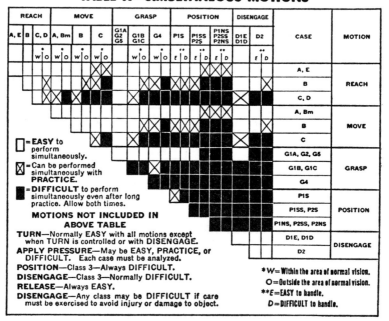

he determines from the methods-time data tables the leveled time in T.M.U.'s for each motion. The nonlimiting motion values should be circled or deleted, as only the limiting motions will be summarized, providing it is "easy" to perform the two motions simultaneously (see section x of Table IX), to determine the time required for a normal performance of the task. For example, if the right hand reached 20 inches to pick up a nut, the classification would be R20C and the time value would be 19.8 T.M.U.'s. If, at the same time, the left hand reached 10 inches to pick up a cap screw, a designation of R10C with a T.M.U. value of 12.9 would be in effect. The right hand would be limiting, and the 12.9 value of the left hand would not be used in calculating the normal time.

The tabulated values presented do not carry any allowance for personal delays, fatigue, or unavoidable delays, and when used for establishing time standards, an appropriate allowance must be added to the summary of the synthetic basic motion times.

Comparison of Work-Factor and Methods-Time Measurement

An interesting comparison of the Work-Factor and the M.T.M. techniques was made by *Modern Industry* magazine.[9] An accomplished engineer familiar with Work-Factor was provided photographs and a complete description of changing an arc-welding electrode for a 400-ampere holder (3/16" × 18" electrode) and was requested to analyze the operation, determining the allowed time. A similar request was given to an exponent of M.T.M. The charts illustrating the techniques of analyzing the motions in this operation are shown in Table X. The final adjusted times by the two techniques showed some difference. The Work-Factor system indicated a time of .0998 minute, while the M.T.M. system showed a time of .00189 hour or .1134 minute. Work-Factor expresses its standards in terms of an experienced, skilled worker while M.T.M. is based on a "normal" or "average" worker. The 12.1 per cent differential found in the preceding example may be in part due to a difference in the base or conception of standard upon which the two systems were established. It was especially significant that both the M.T.M. and the Work-Factor engineers emphasized the fact that the electrode holder was poorly designed, thus prolonging the job unnecessarily. It was pointed out that with a better-designed electrode holder, cycle time would be substantially diminished by eliminating the right-hand motion of opening the holder.

Basic Motion Timestudy

The Basic Motion Timestudy procedure developed in the period 1945 to 1951 by Ralph Presgrave and his associates in J. B. Woods & Gordon,

---

[9] *Modern Industry*, published by Dun's Review and Modern Industry, 99 Church Street, New York, N.Y. The comparison mentioned appeared in the May, 1950, issue.

TABLE X

ILLUSTRATION OF USE OF WORK-FACTOR SYSTEM
(Operation: Change Arc Welding Electrode, 400-Ampere Holder—$\frac{3}{16}''$ x 18″ Electrode)

No.	L. H. Description	Symbol	Time (In Units)*	Symbol	R. H. Description
1	Reach to helmet	A20D	80	. . .	Break arc and
2	Contact helmet	Contact	. .	. . .	move away
3	Raise helmet	A6P	47	. . .	from work and
4	Remove hand	Contact	. .	. . .	hold holder
5	Reach to holder	A10	42	. . .	hold holder
6	Transfer holder from RH	GR-45A	28	. . .	transfer holder to LH
7	Hold holder	. . .	26	A4	Reach to trigger
8	Transfer holder to RH	. . .	28	GR-45A	Transfer holder from LH
9	Reach to rods	A18D	76	. . .	Hold holder
10	Grasp rod	GR-43	36	. . .	
11	Move rod to holder	A12SD	85	. . .	
12	Strike stub with rod to knock stub out of holder	2A2X50	20	. . .	(Assuming this is necessary with one out of two rods)
13	Move rod to holder	A35D	41	. . .	Open holder
14	Assemble rod to holder	ASY-77	42	. . .	Hold holder open
15	Hold rod	. . .	23	H1W	Close holder
16	Release rod	½F1	8	. . .	Hold holder
17	Reach along rod	A6	32	. . .	Hold holder
18	Grasp rod	½F1	8	. . .	Hold holder
19	Turn rod to angle	A3D	32	. . .	Hold holder
20	Release rod	½F1	8	. . .	Hold holder
21	Reach to holder	A6	32	. . .	Transfer holder to RH
22	Transfer holder from RH	GR-45A	28	. . .	Transfer holder to LH
23	Hold holder	. . .	26	A4	Reach to trigger
24	Transfer holder to RH	. . .	28	GR-45A	Transfer holder from LH
25	Idle	. . .	84	A8SWD	Move rod to bead
26		. . .	34	A1SW	Align rod to bead
27	Drop arm to side	. . .	40	HT-450	Nod head to drop helmet
28	Or reach to	. . .	30	MT	Wait for helmet to drop
29	Support right arm	. . .	34	A1SW	Strike arc
		Total..	998		

* Time expressed in .0001 minute.
Source: "Short Cuts to Productivity," *Modern Industry*, May 15, 1950, pp. 41–46.

Limited, of Toronto was a result of a research program endeavoring to measure accurately the effect of the various physical factors influencing the time of hand motions.

According to B.M.T., a basic motion is one in which a body member at rest moves and again comes to rest. For example, in reaching for a pencil lying on the table a basic motion would occur. The beginning of the motion would be the pause or point of rest just prior to the reach,

TABLE X (Continued)

ILLUSTRATION OF USE OF METHODS-TIME MEASUREMENT SYSTEM
(Operation: Change Rods in 400-Ampere Holder)

No.	L. H. Description	Symbol	Time (In Units)*	Symbol	R. H. Description
1	Reach to helmet	R20B	18.6	MBE	Raise holder
2	Contact helmet	G5	0.0	. . .	
3	Raise helmet	M6A	8.1	. . .	
4	Take hand from helmet	RL2	0.0	. . .	
5	Reach to holder	R10A	8.7	. . .	
6	Take holder from RH	G3	5.6	. . .	
7		. . .	7.1	R4B	Reach to trigger
8		. . .	6.5	G3	Take holder from LH
9	Reach to rods	R18C	18.4	AP	Squeeze trigger to open
10	Grasp one rod	G4	8.6	. . .	Holder
11	Move rod to holder	M12E	13.4	M10E	Move rod to holder
12	Strike stub with rod to	M2A	1.8	. . .	Allow 1 out of 2 rods
13	knock it out of holder	M2E	2.1	. . .	
14	Move rod to holder	M3C	5.7	. . .	
15	Position rod in holder	P1SD	11.2	. . .	(P1SE if rod held close to end)
16		. . .	1.7	M1A	Close holder
17	Release rod	RL1	1.7	. . .	
18	Reach to end of rod	R6B	8.6	. . .	
19	Grasp rod	G1a	1.7	. . .	
20	Turn rod to angle	M3E	5.7	. . .	
21	Release rod	RL1	1.7		
22	Reach to holder in RH	R6A	7.0	. . .	
23	Take holder from RH	G3	5.6	. . .	
24		. . .	7.1	R4B	Reach to handle
25		. . .	5.6	G3	Take holder from LH
26		. . .	11.8	M8C	Move rod to bead
27		. . .	5.6	P1SE	Position rod to bead
28	Drop helmet (nod head)	ET30°	9.0	. . .	
29	Strike arc	M1B	1.7	. . .	
		Total..	189.4		

* Time expressed in .00001 hour.

and the termination of the basic motion would be the pause that occurs immediately after the fingers have grasped the pencil. B.M.T. was developed through laboratory study and experiment rather than analysis of uncontrolled factory operations. B.M.T. values have been established in ten thousandths of a minute, as shown in Table XI.

The basic motions identified for purposes of B.M.T. are as follows:

Arm, Hand, and Finger Motions:
   1. Reach
   2. Move
   3. Turn

Body Motions:

1. Foot motion	7. Arise
2. Leg motion	8. Sit
3. Sidestep	9. Stand
4. Bend	10. Turn body
5. Stoop	11. Walk
6. Kneel	12. Eye motions

Finger, hand, and arm motions are identified in terms of the muscular and visual controls that the operator must use to complete them according to the above specifications. The variable factors that affect these motions are described verbally and numerically.

The time data provide a bonus opportunity of some 25 to 30 per cent for the average operator on incentive. They do not include provision for rest and personal requirements of the operator. These must be added to suit the individual jobs.

Basic Motions

B.M.T. recognizes three distinct classes of arm motions. Class A motions are motions that are stopped by impact with a solid object. All muscular effort is used to move the arm in the direction of the motion and none is required to slow down or stop the action. Examples include the downstroke in hammering and the motion to push a flat sheet of metal against a stop in metal shearing.

Class B motions are motions that are stopped entirely by muscular control. Examples include the upstroke in hammering, the motion to toss an object aside, the motion to move the hands aside after placing a part in a foot-operated punch press, and the back-and-forth motions in using a rubber eraser.

Class C motions are motions that are stopped by the use of muscular control to slow the arm before coming to a stop in a grasping or placing action. Examples include reach to a machine lever and grasp, reach to pencil in other hand and grasp, and carry pencil to desk and place down.

The time to perform B and C class motions (motions requiring muscular control in the stopping action) is influenced by the type of visual control required to complete the motion. Whenever the eyes are needed to direct a motion to its destination, but cannot be focused on the end point before the motion begins, the time for the motion will be increased. Motions that are delayed by this form of eye activity are referred to as visually directed motions and are recognized in the B.M.T. time data by the introduction of two additional motion classifications BV and CV. This arrangement provides for five classes of motion, each requiring a different set of time data as shown in Table XI.

B.M.T. makes no distinction between the times to perform basic reaches (transport empty) and basic moves (transport loaded). The

TABLE XI

BASIC MOTION TIMESTUDY VALUES
(Expressed in Ten Thousandths of a Minute)

.0001

REACH OR MOVE

Inches	½	1	2	3	4	5	6	7	8	9	10	12	14	16	18	20	22	24	26	28	30
A	27	30	36	39	42	45	47	50	52	54	56	60	64	68	72	76	80	84	88	92	96
B	32	36	42	46	49	52	55	58	60	62	64	68	72	76	80	84	88	92	96	100	104
BV	36	42	48	53	57	60	63	66	68	70	73	77	81	85	89	93	97	101	105	109	113
C	41	48	55	60	64	68	71	74	77	79	81	86	90	94	98	102	107	111	115	119	123
CV	45	54	62	67	72	76	79	82	85	87	90	95	99	104	108	112	116	120	124	128	132

PRECISION

Inches	1	2	3	4	5	6	7	8	9	10	12	14	16	18	20	22	24	26	28	30
1/2" tol.	3	4	6	7	8	9	10	11	12	13	14	16	17	18	19	20	21	22	23	24
1/4" tol.	13	16	18	21	23	25	27	29	31	32	36	39	42	45	48	51	53	55	57	59
1/8" tol.	33	37	41	45	48	52	55	58	60	62	67	72	76	80	83	87	91	94	98	101
1/16" tol.	60	65	69	73	76	80	83	87	90	93	98	103	107	112	115	119	123	127	131	135
1/32" tol.	90	97	102	106	110	114	117	120	123	126	131	135	139	143	147	150	153	157	161	165

SIMULTANEOUS MOTIONS

Separation Distance	0	2	4	6	8	10	12	14	16	18	20	22	24
1/4" tolerance and over	0	10	18	27	34	41	47	54	59	65	69	74	78
1/8" ...."......".....	0	12	21	30	37	44	51	57	63	68	73	78	82
1/16"...." ....".....	0	15	27	37	45	53	61	68	75	80	86	91	96
1/32"...."......".....	0	19	34	47	58	68	77	84	90	97	103	107	111

FORCE

Apply Pressure, Start or Stop

Inches	6	12	24
2 pounds	2	3	3
4	6	6	7
6	8	9	10
8	10	11	13
10	13	14	16
15	18	20	22
20	23	26	28
30	31	35	38
40	38	43	47
50	45	50	55

TURN

Degrees	30	45	60	75	90	120	150	180
A	26	29	32	34	37	43	49	54
B	33	36	40	43	47	54	60	67
BV	40	44	48	52	56	65	72	80
C	56	60	64	68	72	81	88	96
CV	73	77	81	85	89	98	105	113

EYE TIME

80

BODY MOTIONS

LM (1'-6") 50	Leg Motion		TB_1 110	Turn Body	
Add per inch .. 2			TB_2 220	Turn Body	
			B 180	Bend	
FM 55	Foot Motion		S 180	Stoop	
W 100	Walk One Pace		K_1 180	Kneel on one Knee	
SS_1 (1'-6") 60	Side Step		AB etc. 200	Arise	
Add per inch.. 2			K_2 440	Kneel on Knees	
SS_2 (1'-6") 120	Side Step		AK_2 480	Arise from Knees	
Add per inch.. 4			SIT 220	Sit	
			STAND 270	Stand	

effect of the weight of an object being carried is provided for, when necessary, in the form of an allowance to the basic time as described later. For purposes of analysis, reaches and moves are identified by the code letters R and M respectively. A class C reach is coded R–C while a class C move is coded M–C.

Variable Factors

The time to perform each of these basic motions is influenced by one or more variable factors.

One factor that affects all classes of motion is the distance covered by the motion. A direct relationship exists between the distance through which the motion is performed and the time to perform it. The amount of the variable that is present is expressed in inches. The complete coding for a class C reach 12 inches long is R12C.

Another factor that influences all classes of motion is defined as "force." The amount of the force factor to be allowed for handling a given weight depends upon the method of handling the weight and the distance through which it is handled. For example, the force allowance for tossing aside a 10-pound object that is already held in the hand, using a 24-inch arm motion, will require the basic allowance of 16, which is shown in the force time table. If the weight had to be picked up from a bench before being tossed aside, the allowance would be twice basic or 32. If the weight were picked up, carried 24 inches and again placed down, the allowance would be three times basic or 48.

These allowances are in the form of additions to the time for a basic motion. The complete code and standard time for the three examples used will be as follows:

1. Toss aside weight already held using a 24-inch motion

M24B..........	92
1F10..........	16
	108 or .0108 min.

2. Pick up weight and toss aside

M24B..........	92
2F10..........	32
	124 or .0124 min.

3. Pick up weight, carry and place down

M24C..........	111
3F10..........	48
	159 or .0159 min.

A third variable factor is referred to in B.M.T. as "precision." It is described as the extra care that is required when motions that use muscular control in the stopping action are completed within close limits.

Precision becomes a factor whenever the limits within which the finger tips can move to complete the action are reduced to ½ inch or less.

The allowance for precision is also in the form of additions to the time for a basic motion. The amount of the allowance depends upon the degree of precision and the length of the motion with which it is associated. The time data recognize five degrees of precision from ½ inch to $\frac{1}{32}$ inch for motion distances up to 30 inches. The standard time for a motion that ends in grasping an object, where the limits within which the fingers can complete the action is no more than $\frac{1}{4}$ inch, is developed as follows:

$$
\begin{array}{ll}
\text{R12C} & 86 \\
\text{P}\frac{1}{4} & \underline{36} \\
& 122 \text{ or } .0122 \text{ min.}
\end{array}
$$

Turns

Arm motions that are performed by turning or rotating the hand and forearm around the long axis of the forearm are treated as a special type of arm motion and are called "turns." Separate time data are shown for the five classes of basic arm turns.

The influence of distance is expressed in degrees rather than inches and the code for a 90-degree C class turn is shown as T90C.

Simultaneous Arm Motion

B.M.T. provides an allowance for arm motions that are performed separately but simultaneously if each arm requires visual direction. The allowance is to compensate for the delay that is caused by one arm having to slow down or come to a complete stop at some point short of the destination while the eyes direct the other arm to its destination.

The amount of allowance depends upon the degree of precision in the ending actions and the distance separating the two end points. This allowance is also in the form of an addition to the time for a basic motion. The complete code and standard time for simultaneous arm motion are recorded in two stages. The first stage establishes the details for a one-handed operation. The second stage provides the allowance to cover the delay when simultaneous motions are performed. The procedure is illustrated by showing the separate stages for simultaneous arm motion 12 inches long to place objects within limits of $\frac{1}{8}$ inch, where the end points are 12 inches apart.

$$
\begin{array}{lll}
\text{1st stage:} & \text{M12CV} & 95 \\
\text{1st stage:} & \text{P}\frac{1}{8} & \underline{67} \\
& & 162 \\
\text{2nd stage:} & \text{Simo 12 inch} & \underline{51} \\
& & 213 \text{ or } .0213 \text{ min.}
\end{array}
$$

Application Technique

The B.M.T. procedures outline methods to be used for developing standards for other types of arm motions such as those that follow curved or circular paths. They also include time data for body motions such as steps, body bending, and turning actions, and describe procedures for developing standards that involve combinations of arm and body motion.

Figure 10-2 illustrates the technique used in identification of the basic motions employed in a given method for the assembly of a cap to a fountain pen.

Motion-Time Analysis

Motion-Time Analysis was developed by A. B. Segur in the middle 1920's as a method of establishing time standards. Today, this fundamental motion procedure system, similar to the others discussed in this text, is finding its greatest use as a tool of the methods analyst for improving existing operations, and correctly planning and controlling future operations.

It is similar to the others mentioned in this chapter in that the analyst first makes a listing of the motions being performed by both hands. For each motion, an appropriate time value is assigned. If the motion is classified as being ineffective, (of doubtful value in the job) the figures for its time are entered in red pencil. If the motion is classified as being effective (motion should be generally allowed), its value is posted in black. The number and extent of the red figures are an indication of the method improvement possibilities.

The basic concept of motion time analysis is that the time required to perform basic motions tends to be constant for different individuals. Consequently, time is a function of method. In other words, if the correct method is followed by any operator, he will achieve the standard that was established by that method.

Dimensional Motion Times

Dimensional Motion Times, referred to as DMT, is a procedure developed by the General Electric Company for measuring the work content by predetermined time values. This system has developed the following tables of values:

1. Grasp—jumbled parts in trays, rod—type parts
2. Grasp—jumbled parts in trays, block—type parts
3. Grasp—scattered parts on bench
4. Grasp—isolated parts on surface
5. Grasp—prepositioned tools
6. Grasp—parts from confined area
7. Position hole to pin or pin to hole
8. Position parts to various nest
9. Position and start nut to screw, one hand
10. Position and start nut to screw, simo
11. Restricted area position
12. Rotate
13. Release
14. Transport
15. Time to turn crank
16. Directional turn
17. Weight factors applicable to move, grasp, position, and release
18. Miscellaneous motion times

DMT has emphasized "dimension" as the principal criteria affecting time to perform a motion. As in other fundamental motion data systems, this technique has its greatest application in the study and the improvement of methods and establishment of standards on manual, bench type, high volume work.

Applying Synthetic Basic Motion Times

As a means of improving methods, a general knowledge of the fundamentals of synthetic motion-time standards will prove invaluable. For example, if the methods analyst has a grounding in M.T.M., he will design work stations to utilize the "G1A" grasps requiring but 2 T.M.U.'s rather than the more difficult grasps which require as much as 12.9 (G4C) T.M.U.'s. Likewise, he will endeavor to design for utilization of contact releases rather than normal releases and for symmetrical positioning rather than semisymmetrical or nonsymmetrical positioning. One of the important uses for any of the synthetic basic motion-time techniques lies in the area of methods. Once an analyst has an appreciation of this tool, he will find himself looking more critically at each and every work station, thinking how improvement may be made. Reaches and moves of 20 inches will appear unduly long to him, and he will immediately consider the savings possible through shortened motion patterns. Positioning elements that involve heavy pressure are automatically a sign of need for improvement. Operations that require eye travel and eye focus time can usually be improved.

BASIC ELEMENT STUDY   SHEET___1_OF____1____

DEPT._____ DATE_____ SHEET_____OF_____
OPERATION___ Assemble Cap to Fountain Pen ___OPERATOR _____OBSERVER _____
DATA_____

MAJOR ELEMENT	L.H. BASIC ELEMENT	SYMBOL	TIME	SYMBOL	R.H. BASIC ELEMENT
	Reach to cap on table	R			Hold barrel
	Move cap to pen point	M			"
	Move cap along barrel	M			"
	Hold cap			T	Rotate barrel half turn
	"			T	Regrasp barrel
	"			T	Rotate barrel final half turn
	"			M	Place pen on desk

FIG. 10–2. Basic element breakdown of assembling cap to fountain pen.

Of course, standards of performance may be established through the medium of synthetic basic motion times. If the data are to be used for this purpose, a much greater knowledge of the techniques of application is required. In no case should an analyst endeavor to establish time standards to be used for rate purposes until he has had thorough training and has demonstrated his ability to use the tool precisely. Thus, the analyst must know if the distance moved is the linear distance taken by the hand or the circumferential distance taken by the arc that the hand makes. He must know if the distance is measured from the center of the hand, the knuckles, or the finger tips. He must know when application of pressure prevails and when it does not. He must clearly understand the elements of alignment and orientation as they affect positioning time. These and many other considerations must be mastered before an analyst can expect to establish consistent and accurate time standards with this tool.

Mr. A. B. Segur has not made the derivations and use of his Motion-Time Analysis values available to the public. He defends his position as follows:

> Now I have heard in the last few years a great deal of criticism because the motion values that have gone with Motion-Time Analysis have not been generally published. As a matter of fact, these motions values have been very freely given to anyone who is sufficiently trained in the art of fundamental motion study to be able to use them correctly. But, as a matter of course, we know what would happen in a large plant if someone who is not sufficiently trained undertook to equate the working conditions, the exact motions and the correct times. The principle of fundamental motions could not be used, and the result would be disastrous. That is to say that those who are going to use this principle should be trained. By insisting upon that training, we get away from having our work discredited.[10]

It is only after thorough training that a group of analysts will arrive at consistent time standards using any of the synthetic motion-time techniques. In no case should any analyst endeavor to establish time standards with only a superficial knowledge of this tool.

Summary

Basic Motion Timestudy, Work-Factor, Methods-Time Measurement, Dimensional Motion Times, Motion-Time Analysis as well as several leading industries, have made substantial contributions to a fund of knowledge that is available for analysis of fundamental motions. Frederick Taylor, many years ago, visualized the development of standards for basic divisions of work similar to what is currently being accomplished. In his paper on "Scientific Management" he brought out the fact that the time would come when a sufficient volume of basic standards would be developed so as to make further stop-watch studies unnecessary.

As has been pointed out, the data that have been developed to date

---

[10] *Proceedings, National Time and Motion Study Clinic, 1940,* Industrial Management Society.

are comparatively new, and since the various tables of motion differ, there is some question as to their accuracy. In applying various published data, broad differences in time values are realized on certain motion patterns. All values cannot be correct, but once valid values have been conclusively proven, they should be made available to practitioners of the science. For example, one study developed the fact that 79 per cent more time was required to move a 15-pound weight a given distance than was necessary to move a 1-pound weight of the same size the same distance.[11] Other studies show considerably less influence of weight on time.

Inevitably, synthetic basic motion time values are becoming more accurate as additional studies are being made. There is still a need for further research, testing, and refinement in this area. For example, there is a question as to the validity of adding basic motion times for the purpose of determining elemental times in that therblig times may vary once the sequence is changed. Thus, the time for the basic element "reach 20 inches" may be affected by the preceding and succeeding elements and is not dependent entirely on class of reach and distance. Further study will probably allow the tabulation of the majority of variables influencing time so that it should be only a matter of a few years until completely reliable values will be available to practicing methods analysts and time study engineers. This will be a useful tool to supplement the stop watch and moving-picture camera.

One of the paramount uses of basic motion times is that the analyst who endeavors to apply the synthetic procedure must carefully examine all factors affecting the motion pattern of a job. This minute scrutiny inevitably reveals opportunities for refinement of work methods.

In one company, $40,000 was allocated in an effort to provide advanced tooling so as to increase the rate of production on a brazing operation. Prior to retooling, a work-measurement study of the existing method was made, and it developed that by providing a simple fixture and rearranging the loading and unloading area, production could be increased from 750 to 1,000 pieces per hour. The total cost of the synthetic basic motion time study was $40, and as a result of its application it was not necessary to embark on the retooling program of $40,000.

Another manager of one of our leading electrical appliance companies has emphasized the fact that basic motion times permit predetermining whether or not expenditures for new facilities and tools are warranted, and can accurately forecast the cost of reductions that may be achieved. This same manager states:

We can recommend improvements in tool design for motion economy and better methods. We can accurately predetermine our labor costs for production. We can advise our product-design engineers so that parts can be designed

---

[11] B. W. Niebel and G. L. Thuering, "Let's Have More Accurate Time Standards for Basic Motions," *Factory Management and Maintenance*, September, 1951, p. 101.

for more efficient manufacture. We can establish consistent incentive-standard data.[12]

The above examples are representative of the methods improvement possibilities that can be gained with this tool which the methods analyst is rapidly realizing is essential in his kit of knowledge.

It can be concluded that predetermined time systems have a definite place in the field of methods and work measurement and that they are no better than the people using them, that is, they should not be installed without professional help or a complete understanding of their application.

TEXT QUESTIONS

1. About when did synthetic time values begin to be used in industrial work?
2. What are the advantages of using synthetic basic motion times?
3. What variables are considered by the Work-Factor technique?
4. How did Work-Factor develop its values?
5. What is the time value of one T.M.U.?
6. Who pioneered the M.T.M. system?
7. How was the development of the Basic Motion Timestudy values different from both M.T.M. and Work-Factor?
8. What variables are considered in the B.M.T. technique?
9. Who was originally responsible for thinking in terms of developing standards for basic work divisions? How did he contribute?
10. Calculate the equivalent in T.M.U.'s of .0075 hours per piece, of .248 minutes per piece, of .0622 hours per hundred, of .421 seconds per piece, of 10 pieces per minute.
11. How is M.T.M. related to the analysis of method?
12. Why has Mr. A. B. Segur been reluctant to make his fundamental motion data available to the public?

GENERAL QUESTIONS

1. Select a simple operation and preprice the method using M.T.M., Work-Factor, and B.M.T. Which technique establishes the "tightest" standard?
2. What does the future hold for synthetic basic time values?
3. Which of the three techniques outlined is the easiest to apply?
4. Which in your opinion will give the most reliable results? Why?
5. Describe as vividly as you can how you would explain to a workman in your forge shop who knows nothing about M.T.M. what it is and how it is applied.
6. Give several objections which you might receive from a workman in the application of M.T.M. and explain how you would overcome them.
7. Some companies have been experiencing a tendency for their time study men to become more liberal in their performance rating over a period of years. How does fundamental motion data offset this tendency toward creeping loose standards?

---

[12] "Short Cuts to Productivity," *Modern Industry*, May 15, 1950, p. 42.

CHAPTER 11

Determination of Factory Cost

F<small>ACTORY COST OF A PRODUCT IN-</small>cludes the cost of direct labor, direct material, and factory expense. Factory expense consists of such items as light, heat, rent, service supplies, and factory supervision. A close review of expense or overhead items will show that these costs are made up of but two components: material and labor, or a combination of the two. So, in effect, factory cost is made up of just labor and material. Therefore:

FACTORY COST = COST OF LABOR + COST OF MATERIAL

Material cost is easily determined, no matter what the product may be. In every instance, it is determined by multiplying the cost per unit of measure by the number of measures involved. Thus, some yardstick always governs its basis of cost. Steel is bought by the ton, castings and forgings by the piece, water and gas by the cubic foot, electricity by the kilowatt hour, tubing by the foot, silver by the ounce, cloth by the square yard, oil by the gallon, and so forth. In every case, material cost can be prorated so that it is possible to determine the proportional share each product item should absorb.

The only other item of cost entering into factory cost is the cost of labor either direct or indirect. Labor cost, in most commodities, represents the major portion of total costs. In order to have some conception of true costs of specific products, standards must be established on labor elements. Hourly monetary rates mean nothing unless they are supplemented with performance standards. If an operator running a No. 2 Brown & Sharpe Universal Mill is paid a base rate of $1.70 per hour while milling a profile on a forging, there is no conception of the unit milling cost until a standard has been established on the job in terms of

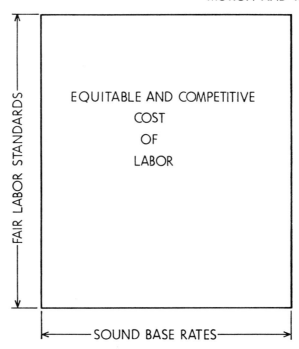

time. If a standard allows six minutes per piece, then a labor cost of $0.17 can be assigned to the operation. However, time standards alone do not give the entire story with regard to labor costs. They do form one side of the rectangle whose area may be thought of as equitable and competitive costs of labor. The other side of the rectangle is sound base rates.

Base rates that are sound must assure money rates commensurate with area rates for similar work; they must allow adequate differentials for jobs requiring higher skills and responsibilities; they must be based on techniques that can be explained and justified.

Job Analysis

Appropriate base rates are determined by job evaluation, which was defined in Chapter 1 as a technique for equitably determining the relative worth of the different work assignments within an organization. The basis of job evaluation is job analysis, which is the procedure for making a careful appraisal of each job and then recording the details of the work so that it can be evaluated fairly by a trained analyst. Figure 11–1 illustrates an analysis of a clerical job for use in a point job evaluation plan. It should be clearly understood that before a job description is developed, all aspects of the opportunity should be carefully studied to assure that the best methods are being used and that the operator is thoroughly trained in the prescribed method.

JOB TITLE____Shipping and Receiving Clerk_____ DEPT.___Shipping_____

MALE_x_FEMALE____DATE_____TOTAL POINTS__280__CLASS__7_

JOB DESCRIPTION

Directs and assists in loading and unloading, counting, and receiving or rejecting purchased parts and supplies, and later delivers to proper departments.
Examines receivals out of line with purchase orders. Maintains file on all purchase orders and/or shipping orders and keeps open orders up to date. Maintains daily and weekly shipping reports and monthly inventory reports.
Assists in packing of all foreign and domestic shipments. Makes up request for inspection form on certain materials received and rejection form for all items rejected.
Job requires thorough knowledge of parking, shipping, and receiving routine, knowledge of plant layout, shop supplies and finished parts. Needs to have a knowledge of simple office routine. Ability to work with other departments, as a service department, and to deal effectively with vendors. Job requires considerable accuracy and dependability.

JOB EVALUATION	DEGREE	POINTS
EDUCATION	1	15
EXPERIENCE AND TRAINING	2	50
INITIATIVE AND INGENUITY	3	50
ANALYTICAL ABILITY	3	50
PERSONALITY REQUIREMENTS	2	30
SUPERVISORY RESPONSIBILITY	1	25
RESPONSIBILITY FOR LOSS	1	10
PHYSICAL APPLICATION	6	25
MENTAL OR VISUAL APPLICATION	1	5
WORKING CONDITIONS	5	20
		280

FIG. 11-1. Job analysis for shipping and receiving clerk.

Job Evaluation

There are four principal methods of job evaluation being practiced in this country today. These are:

1. The classification method.
2. The point system.
3. The factor comparison method.
4. The ranking method.

The classification method, sometimes called the grade description plan, consists of a series of definitions which are designed to differentiate jobs into wage groups. Once the grade levels have been defined, each job is studied and assigned to the appropriate level on the basis of the complexity of duties and responsibilities. This plan is used extensively in the United States Civil Service.

When using this method of job evaluation, the following steps must be considered:

1. Prepare a grade description scale for each type of job, e.g. machine operations, manual operations, skilled (craft) operations, inspection.
2. Write the grade descriptions for each grade in each scale, using factors such as,
   a) Type of work and complexity of duties,
   b) Education necessary to perform job,
   c) Experience necessary to perform job,
   d) Responsibilities,
   e) Effort demanded.
3. Prepare job descriptions for each job. Classify each job by "slotting" (placing in a specific category) the job description into the proper grade description.

Both the point system and the factor comparison method are more objective and thorough in their evaluations of the various jobs involved, in that both of these two plans make a study of the basic factors that are common to most jobs and influence their relative worth. Of the two plans, the point plan is generally considered to be the most accurate method for occupational rating. In this method, all the different attributes of a job are compared directly with these attributes in other jobs.

When a point system is to be installed, the following procedure should be followed:

1. Establish and define basic factors which are common to most jobs and which indicate the elements of value in all jobs.
2. Specifically define the degrees of each factor.
3. Establish the points to be accredited to each degree of each factor.
4. Prepare a job description of each job.
5. Evaluate each job by determining the degree of each factor contained in it.
6. Sum points for each factor to get total points for job.
7. Convert the job points into a wage rate.

The factor comparison method of job evaluation usually has the following elements:

1. Factors are determined that will establish the relative worth of all jobs.
2. An evaluation scale is established which is usually similar to a point scale except that the units are in terms of money.
3. Job descriptions are prepared.
4. Key jobs are evaluated factor by factor by ranking each job from the lowest to the highest for each factor.
5. The wages paid on each key job are allocated to the various factors. The money allocation automatically fixes the relationship between jobs for

each factor, and therefore establishes the ranks of jobs for each factor.

6. On the basis of the monetary values assigned the various factors in the key jobs, other jobs are evaluated factor by factor.
7. By adding the money value for each factor, a wage is determined.

The ranking method arranges the jobs in their order of importance or according to their relative worth. This method became popular in the United States during World War II because of its simplicity and ease of installation. It was at this time that the National War Labor Board set up the requirement that all companies working on government contracts must have some type of wage classification system. This ranking method satisfied this requirement. Generally speaking, the ranking method is less objective than the other techniques; consequently, greater knowledge of all jobs is necessary. For this reason, it has not been extensively used in recent years but has been superseded by the other plans. The following steps are followed when installing the ranking plan:

1. Prepare job descriptions.
2. Rank jobs (usually departmentally first) in order of their relative importance.
3. Determine the class or grade for groups of jobs using a bracketing process.
4. Establish the wage or wage range for each class or grade.

Selection of Factors

It is generally considered preferable to use a small number of factors. Under the factor comparison method, most companies use five factors. In some point programs, ten or more factors may be used. The objective is to use only as many factors as is necessary to provide a clear-cut difference between the jobs of the particular company. The elements of any job may be classified as to:

1. What the job demands the employee to bring in the form of physical and mental factors.
2. What the job takes from the employee in the form of physical and mental fatigue.
3. The responsibilities that the job demands.
4. Conditions under which the work is done.

The selection of factors is usually the first basic task to be undertaken when introducing job evaluation.

The National Electrical Manufacturers Association states that the relative value of a job is considered to depend on the following factors:

1. Education
2. Experience
3. Initiative and Ingenuity
4. Physical Demand
5. Mental and/or Visual Demand
6. Responsibility for Equipment or Process

  7. Responsibility for Material or Product
  8. Responsibility for Safety of Others
  9. Responsibility for Work of Others
 10. Working Conditions
 11. Hazards

These factors are present in varying degrees in the various jobs, and any job under consideration will fall under some one of the several degrees of each factor. The various factors are not of equal importance. To give recognition to these differences in importance, weights or points are assigned to each degree of each factor as shown in Table XII. Figure 11–2 illustrates a job rating and substantiating data sheet based on the National Electrical Manufacturers Association plan.

It has been seen how one side of the rectangle whose area is competitive cost of labor can be determined. Job evaluation will provide the means for compensating all employees within an organization in proportion to their responsibilities and to the difficulty of their work. At the same time, it will lead to base pay rates that are in line with remuneration for similar work in the community. The benefits effected through job evaluation will enhance ideal personnel relations.

Determination of Labor Standards

In order to assure equitable and competitive costs of labor, it is important to establish fair labor standards in addition to sound base rates.

TABLE XII

POINTS ASSIGNED TO FACTORS AND KEY TO GRADES

FACTORS	1st Degree	2nd Degree	3rd Degree	4th Degree	5th Degree
SKILL					
1. Education	14	28	42	56	70
2. Experience	22	44	66	88	110
3. Initiative & Ingenuity	14	28	42	56	70
EFFORT					
4. Physical Demand	10	20	30	40	50
5. Mental or Visual	5	10	15	20	25
RESPONSIBILITY					
6. Equipment, Process	5	10	15	20	25
7. Material or Product	5	10	15	20	25
8. Safety of Others	5	10	15	20	25
9. Work of Others	5	10	15	20	25
JOB CONDITIONS					
10. Working Conditions	10	20	30	40	50
11. Unavoid. Hazards	5	10	15	20	25

Source: National Electrical Manufacturers Association

JOB RATING - SUBSTANTIATING DATA
DORBEN MFG. CO.
UNIVERSITY PARK, PA.

JOB TITLE: Machinist (General)   CODE: 176   DATE: Nov. 12, 1958

FACTORS	DEG.	POINTS	BASIS OF RATING
Education	3	42	Requires the use of fairly complicated drawings, advanced shop mathematics, variety of precision instruments, shop trade knowledge. Equivalent to four years of high school or two years of high school plus two to three years of trades training.
Experience	4	88	Three to five years installing, repairing, and maintaining machine tools and other production equipment.
Initiative and Ingenuity	3	42	Rebuild, repair, and maintain a wide variety of medium-size standard automatic and hand-operated machine tools. Diagnose trouble, disassemble machine and fit new parts, such as antifriction and plain bearings, spindles, gears, cams, etc. Manufacture replacement parts as necessary. Involves skilled and accurate machining using a variety of machine tools. Judgment required to diagnose and remedy trouble quickly so as to maintain production.
Physical Demand	2	20	Intermittent physical effort required tearing down, assembling, installing, and maintaining machines.
Mental or Visual Demand	4	20	Concentrated mental and visual attention required. Laying out, setup, machining, checking, inspecting, fitting parts on machines.
Responsibility for Equipment or Process	3	15	Damage seldom over $300. Broken parts of machines. Carelessness in handling gears and intricate parts may cause damage.
Responsibility for Material or Product	2	10	Probable loss due to scrapping of materials or work, seldom over $150.
Responsibility for Safety of Others	3	15	Safety precautions are required to prevent injury to others; fastening work properly to face plates, handling fixtures, etc.
Responsibility for Work of Others	2	10	Responsible for directing one or more helpers a great part of time. Depends on type of work.
Working Conditions	3	30	Somewhat disagreeable conditions due to exposure to oil, grease, and dust.
Unavoidable Hazards	3	15	Exposure to accidents, such as crushed hand or foot, loss of fingers, eye injury from flying particles, possible electric shock, or burns.

REMARKS: Total 307 Points--assign to job class 5.

FIG. 11-2.

Three techniques have been used for determining labor standards. These
are estimates, historical records, and work measurement procedures.
Estimates as a means of establishing standards were used to a greater
extent in years past than today. With the growth of the organized labor
movement, there has been an increasing effort to establish standards

based on facts rather than judgment. Experience has shown that no individual can establish consistent and fair standards of production by the simple procedure of taking a look at a job and then judging the amount of time required to produce it. Where estimates are used, standards will be out of line an average of about 25 per cent. Compensating errors sometimes will diminish this figure, but over a period of time, experience has shown that estimated values deviate substantially from measured standards. Both historical records and work measurement techniques will give much more accurate values than will the use of estimates based on judgment alone.

Under the historical method, production standards are based on the records of previously produced, similar jobs. In common practice, the worker "punches in" on a time clock every time he begins a new job, and then "punches out" on the job when he has completed it. This technique tells us how long it took to do a job, but never indicates how long it should have taken. Since operators wish to justify their entire working day, some jobs carry personal delay time, unavoidable delay time, and avoidable delay time to a much greater extent than they should, while other jobs will not carry their appropriate share of delay time. I have seen historical records deviate consistently as much as 50 per cent on the same operation of the same job. Historical records as a basis of determining labor standards are better than no records at all. This method will give more reliable results than using estimates based on judgment alone, but it does not provide sufficiently valid results to assure equitable and competitive cost of labor.

Any of the work measurement techniques—stop watch time study, standard data, time formulas or work sampling studies—represents a better way to establish fair production standards. All of these methods are based on facts. All of these techniques consider each detail of the work and its relation to the normal time required to perform the entire cycle. Accurately established time standards make it possible to produce more within a given plant, thus increasing the efficiency of equipment and operating personnel. Poorly established standards, although better than no standards at all, will lead to high costs, labor dissension, and eventually possible failure of the enterprise.

Conclusion

In order to predetermine factory cost, so necessary from the standpoint of submitting bids and quotations, it is essential that cost of the various direct and indirect materials and the cost of all labor be precisely predetermined.

Predetermined material costs can easily be calculated. Predetermined labor costs can also be readily computed if good labor standards developed by one of the work measurement techniques prevail. Standards determined by estimates and historical records usually will not be sufficiently accurate to meet competitive prices or will not allow manufacture at a necessary profit.

Although labor standards determine "how long," it is necessary to have sound base rates in order to measure fairly the "how much" in terms of dollars and cents. Of the various methods of job evaluation used in establishing sound base rates, the point plans tend to give the most reliable results. Point job evaluation systems patterned after the National Metal Trades and the National Electrical Manufacturers Association techniques represent a logical approach toward developing the relative worth of the different work assignments within an organization.

TEXT QUESTIONS

1. What are the three basic components of cost?
2. Is time a common denominator of labor cost? Why?
3. What is job analysis?
4. What four methods of job evaluation are being practiced in this country today?
5. Explain in detail how a "point" plan works.
6. What factors influence the relative worth of a job?
7. Why are estimates unsatisfactory for determining direct labor time standards?
8. What is the weakness of using historical records as a means of establishing standards of performance?
9. What work measurement techniques will give valid results when undertaken by competent trained analysts?

GENERAL QUESTIONS

1. When plotting area rates against job point values, is it necessary that the resulting curve be a straight line? Why?
2. Should cost of living increases be given as a percentage of base rates or as a straight hourly increment? Why?

CHAPTER 12

Time Study Requirements

In CHAPTER 1, TIME STUDY WAS defined as a technique of establishing an allowed time standard to perform a given task. This technique is based upon measurement of work content of the prescribed method, with due allowance for fatigue and personal and unavoidable delays. Frequently, time study is defined by the layman as a method of determining a "fair day's work," and this concept will be discussed before the requirements and responsibilities of those associated with time study are explained. It is necessary to have a clear understanding of what is involved in a fair day's work.

A Fair Day's Work

Practically everyone connected with industry in any way has heard many times the expression, "a fair day's work," yet if asked to define just what is a fair day's work, he is immediately perplexed to establish a sound definition. The intraplant wage rate inequities agreements of the basic steel industries[1] contain the provision that "the fundamental principle of the work and wage relationship is that the employee is entitled to a fair day's pay in return for which the company is entitled to a fair day's work." A fair day's work is defined in these agreements as the "amount of work that can be produced by a qualified employee when working at a normal pace and effectively utilizing his time where work is not restricted by process limitations." This definition is limited as to what is exactly meant by "qualified employees," "normal pace," and "effective utilization." Although all of these terms have been defined by the steel industries, a certain amount of flexibility prevails because firm benchmarks cannot be established on such broad terminology. For ex-

---

[1] With United Steelworkers of America.

224

ample, a "qualified employee" is defined as "a representative average of those employees who are fully trained and able satisfactorily to perform any and all phases of the work involved, in accordance with the requirements of the job under consideration." This definition leaves a doubt as to what is meant by a "representative average employee."

Then the term "normal pace" is defined as "the effective rate of performance of a conscientious, self-paced, qualified employee when working neither fast nor slow and giving due consideration to the physical, mental, or visual requirements of the specific job." The intraplant wage rate inequities agreements specify as an example "a man walking without load, on smooth, level ground at a rate of three (3) miles per hour." Although the three miles an hour concept tends to tie down what is meant by normal pace, still a notable amount of latitude can prevail, when we think of normal pace on the thousands of different jobs in American industry.

Again, a feeling of uncertainty arises when one considers the definition of "effective utilization." This is explained in the agreements as "the maintenance of a normal pace while performing essential elements of the job during all portions of the day except that which is required for reasonable rest and personal needs, under circumstances in which the job is not subject to process, equipment or other operating limitations."

In general, a fair day's work is one that is fair to both the company and the employee. This means that the employee should give a full day's work for the time that he gets paid, with reasonable allowances for personal delays, unavoidable delays, and fatigue. He is expected to operate in the prescribed method at a pace that is neither fast nor slow, but one which may be considered representative of all-day performance by the experienced, co-operative employee.

Time Study Requirements

Certain fundamental requirements need to be realized before the time study should be taken. If the standard is required on a new job, or if it is required on an old job on which the method or part of the method has been altered, the operator should be thoroughly acquainted with the new technique before the operation is studied. Also, it is important that the method to be studied has been standardized at all points where it is to be used. Unless all details of the method and working conditions have been standardized, the time standards will have little value and will be a continual source of mistrust, grievances, and internal friction.

It is also important that the union steward, the departmental foreman, and the operator are cognizant of the fact that the job is to be studied. Each of these parties will then be able to make any specific plans in advance and thereby take the necessary steps to allow a smooth, coordinated study. The operator should verify that he is performing the correct method and endeavor to acquaint himself with all details of the operation. The foreman should check the method in order to make sure that feeds, speeds, cutting tools, lubricants, and so forth, conform to standard practice as established by the methods department. Also, the foreman must investigate the amount of available material so that no shortage will take place during the course of the study. If several operators are available for study of the operation in question, the foreman should determine to the best of his ability which operator will be likely to give the most satisfactory study. The union steward should then make sure that only trained competent operators are selected for time study observation. He should explain to the operator why the study is being taken and answer pertinent questions that come to the operator's attention from time to time.

Responsibilities of the Time Study Man

All work involves varying degrees of skill and physical and mental effort in order to accomplish the task satisfactorily. In addition to the variations in job content, there are differences in aptitude, physical application, and dexterity of the workmen. It is an easy matter for the analyst to observe an employee at work and measure the actual time taken to perform a task. It is a considerably more difficult problem to evaluate all variables and determine the time required for the "normal" operator to perform the job.

Because of the many human interests and reactions associated with the time study technique, it is essential that there be a full understanding of its principles and practice. There must be, also, complete co-operation of the foremen, the employee, the union steward, and the time study analyst.

In general, the time study analyst is charged with these responsibilities:

1. To probe, question, and examine the present method so as to assure that it is correct in all respects before the standard is established.
2. To discuss equipment, method, and operator's ability with the foreman before studying the operation.
3. To answer questions relating to time study practice or to a specific time study which may be asked by the union steward, the operator, or the foreman.
4. To co-operate with the foreman and the operator at all times in order to obtain maximum help from both.
5. To refrain from any discussion with the operator or other operators, since this might be construed as criticism of the individual being studied.
6. To show on each time study, complete and accurate information, thus specifically identifying the method under study.
7. To record accurately times taken to perform the individual elements of the operation being studied.
8. To evaluate the performance of the operators honestly and fairly.
9. To conduct himself at all times in such a manner as to obtain and hold the respect and confidence of the representatives of both labor and management.

The qualifications of a time study man that are necessary for him to meet successfully the responsibilities of his position are similar to those required for success in any field in which the major efforts are directed toward establishing ideal human relations.

First of all, a good time study man must have the mental ability to analyze diversified situations and make rapid, sound decisions. He should have an inquisitive, probing, and open mind that seeks to improve and always to be cognizant of the "why" as well as the "how."

Supplementing a keen mind, it is essential that the time study analyst have practical shop training in the areas in which he will be establishing standards. If he is to be associated with the metal trades, he should have a background as a journeyman machinist or the equivalent knowledge of machines, hand tools, jigs, fixtures, gages, and their correct use and application. This would include specific knowledge of cutting feeds, speeds, and depths of cut in order to get the maximum results consistent with desired quality of the product and ultimate tool life.

Since the time study man directly affects the pocketbook of the worker and the profit and loss statement of the company, it is essential that his work be completely dependable and accurate. Inaccuracy and poor judgment will not only affect the operator and the company financially but may also result in complete loss of confidence by the operator and the union, which may undo harmonious labor relations that have taken management years to build up.

In order to achieve and maintain good human relations, the following personal requirements can be considered essential for the successful time study man:

1. Honesty.
2. Tact, human understanding.
3. Resourcefulness.
4. Self-confidence.
5. Good judgment, analytical ability.
6. Pleasing, persuasive personality, supplemented with optimism.
7. Patience with self-control.
8. Bountiful energy tempered with a co-operative attitude.
9. Well-groomed, neat appearance.
10. Enthusiasm for the job.

A review of all of the qualifications essential for a successful time study man may give the reader the opinion that he should be on a staff level with the president of the company. In fact, it is questionable if all of these attributes would be required of top executives of a concern. However, when one considers the magnitude of the labor relations problem today, it is essential that only the most competent people enter the field of time study. No other one individual within a company comes in contact with as many personnel from different levels of the organization as the time study analyst. Therefore, it is imperative that he have the best qualifications.

In the time study man's approach to various employees, he should learn to recognize the human qualities in a man and then be guided by a realization of the limitations of human nature. Thus, in order to receive co-operation he must determine and follow through with the best method of approach to the workman. This calls for analysis of the employee's attitude toward his job, his fellow workmen, the company, and toward the time study man himself.

Foreman's Responsibility

Any and all foremen are management's representatives throughout the plant. Next to the operator, the foreman is closer to specific jobs than any other man in the plant. In view of this, he must accept certain responsibilities in connection with the establishment of time standards.

To begin with, the foreman, in the interest of harmonious labor relations within the department in which he supervises, finds it mandatory that equitable time standards prevail. Both "tight" and "loose" standards are the direct cause of endless personnel problems, and the more of these that can be avoided, the easier and more pleasant will be his job. Of course, if all standards were loose, he would find his supervisory responsibilities relatively easy. However, this situation could not exist practically, as competition would not be met where all standards are loose.

The foreman should notify the operator in advance that his work assignment is to be studied. This clears the way for both the time study analyst and the operator. The operator has the assurance that his direct superior is cognizant of the fact that a rate is to be established on the job and will have the opportunity to bring out specific difficulties that he feels should be corrected before a standard is set. The time study analyst will of course feel considerably more at ease, knowing that his presence has been anticipated.

It should be the foreman's responsibility to see that the proper method established by the methods department is being utilized and that the operator selected is competent and has adequate experience on the job. Although the time study analyst is required to have a practical background in the area of work that he is studying, he can hardly be expected to be infallible in specifications of all methods and processes. Thus, he should consider the foreman as his ally to verify that the cutting tools are properly ground, the correct lubricant is being used, and that proper selection of feeds, speeds, and depths of cut have been considered.

If, for any reason, conditions are such that the operation will be so affected that it is questionable whether a fair time study can be taken, the foreman should immediately make this fact known to the time study analyst.

In general, the foreman is responsible for assisting and co-operating with the time study man in any way that will aid in defining or clarifying an operation. He should carefully consider any suggestions for improvement brought out by the time study man, and fully utilize his own background and influence to establish an ideal method in conjunction with the methods department, prior to stop-watch study.

The foreman is responsible for seeing that his men use the prescribed method, and he should conscientiously assist and train all those employees coming under his jurisdiction in perfecting this method. He should freely answer any questions asked by the operator regarding the operation.

Any time a methods change takes place within his department, the foreman should notify the time study department immediately so that an appropriate adjustment of the standard can be made. This procedure should be followed regardless of the degree of the methods adjustment. It would include such things as changes in material handling to and from the work station, changes in inspection procedure, changes in feeds and speeds, changes in work station layout, and process changes.

Upon completion of a time study, the foreman should be required to sign the original study, thus indicating that he has complied with all of his responsibilities relative to the study taken. Foremen who accept and carry out their responsibilities toward time study practice can be assured of operating harmonious departments that will be looked on with favor by management, the union, and the employees themselves. Foremen who fall short of these responsibilities can contribute to the establishment of inequitable rates which will result in numerous labor grievances, pressure from management, and considerable dissatisfaction from the union.

The Union's Responsibility

As every union steward knows, poor time standards are just as much of a problem to him as they are to the management of the company. In the interests of operating a healthy union within a profitable business, the union must accept certain responsibilities toward time study.

Through training programs, the union should educate all of its members in the principles, theories, and economic necessity of time study practice. All of us tend to fear anything on which we are poorly informed. Operators can hardly be expected to be enthusiastic about time study if they know nothing about it. This is especially true in view of its background (see Chapter 2). Therefore, the union should accept the responsibility of helping to clarify and sell this important tool of management.

The union should accept the responsibility of seeing that adjusted standards are put into effect whenever a methods change is made. When methods are revised, the union should see that the time study department is notified through specified lines of authority.

The union should encourage its members to co-operate with the time study analyst and have the operators refrain from practices which would tend to place their performances at the low end of the rating scale. Encouraging operators to deceive the time study man will, in the final analysis, add up to but one thing—a poor standards structure, which will include both loose and tight rates.

Unions that train their members relative to the elements of time study, encourage co-operativeness, and stay abreast of management's program will benefit by more co-operation at the bargaining table, fewer work stoppages, and better satisfied members. Those unions that encourage distrust of time study, and facilitate a program of "keeping the operator in the dark," will be faced with a multitude of grievances from their members, a balky management team to negotiate with, and over a period of time, sufficient work stoppages to create a hardship on all parties concerned.

Operator's Responsibility

Every employee should be sufficiently interested in the welfare of his company to give his wholehearted support to every practice and procedure inaugurated by management. Unfortunately, this situation is seldom realized, but it certainly can be approached if a company's management demonstrates its desire to operate with fair standards, fair base rates, good working conditions, and adequate employee benefits in the form of insurance and retirement programs. Once management has taken the initiative in these areas, every employee can be expected to cooperate in all operations and production control techniques.

The individual operators should be responsible for giving new methods a fair trial when introduced. They should wholeheartedly co-operate in helping to work out the "bugs" characteristic of practically every innovation. Suggestions for further improvement of the method should be accepted as a part of each operator's responsibilities. The operator is closer to the job than anyone else, and he can make a real contribution to the company and to himself by doing his part in establishing ideal method procedures.

The operator should be responsible for assisting the time study analyst in breaking down the job into elements, thus assuring that all details of the job are specifically covered. He should also be responsible for working at a steady, normal pace while the study is being taken and should introduce as few foreign elements and extra movements as possible. He should be responsible for using the exact prescribed method and make no effort to deceive the time study analyst by introducing an artificial method with the thought of lengthening the cycle time and thereby receiving a more liberal standard.

Conclusion

To many practicing time study men, the aforementioned responsibilities of the operator, the union, and the foreman may be considered a utopian approach which can never be realized. However, as stated, if management takes the initiative, these conditions can be approximated and the result will be a competitive, profitable business for all parties. For example, Howard M. Hinkel, Personnel Director of American Type Founders, Inc., reports that by establishing an "appreciation" course in time study and incentive techniques for union stewards and committee-men in his company, they have almost eliminated rate discussions that go beyond the operator's initial complaint.[2]

Time study procedures are the only known methods for supplying accurate information relative to standard times which are so essential for the profitable, efficient operation of industry and business. In order to assure the most valid results from time study practice, the time study analyst must receive complete co-operation from the foreman, the union steward, the operator, and company management.

Time study represents one of the most important and exacting forms of work in any industrial, commercial, or governmental enterprise. When intelligently used and fully understood by all parties, it offers marked benefits to workmen, management, and the general public.

TEXT QUESTIONS

1. How is a fair day's pay determined by the intraplant wage rate inequities agreements of the basic steel industries?
2. What benchmark for normal pace is given under these agreements?
3. Why should the foreman sign the time study?
4. Why should the time study man have excellent personal qualities?
5. Explain how poor time standards increase the difficulties of the union steward?
6. How can management increase the co-operation of the union steward, the foreman, and the operator in their dealings with the time study analyst?

GENERAL QUESTIONS

1. Is it customary for the union to co-operate with the time study department to the extent recommended in this text? Is this co-operation likely to occur?
2. If the requirements for a time study man are so high, why is it that industry does not pay more for time study work?

---

[2] "Time Study Training for Stewards and Committeemen," *Factory Management and Maintenance*, August, 1947.

CHAPTER 13

Time Study Equipment

The minimum equipment that is required to carry on a time study program includes:

1. Stop watch.
2. Time study board.
3. Time study forms.
4. Slide rule.

In addition to the above, time-recording devices that are being used successfully and that offer some advantages over the stop watch are:

1. Time-recording machines.
2. Motion-picture camera.

It will be noted that the equipment needed for time study or work measurement is not nearly as elaborate or costly as that required for micromotion study work. In general, the ability and personality of the time study analyst represent the criteria of success rather than the equipment he chooses to use.

The Stop Watch

There are several types of stop watches in use today, the majority of which are included in one of the following classifications:

1. Decimal minute watch (.01 minute).
2. Decimal minute watch (.001 minute).
3. Decimal hour watch.

The decimal minute watch (.01 minute shown in Figure 13–1) has 100 divisions on its face, and each division is equal to .01 minute. Thus, a complete sweep of the long hand would require 1 minute. The small dial

FIG. 13–1

FIG. 13–2

FIG. 13–1. Decimal minute watch.

FIG. 13–2. Decimal minute split (double action) watch.

FIG. 13–3. Decimal hour watch.

Courtesy: Meylan Stopwatch Co.

FIG. 13–3

on the watch face has 30 divisions, and each division here is equal to 1 minute. For every revolution of the sweep hand, the small hand will move 1 division or 1 minute.

To start this watch, the side slide is moved toward the crown. In order to stop the watch and have the hands retain their respective positions, the side slide is moved away from the watch crown. To continue operation of the watch from the point where the hands stopped, the slide is moved toward the crown. In order to move both the sweep hand and the small hand back to zero, the crown is depressed. Release of the crown will put the watch back into operation unless the side slide is moved away from the crown.

The decimal minute watch tends to be a favorite with time study men because of its ease of reading and ease of recording. The sweep hand moves only 60 per cent as fast as the long hand of the decimal hour watch, and thus terminal points are more discernible. In recording the time values, the analyst's task is simplified by the fact that the elemental readings are in one hundredths of a minute, eliminating the need for the ciphers that are registered when using the decimal hour watch, which is read in ten thousandths of an hour.

The decimal minute watch (.001 minute) is similar to the decimal minute watch (.01 minute). In the former, each division of the larger hand is equal to one thousandth of a minute. Thus, it takes .10 minute for the sweep hand to circle the dial rather than 1.00 minute as in the .01 decimal minute watch. This watch is used primarily for timing short elements for standard data purposes (see Chapter 18). In general, the .001 minute watch has no starting slide on its side, but is started, stopped, and returned to zero by successive depressions of the crown.

A special adaptation of the decimal minute watch that many time study men find convenient to use is illustrated in Figure 13–2. The two long hands indicate decimal minutes and will complete one turn of the dial in one minute. The upper small dial is graduated in minutes, and a complete sweep of its hand represents 30 minutes. The lower small dial is graduated in seconds, and a complete sweep of the small hand here takes 1 minute.

To start this watch, the crown is depressed and both sweep hands will simultaneously start from zero. At the termination of the first element, the side pin is depressed and this will stop the lower sweep hand only. The time study man can then observe the elapsed time for the element without the difficulty of reading a moving hand. He then depresses the side pin, and the lower hand will rejoin the upper hand which has been moving uninterruptedly. At the end of the second element, the side pin is depressed and the procedure is repeated.

The decimal hour stop watch has 100 divisions on its face also, but each division on this watch represents 1 ten thousandth (.0001) of an hour. Thus a complete sweep of the large hand on this watch would represent 1 one hundredth (.01) hour or .6 minute. The small hand registers each turn of the long hand, and a complete sweep of the small hand would take 18 minutes or .30 hour (see Figure 13–3).

The decimal hour watch is started, stopped, and its hands are returned to zero in the same manner as in the decimal minute (.01) stop watch.

Since the hour represents a universal unit of time in measuring output, the decimal hour watch is a practical timer and is widely used. Somewhat more skill is required to read this watch while timing short elements on account of the speed of the sweep hand. For this reason, some time study men prefer the decimal minute watch with its slower moving hand.

It is possible to mount three watches on a board, with linkage between them, so that the analyst, during the course of a study, can always read one watch which has stopped hands. Figure 13–4 illustrates such an arrangement. Here are shown three crown action watches which are actuated by a lever shown at the right. First pressure on lever starts Watch 1 (far left), cocks Watch 2, and stops Watch 3. At end of first

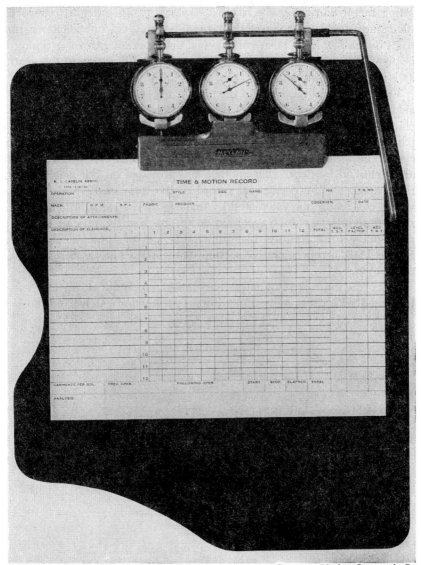

Courtesy: Meylan Stopwatch Co.

FIG. 13–4. Time study board with watches and form mounted, placed in proper position.

element, the lever is again pressed. This will stop Watch 1, start Watch 2, and reset Watch 3 to zero. Watch 1 is now waiting to be read, while the next element is being timed by Watch 2.

Time-Recording Machines

It is obvious that considerable training is required to be able to read the stop watch, record the reading on the time study form, and still be cognizant of the operative performance so that the correct leveling or rating factor can be applied (see Chapter 15). In order to relieve the time study analyst of some of these required simultaneous functions, time study machines have been constructed that "permit precision timing of elements or movements as small as .01 minutes in duration to the nearest .001 minute in sequence."[1]

One time study machine on the market today, available for use by the analyst, will correctly record values accurate to .025 minute. The machines are built to drive a graduated tape at a constant rate of speed past a key or indicator, which when depressed will mark the tape indicating the termination of an element. Interruptions or foreign elements are identified by depressing another key provided on the machine. The tape represents the permanent record of the time study, and elemental values can readily be calculated by making successive subtractions. Element descriptions can be recorded on the back of the tape or on a supplementary form. Figure 13–5 illustrates one of these machines and Figure 13–6, a representative section of recorded tape as a result of its use.

Since the time study analyst has nothing to write down and is not burdened with continually observing a fast-moving watch hand, he is in

Courtesy: Black & Webster Inc.

FIG. 13–5. Marsto-chron timing instrument.

[1] Dale Jones, "A New Time Study Tool," *Advanced Management*, April, 1953.

a much better position to do an accurate job of "rating" the operator, as all of his attention can be directed to operator performance. This is especially true on short elements (.08 minute and less). The time study machine offers no particular advantage on studies composed of only long elements (over .08 minute), as studies of this nature allow the analyst ample time to record the terminal points as well as observe the operator's skill and effort.

The principal disadvantage of the time study machine is the added clerical work necessitated by the transcription of the data taken on the tape to the time study work sheet.

Other disadvantages of the time study machine are its cumbersomeness in comparison to the stop watch and the difficulty of securing 110 A.C. outlets throughout a shop.

Motion-Picture Camera

The motion-picture camera is ideal for recording operator methods and elapsed time. Unfortunately, the cost of film and the delay necessitated by having to send the films out to be developed, prohibit the use of the method in a great many instances.

More and more industries are resorting to the motion-picture camera for establishment of standards with the development of synthetic motion-time values. By taking pictures of the operator and then

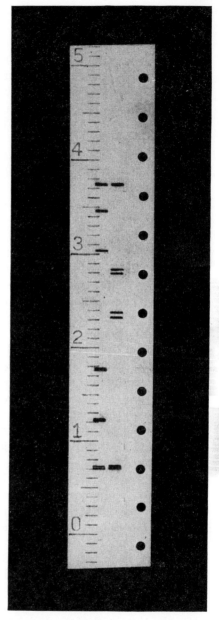

FIG. 13–6. Graduated tape as used in the Marsto-chron timing instrument.

studying them a frame at a time, the analyst can record exact details of the method used and assign time values. It is also possible to establish standards by projecting the exposed films at the same speed that the pictures were taken and then performance rating the operator. All the facts necessary to accomplish a fair and accurate job of rating are available by observing the exposed film. Then, too, potential method improvements are revealed through the camera eye that would never be uncovered with the stop watch or time study machine.

These advantages, supplemented with the "Memomotion" precedure, which allows longer cycle filming with minimum exposure of film, have increased the popularity of the camera as an effective tool of the time study analyst (see Chapter 9). Figure 9–8 illustrates a portion of a memomotion film taken at the rate of 1 frame per second.

The motion-picture camera described and illustrated in Chapter 8 will also do an excellent job when filming for the purpose of establishing time standards.

Time Study Board

When the stop watch is being used, it will be necessary to provide a suitable board to hold the time study form and the stop watch. The board should be light, so as not to tire the arm, and yet strong and hard enough to provide a suitable backing for the time study form. One-quarter-inch plywood or a smooth plastic, such as bakelite, make suitable materials. The board should have arm and body contacts (see Figure 13–7) for comfortable fit and ease of writing while it is being held.

In the upper right-hand corner of the board (for right-handed people) is mounted the watch, and to the left, a spring clip holds the time study form. By standing in the proper position, the time study analyst can look over the top of his watch to the work station, and follow the operator movements while keeping both the watch and the time study form in his immediate field of vision.

In order to assist the analyst in performance-rating the operation under study, an alignment chart, developed by the author, may be attached to the board (see Figure 13–7). This chart permits the analyst to determine synthetically the allowed time for several of the effort elements comprising the study. The ratio of the synthetic value for a particular element to the mean value actually taken by the operator serves as a guide for determining the performance factor. This chart establishes standards for the therbligs reach, grasp, move, position, and release when performed collectively.

Time Study Forms

On the time study form is recorded all details of the study. To date there has been little standardization of the design of forms used by various industries. It is important that the form provide space to record all pertinent information concerning the method being studied. This is often done by constructing an operator process chart (see Chapter 6) on one side of the form. In addition to making a permanent record of the relative location of the tools and materials in the work area, the analyst should

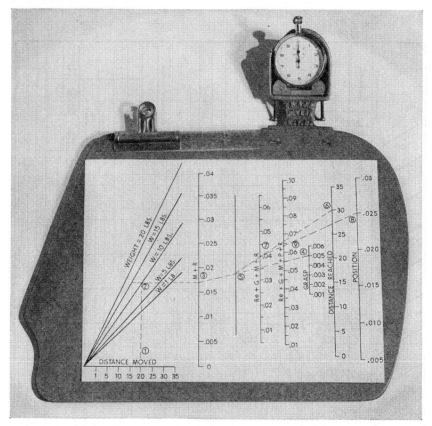

FIG. 13–7. Time study board for right-handed observer. Note alignment chart on board to assist observer in the determination of performance rating factor.

record such method data as feeds, depth of cut, speeds, and inspection specifications. Of course, it is also necessary to identify completely the operation being studied by including such information as the operator's name and number, operation description and number, machine name and number, special tools used and their respective numbers, department where operation is performed, and the prevailing working conditions. It is always better to provide too much information on the job being studied than too little. This will be discussed in a subsequent chapter.

The time study form should also include space for the signature of the foreman in the department and the time the study was conducted, thus indicating his approval of the method under observation. Likewise, the inspector should sign every study taken, thus acknowledging his acceptance of the quality of the parts produced during the course of the time study.

The form should be designed so that the analyst can conveniently record watch readings, foreign elements (see Chapter 14), rating factors

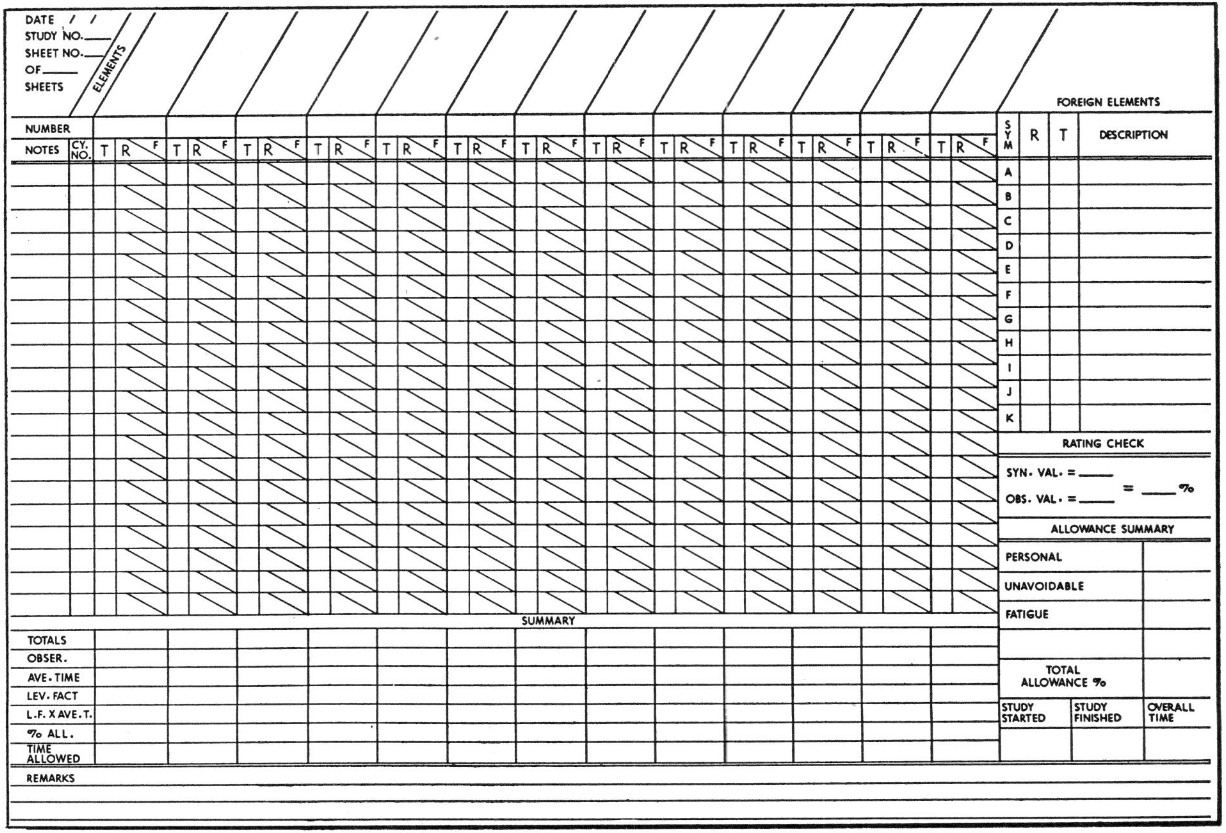

FIG. 13–8. Time study form (front) designed for either elemental or over-all rating.

SKETCH

STUDY NO._____DATE_____

OPERATION_____

DEPT._____OPERATOR_____NO._____

EQUIPMENT_____

_____

_____MCH. NO._____

SPECIAL TOOLS, JIGS, FIXTURES, GAGES_____

_____

_____

CONDITIONS_____

MATERIAL_____

PART NO._____DWG. NO._____

PART DESCRIPTION_____

ACT BREAKDOWN		ELEM. NO.	SMALL TOOL NUMBERS, FEEDS, SPEEDS, DEPTH OF CUT, ETC.	ELEMENTAL TIME	OCC. PER CYCLE	TOTAL TIME ALLOWED
LEFT HAND	RIGHT HAND					
		EACH PIECE_____		TOTAL		
		SET-UP_____		HRS. PER C		
		FOREMAN		INSPECTOR		
		OBSERVER		APPROVED BY		

FIG. 13–9. Time study form (back). Note space for operator chart (act breakdown) so that all details of method under study may be recorded.

(see Chapter 15), and still use the sheet to calculate the allowed time. Figures 13–8 and 13–9 illustrate a time study form that has been developed by the author which allows sufficient flexibility to study practically any type of operation.

In this form, the various elements comprising the operation are recorded horizontally across the top of the sheet and the various cycles studied are recorded vertically row by row.

The "R" column is divided into two sections. The large area is for recording the watch readings and in the small section marked "F" is shown the element performance factor if elemental rating is used. The "T" column is provided for elemental elapsed values (see Chapter 14).

Auxiliary Equipment

The time study analyst will fine it necessary to provide certain additional equipment to facilitate calculation of studies rapidly and accurately. Foremost of these items is the slide rule by means of which calculation of the time study involving multiplication, division, and proportion can be solved correctly and rapidly in a small fraction of the time required to work it out by longhand arithmetical procedures.

It is recommended that the time study analyst use a slide rule with a 10-inch scale, as this will give results correct to within about 1 part in 1,000 or one-tenth of 1 per cent. The shorter the rule, the less accurate will be the readings, and of course the larger the scales, the more precise will be the results.

Although, in most cases, modern machine tools, being self-powered, show their speeds in an obvious place, there will be occasions when the running sped will not be evident. Then too, speeds indicated by the manufacturer are based upon certain pulley diameters which may have been altered during the setup or changed during maintenance or overhaul of the machine.

In order to determine the speed being used, the time study analyst will find it convenient to use a speed indicator. This instrument has few parts, is simple in operation, and will give relatively accurate revolutions of shafting, wheels, and spindles in either direction. Figure 13–10 illustrates a typical speed indicator. To use the speed indicator, it is merely

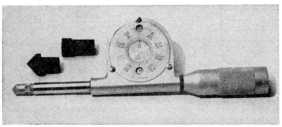

FIG. 13–10. Speed indicator for use in determining speeds in revolutions per minute.

Courtesy: Brown & Sharpe Manufacturing Co.

FIG. 13–11. Checking spindle speed with speed indicator.

necessary to place the point of the indicator on the spindle or shaft and watch the dial for a given period of time. In the illustration, the figures showing through the small, round windows on the dial read every 5 revolutions. The inside dial reads every 100 revolutions. The dials may be quickly returned to zero for repeated use by turning a knob on the back of the indicator.

TEXT QUESTIONS

1. What equipment is needed by the time study analyst to carry on a program of time study?
2. What features of the decimal minute watch make it attractive to time study men?
3. Where does the decimal minute watch (.001 minute) have application?
4. How does the duration of one division on the decimal hour watch compare to one division on the decimal minute watch?
5. What is the principal advantage of the time-recording machine?
6. What is the "Memomotion" procedure? What are its advantages and limitations?
7. Why is it desirable to provide space for an operator process chart on the time study form?
8. Describe the speed indicator and how it is used.

9. How many feet of film would be exposed on a 5-minute cycle while using the Memomotion technique?

GENERAL QUESTIONS

1. Explain the statement, "the ability and personality of the time study engineer represent the criteria of success rather than the equipment he chooses to use."
2. Why has there not been a standardized time study form adopted by industry?
3. Do you feel that the typical shop workman would favor the time study machine? Why?
4. What would be the advantages of having a time study machine that would be able to record and play back sound as well as record end points of progressive elements?

CHAPTER 14

Elements of Time Study

THE ACTUAL TAKING OF A TIME
study is both an art and a science. In order to be sure of success in this
field the analyst must have developed the art of being able to inspire
confidence, exercise judgment, and create a personable approach to all
with whom he comes in contact. In addition, it is essential that his background and training have been such that he thoroughly understands and
is able to perform the various functions related to each step in the taking
of the study. These elements include selecting the operator, analyzing the
job and breaking it down into its elements, recording the elapsed elemental values, performance rating the operator, assigning appropriate allowances, and working up the study.

Choosing the Operator

The first approach to beginning a time study is made through the departmental foreman or line supervisor. Upon review of the job in operation, both the foreman and the time study man should agree that the job
is ready to be studied. If more than one operator is performing the work
assignment on which the standard is to be established, several things
should be taken into consideration in selecting just which operator to use
in taking the study. In general, the operator who is average or somewhat
above average in performance will give a more satisfactory study than
the low-skilled or highly superior operator. The average operator usually
will perform the work consistently and systematically. His pace will tend
to be in the approximate range of normal (see Chapter 15), thereby
making it easier for the time study analyst to apply a true performance
factor.

Of course, the operator should be completely trained in the method
being used and should possess a liking for his work and an interest in

doing a good job. He should be familiar with time study procedures and practice, and have confidence in time study methods as well as in the time study analyst. It is desirable that the operator have a co-operative spirit, so that he will follow through willingly with suggestions made by both the foreman and the time study analyst.

At times, the analyst will have no choice as to whom he studies, in that the operation is performed by only one man. In cases of this nature, the analyst must be very careful when he establishes his performance rating because the operator may be performing at either of the extreme ends of the rating scale. In one-man jobs, it is also especially important that the method being used is correct and that the analyst approach the operator tactfully.

Approach to the Operator

The technique used by the time study man in approaching the selected operator will have much to do with the extent of co-operation received. The operator should be approached in a friendly manner and be informed that the operation is to be studied. He should then be given the opportunity to ask any questions relative to such matters as the timing technique, method of rating, and application of allowances. In some instances, the operator may have never before been studied, and the time study man will find it worthwhile to answer all his questions frankly and patiently. He should encourage the operator to offer suggestions and, when the operator does so, should receive them willingly, thus recognizing that he respects the skill and trade knowledge of the operator.

The time study man should show interest in the workman's job, and at all times be fair and straightforward in his behavior toward the workman. This approach will establish the workman's confidence in the time study man's ability, and the analyst will find the respect and goodwill resulting will not only help in establishing a true standard, but will also make his future work assignments on the production floor more pleasant.

Analysis of Materials and Methods

Perhaps the most common mistake made by time study analysts is neglecting to make sufficient analysis and records of the method being studied. The time study form illustrated in Chapter 13 allows space for a sketch or photograph of the work area. If a sketch is make, it should be drawn to scale and should show all pertinent details that affect method. The sketch should clearly show the location of the raw material and finished parts bins with respect to the work area. Thus, distances that the operator must move or walk are clearly recorded. The location of all tools involved in the operation should be indicated, thus illustrating the motion pattern utilized in performing successive elements.

Immediately below the pictorial presentation of the method, space frequently is allotted for an operator process chart (see Chapter 6) of the method being studied. On high activity work, it is recommended that this chart be completed before the actual timing of the operation begins. By completing this right- and left-hand chart, the analyst can entirely identify the method under study and can observe opportunities for methods improvement. Elemental breakdown of the study to be taken will be facilitated, and the analyst will be able to acquire a better conception of the skill being executed.

The value of completely identifying the method under study cannot be overemphasized. Since management usually guarantees a standard as long as the method studied is in effect, it is mandatory that the method studied be completely known. For example, after machining a casting, the operator may have been studied as placing the casting in a tote box on a pallet 4 feet from the work station. The element "lay aside finished casting" may have consumed .05 minute. Let us assume that sometime after the standard was established the location of the skid was changed so that a chute and drop delivery could be used to remove the completed part. This could reduce the "lay aside finished casting" element to .01 minute. The savings of .04 minute per cycle would be substantial if the job could be completed in .40 minute or less. This small method change could result in a loose rate that would be troublesome to the union, the company, and the worker's fellow employees. Unless a complete record of the method originally used to "lay aside finished casting" had been established, the time study department would have no authority to restudy the job.

More pronounced methods changes are often made without informing the time study department, such as changing the job to a different machine, increasing or decreasing feeds and speeds, or using different cutting tools. Changes of this nature, of course, seriously affect the validity of the original standard. Often the first time it is brought to the time study department's attention is when a grievance has been submitted that a rate is too tight, or the cost department complains about a loose standard. Investigation will frequently reveal that a change in method has been the cause of this inequitable standard. In order to know what part or parts of the job should be restudied, the analyst must have information as to method used when the job was initially studied. If this information is not available and the rate appears too loose, the only recourse the analyst has is to let the loose rate prevail for the life of the job—a situation that will be resented by management—or to change the method again and then immediately restudy the job—a program that will be strongly criticized by the operator.

Information as to the type of material being used should be recorded, as well as material used in cutting tools (carbon, high-speed, carbide). A design change calling for a part to be made from "60–40 brass" rather than "70–30 brass" could have a pronounced effect on cycle time. Likewise, a change from high-speed tools to carbide tools could decrease machining time by more than 50 per cent.

It has continually been emphasized that a job should not be time studied until it is *ready* to be studied; that is, until the method employed is correct. However, it has also been shown that methods must be continually improved in order to progress. A plant that does not continually emphasize methods improvement will fall into the doldrums and will eventually be unable to operate profitably. Since methods changes are continually taking place, it is necessary that complete analysis of the existing materials and methods be made and recorded prior to beginning the actual watch readings.

Recording the Significant Information

Complete information should be recorded concerning the machines, hand tools, jigs or fixtures, working conditions, materials used, operation performed, name of operator and clock number, department, date of study, and the time study observer's name. Perhaps all this detail will seem unimportant to the novice, but through experience he will realize that the more pertinent information recorded, the more useful will the study be over the years to come. The time study will be a source of establishing standard data (see Chapter 18) and the development of formulas (see Chapter 19). It also will be useful in methods improvement, operator evaluation, tool evaluation, and machine performance.

When machine tools are used, the name, size, style, capacity, and serial or inventory number should be specified. For example "No. 3 Warner & Swasey Ram Type turret lathe, Serial No. 111408, equipped with 2-jaw S.P. air chuck," would identify the facility under use. Cutting tools should be described completely as "½-inch, two-flute, high-speed, 18–4–1, gun drill." Likewise, description of general facilities should be complete and well defined, such as "2-pound ball-peen hammer," "1-inch micrometers," "combination square," "12-inch bastard file."

Dies, jigs, gages, and fixtures can be identified by their number and a short description. For example, "flange trimming die F–1156," "progressive trimming, piercing, forming die F–1202," "Go-No-Go Thread Plug Gage F–1101."

The working conditions should be noted for several reasons. First, the prevailing conditions will have a definite relationship to the "allowance" added to the leveled or normal time. If conditions improve in the future, the allowance for personal time as well as fatigue may be diminished. Conversely, if for some reason, it becomes necessary to alter the working conditions so that they become poorer than when the time study was first taken, it would follow that the allowance factor should be raised.

If working conditions prevailing during the study are different from the normal conditions that exist on that job, then they would have an effect on the usual performance of the operator. For example, in a drop forge shop, if a study were taken on an extremely hot summer day, it can be readily understood that working conditions would be poorer than they usually are, and operator performance would reflect the effect of the intense heat. The following examples will illustrate the description that should be included when recording the job conditions: "Normal for job, wet, hot (90° F.), operator standing," or "poor, temperature 85° F., operator seated, clean, noisy."

It will be noted that it is customary to indicate first the working conditions as they compare with the average conditions for that job. This description is then followed by a short account of the exact conditions which were observed.

Raw materials are identified completely, giving such information as heat number, size and shape, weight, quality, and previous treatments.

The operation being performed is specifically described. For example, "broach ⅜ inch × ⅜ inch keyway in 1-inch bore" is considerably more explicit than the description "broach keyway." There could be several inside diameters on the part, each having a different keyway, and unless the hole that is being broached is specified and the keyway size is shown, misinterpretation may result.

The operator being studied should be identified by name and clock number. There could easily be two John Smiths in one company. Then, too, the clock number does not completely identify an employee, as labor turnover results in assignment of the same clock numbers to more than one employee over a period of years.

Observer's Position

Once the time study analyst has made the correct approach to the operator and has recorded all the significant information, he is ready to record the time consumed by each element.

The time study observer should take a position a few feet to the rear of the operator so as not to distract or interfere with him. It is important that the time study analyst stand while taking the study. A time study man who takes his studies while seated will be subject to criticism from the operators and will soon lose the respect of the production floor. Then, too, when standing, the observer is better able to move about and follow the movements of the operator's hands as he goes through his work cycle. Figure 14–1 illustrates the correct position of the observer with respect to the operator while studying a radial drill operation. It can be seen that the observer is in a position to have a simultaneous view of his watch, his time study form, and the hands of the operator.

During the course of the study, the observer should avoid any conversation with the operator, as this would tend to upset the routine of both the analyst and the workman.

FIG. 14–1. Time study observer studying a radial drill press operation.

Dividing the Operation into Elements

For ease of measurement the operation is divided into groups of ther-bligs known as "elements." So that the operation may be divided into its individual elements, the observer should watch the operator for several cycles. However, if the cycle time is relatively long (over 30 minutes), the observer should write the description of the elements while taking the study. If possible, the elements into which the operation is to be di-vided should be determined in advance of the start of the study. Ele-ments should be broken down into divisions as fine as possible and yet not so small that accuracy of reading will be sacrificed. Elemental divi-sions of about .04 minute are about as fine as can be consistently read by the experienced time study analyst. Of course, if the preceding and suc-ceeding elements are relatively long, an element as short as .02 minute can be readily timed.

In order to identify end points completely and develop consistency in reading the watch from one cycle to the next, elemental breakdown should give consideration to sound as well as sight. Thus, terminal points of elements can be associated with the sounds made when a finished piece hits the container, when a facing tool bites into a casting, when a drill breaks through the part being drilled, and when a pair of microme-ters are laid on a bench.

Each element should be recorded in its proper sequence and include a basic division of work terminated by a distinctive motion or a sound. Thus, the element "up part to manual chuck and tighten" would include the basic divisions of reach for part, grasp part, move part, position part, reach for chuck wrench, grasp chuck wrench, move chuck wrench, position chuck wrench, turn chuck wrench, move chuck wrench, and release chuck wrench. The point of termination of this element would be evidenced by the sound of the chuck wrench being dropped on the head of the lathe. The element "start machine" could include reach for lever, grasp lever, move lever, and release lever. Rotation of the machine with accompanying sound would identify the point of termination so that readings could be made at exactly the same point in each cycle.

Frequently, a standard elemental breakdown is adopted by the different time study analysts within a company for given classes of facilities so as to assure uniformity in establishing terminal points. For example, all single spindle bench type drill press work may be broken down into standard elements and all lathe work may be composed of a series of predetermined elements. Having standard elements as a basis for operation breakdown is especially important in the establishment of standard data (see Chapter 18).

When dividing the job into elements, the analyst should keep machine or cutting time separate from effort or handling time. Likewise, constant elements (those elements for which the time will not deviate within a specified range of work), should be kept separate from variable elements (those elements for which the time will vary within a specified range of work).

Once the proper breakdown is made of all the elements comprising the operation, it is then necessary that each element be accurately described. The termination of one element is automatically the beginning of the succeeding element and is referred to as the "breaking point." The description of this terminal point or breaking point should be such that it will be readily recognized by the observer. This is especially important when the element does not include sound at its ending. On cutting elements, the feed, speed, depth, and length of cut should be recorded immediately after the element description. Typical element descriptions are: "Pk. up pt. from table & pos. in vise" and "Dr. ½" D. .005" F 1200 R.P.M." It will be noted that the analyst, in the interest of brevity, abbreviates and uses symbols to a great extent. This system of notation is acceptable only if the element is completely described in terminology and symbols which are meaningful to all who may come in contact with the study. Some companies use standard symbols throughout their plant, and all connected with the plant are familiar with the terminology.

When elements repeat themselves, it is not necessary to describe the element a second time, but only necessary to indicate in the space provided for a description of the element, the identifying number of the element that was used when it first occurred.

The time study form offers the flexibility required by diversified studies. For example, occasionally, it will not be possible to record an element that successively repeats itself, due to the space limitations of the time study form. This can be handled by recording the watch readings of the repeating elements in the same column as the one in which the first occurrence of the element was recorded. Figure 14–2 illustrates this method of recording.

DATE / /
STUDY NO.__
SHEET NO.__ OF __ SHEETS

NUMBER		1		2		3		4		5		6		7		8		9		10		11		12		13		14		15	
NOTES	CY. NO	T	R F	T	R F	T	R F	T	R F	T	R F	T	R F	T	R F	T	R F	T	R F	T	R F	T	R F	T	R F	T	R F	T	R F	T	R F
	1		5		12		16		26		35																				
	2						39		48		57																				
	3						62		71		80		101		9		19		48		57		62		68		201		11		32
	4		37		44		49		60		71																				
	5						75		83		92																				
	6						97		307		17		36		43		52		81		90		93		400		35		44		63
	7		69		77		82		91		501																				
	8						6		16		24																				
	9						27		38		47		66		78		89		608		17		23		29		59		69		88
	10		93		701		5		14		24																				
	11						9		29		40																				
	12						44		52		64		84		93		805		35		46		52		58		85		94		920
	13		25		33		37		47		56																				
	14						60		69		78																				
	15						83		95		1005		25		33		43		70		81		86		91		1125		35		55
	16		60		68		73		82		91																				
	17						96		1206		15																				
	18						19		29		39		59		67		77		1302		11		17		23		54		64		84
	19		90		97		1401		11		22																				
	20						26		37		47																				

SUMMARY

TOTALS															
OBSER.															
AVE. T.															
LEV. FACT															
L.F. & AV. T.															
% ALL.															
TIME ALLOWED															

FOREIGN ELEMENTS			GENERAL RATING CHECK	SYN. VAL. / OBS. VAL. = %		REMARKS:
	R	T				
A			STUDY STARTED	STUDY FINISHED	OVERALL TIME	
B			____ A.M. P.M.	____ A.M. P.M.	____ MIN.	
C			F			
D			G			
E			H			

FIG. 14–2. Method of recording an element that successively repeats itself.

When more than 15 elements comprise the study, a second sheet should be used to record those elements in excess of 15. If more than 20 cycles are to be observed and the study comprises 7 or less elements, then the right-hand half of the form can be utilized by repeating the elements

DATE / /
STUDY NO.___
SHEET NO.___
OF
SHEETS

CY. NO	1	2	3	4		1	2	3	4		1	2	3	4	
1	4	14	20	23		64	73	80	83		53	65	72	75	
2	27	36	42	46		87	97	503	6		80	91	97	100	
3	51	62	69	74		10	20	25	28		5	15	22	25	
4	78	88	94	98		33	45	52	55		29	39	46	49	
5	101	13	19	23		59	69	75	78		53	61	67	71	
6	26	35	41	44		84	95	602	5		74	84	90	93	
7	48	56	62	65		9	19	26	29		97	1106	13	16	
8	69	79	85	88		34	43	49	52		20	30	37	40	
9	91	200	5	9		55	63	68	72		44	54	60	63	
10	13	22	28	31		76	91	98	702		67	76	82	85	
11	35	45	51	54		5	15	21	24		89	99	1202	5	
12	58	66	71	74		29	39	46	49		9	19	25	28	
13	79	89	97	301		53	63	70	73		32	42	48	51	
14	5	15	22	26		77	86	93	96		55	66	72	74	
15	30	41	46	49		800	10	18	24		78	88	94	98	
16	52	60	66	69		29	37	45	48		1302	12	18	21	
17	73	83	89	92		52	62	69	72		25	35	41	44	
18	96	406	12	15		76	85	91	94		49	61	68	71	
19	19	29	35	38		98	908	15	18		75	85	91	95	
20	42	51	57	60		23	35	45	48		1400	12	18	21	

SUMMARY

TOTALS														
OBSER.														
AVE. T.														
LEV. FACT														
L.F. ŁAV. T.														
% ALL.														
TIME ALLOWED														

FOREIGN ELEMENTS			GENERAL RATING CHECK	SYN. VAL. ___ = % OBS. VAL.	REMARKS:
	R	T			
A				STUDY STARTED	STUDY FINISHED	OVERALL TIME
B				A.M. P.M.	A.M. P.M.	___MIN.
C				F		
D				G		
E				H		

FIG. 14–3. Time study form showing recording of 4-element 60-cycle study.

and continuing the study in the open spaces. However, if more than 7 elements occur and more than 20 cycles are to be recorded, a second sheet should be used. Figure 14–3 illustrates a 60-cycle study comprising 4 elements.

DATE 3/15/55 STUDY NO. 108 SHEET NO. 1 _OF_ SHEETS	Pick up part from table & bring to vise & file edge	Position part in vise & tighten vise by hand. Position table &	Start machine & engage feed	Mill 3/4" slot	Return table eight inches. Stop machine	Open vise & remove part	Brush out chips	Reposition part for second cut	Tighten vise & return table	Start machine	Run table forward & engage feed	Mill second 3/4" slot	Return table eight inches	Stop machine & open vise	Brush machine & aside part
NUMBER	1	2	3	4	5	6	7	8	9	10	11	12	13	14	15
NOTES CY.NO	T R F	T R F	T R F	T R F	T R F	T R F	T R F	T R F	T R F	T R F	T R F	T R F	T R F	T R F	T R F
1	14 14	16 30	4 34	68 102	6 8	19 27	14 41	11 52	21 73	3 76	8 84	77 261	9 70	8 82	18 300
2	12 12	15 27	5 32	73 405	7 12	16 28	15 43	10 53	23 76	5 81	10 91	80 571	9 80	6 86	20 606
3	A 22 36	17 53	4 57	64 1021	5 26	21 47	18 65	10 75	21 96	3 99	11 1110	75 85	11 96	10 1206	16 22
4	12 34	B 16 32	(10) 42	70 1512	8 20	21 41	14 55	11 66	19 85	4 89	9 98	82 1680	11 91	8 99	19 1718
5	12 30	12 42	4 46	70 1818	7 23	22 45	16 61	9 70	22 92	2 94	9 1903	71 74	9 83	8 91	19 2010
Drop Part 6	13 23	17 27/44	4 22/66	66 2118/2044	5 15	20 35	15 50	10 60	20 80	5 85	10 95	80 2275	10 36	9 45	20 C 65
7	16 81	16 97	5 2402	73 75	5 80	(34) 2514	14 28	9 37	21 58	3 61	8 69	76 2645	(4) 49	10 59	18 77
8	15 92	17 2709	4 13	D (50) 64	6 70	18 88	(7) 95	10 3005	20 25	5 30	11 41	80 3732	9 41	12 53	16 69
9	14 83	17 3800	4 4	71 75	6 81	21 3902	14 16	11 27	21 48	5 53	8 61	71 4032	10 42	14 56	15 71
10	17 88	12 4100	– M	– 80	5 85	21 4206	14 20	11 31	22 53	– M	– M	– 4340	10 50	8 58	18 76

SUMMARY

	1	2	3	4	5	6	7	8	9	10	11	12	13	14	15
TOTALS	1.470	1.55	.34	5.55	.60	1.79	1.34	1.02	2.10	.35	.84	6.92	.88	93	1.79
OBSER.	10	10	8	8	10	9	9	10	10	9	9	9	9	10	10
AVE. T.	.147	.155	.043	.694	.06	.199	.149	.102	.210	.039	.093	.769	.098	.093	.179
LEV. FACT	1.10	1.10	1.10	1.00	1.10	1.10	1.10	1.10	1.10	1.10	1.10	1.00	1.10	1.10	1.10
L.F.&AV.T.	.162	.171	.047	.694	.066	.219	.164	.112	.231	.043	.102	.769	.108	.102	.197
%ALL.	15	15	15	10	15	15	15	15	15	15	15	10	15	15	15
TIME ALLOWED	.186	.197	.054	.763	.076	.252	.189	.129	.266	.050	.117	.846	.124	.117	.227

FOREIGN ELEMENTS			GENERAL RATING CHECK	SYN. VAL. #2 $\frac{.164}{.150}$ = 109 %		REMARKS:
	R	T		OBS. VAL.		Investigate use of carbide tipped cutters to replace
A	914 / 606	208	Get drink	STUDY STARTED	STUDY FINISHED	OVERALL TIME	H.S.S. Cutters.
B	1416 / 1234	182	Interrupted by foreman	10:32 A.M. P.M.	11:16 A.M. P.M.	44 MIN.	
C	2326 / 2275	51	Gage part	F		
D	2914 / 2713	201	Chip in eye	G		
E	3652 / 3041	611	Replace milling cutter	H		

FIG. 14–4. Completed time study illustrating the continuous method of watch reading and over-all performance rating (front of form).

Taking the Study

There are two techniques of recording the elemental time while taking the study. The continuous method, as the name implies, allows the stop watch to run for the entire duration of the study. In this method, the watch is read at the breaking point of each element while the hands of the watch are moving. In the snapback technique, the watch is read at the termination point of each element, and then the hands are snapped back to zero. As the next element takes place, the hands move from zero. The elapsed time is read directly from the watch at the end of this element, and the hands are again returned to zero. This procedure is followed throughout the entire study.

When starting the study, using either the continuous method or the snapback, the time study analyst should advise the operator that he is beginning his study, and also let him know the exact time of day at which the study is being taken so that the operator will be able to verify the over-all time. The time of day that the study is started is recorded on the time study form (see Figure 14–4), just prior to starting the stop watch. Figures 14–4 and 14–5 illustrate a completed time study.

Snapback Method

The snapback method has certain advantages and disadvantages as compared to the continuous technique. These should be clearly understood before standardizing on one way of recording the values. In fact, some time study men find it desirable to use both methods, feeling that studies made up predominantly of long elements are adapted to snapback readings, whereas short-cycle studies are better studied with the continuous procedure.

Since elapsed elemental values are read directly in the snapback method, no clerical time is required for making successive subtractions, as is necessary with the continuous method. Then, too, elements that are performed out of order by the operator can be readily recorded without special notation. Proponents of the snapback method also bring out the fact that when using this procedure, it is not necessary to record delays, and since elemental values can be compared from one cycle to the next, a decision can be made as to the number of cycles to study. Actually, observations of the past few cycles, as a means of determining how many additional cycles should be studied is an erroneous procedure. This practice can lead to studying entirely too small a sample.

W. O. Lichtner[1] points out one accepted disadvantage of the snapback method, namely that individual elements should not be removed from the operation and studied independently because elemental times are dependent on preceding and succeeding elements. Consequently, by omit-

---

[1] W. O. Lichtner, *Time Study and Job Analysis* (New York: Ronald Press Co.).

STUDY NO. __132__ DATE __9-15-58__

OPERATION __Mill diagonal slots in regulator clamp__

DEPT. __11-5__ OPERATOR __B.V.Harvey__ NO. __14__

EQUIPMENT __# 2 B. + S. Horizontal Mill__

MCH. NO. __3-17694__

SPECIAL TOOLS, JIGS, FIXTURES, GAGES __Milling fixture__
__# F-14611, 18-4-1 high speed cutters__

CONDITIONS __Normal__

MATERIAL __X - 4130 steel forging__

PART NO. __S-11694-1__ DWG. NO. __SA-11694__

PART DESCRIPTION __2" clamp for series 411__

SKETCH

2 B. + S. Mill

Bin with Raw Forgings ← 3' → Operator 1½' Finished Parts Bin on Pallet

ACT BREAKDOWN

LEFT HAND	RIGHT HAND	ELEM. NO.	SMALL TOOL NUMBERS, FEEDS, SPEEDS, DEPTH OF CUT, ETC.	ELEMENTAL TIME	OCC. PER CYCLE	TOTAL TIME ALLOWED
Reach 12", grasp (simple)	Reach 8" grasp file,	1		.186	1	.186
forging on mill bed, Move	Move file to forging,	2		.197	1	.197
12", hold.	file edge (3 strokes)	3		.054	1	.054
Position forging in vise	Move file 8", release.	4	95 R.P.M. 5⅝"/Min.	.763	1	.763
	Reach 12" for vise handle,	5		.076	1	.076
	grasp handle, turn handle	6		.252	1	.252
	90 to 180 degrees	7		.189	1	.189
Idle	Reach for start button	8		.129	1	.129

Description	Element				
for feed lever, grasp lever, Move lever	10				.266 / .050
Get new piece from bin. — Idle during mill cut	11			.050	.117
Reach for stop button, apply pressure. — Reach 8" grasp control wheel, Move 45°, release wheel.	12	95 R.P.M. 5⅜"/Min.		.117	.846
Reach 15" to part, grasp part, Move part 8" and release. — Reach 16" for vise handle, grasp handle, turn handle 90-180°.	13			.846	.124
Idle — Reach 12", grasp brush, move brush to vise 12" and brush chips.	14			.124	.117
Reach 8" to part, grasp, Move 8" to vise, position — Move brush to table (12"), release brush, reach for vise handle	15			.117	.227
Grasp vise handle, turn handle 90 to 180 degrees.				.227	
Idle — reach 8", grasp control wheel move 45 degrees and release					
Idle — Reach 14" for Start button, apply pressure.					
Reach 14" for control wheel,					
Reach 18" grasp feed lever move lever — grasp wheel, turn wheel 15 degrees, release.					
Idle during mill cut — Lay aside finished piece.					
Reach for control wheel					
Idle — 14", grasp wheel, turn 60 degrees.					
Reach 16" for stop button, apply pressure. — Release control wheel, reach 12" and grasp vise handle, move handle 90°					
Reach for part 12", grasp, Move part to table — Reach 12", grasp brush, move brush to vise 12", brush					
release. — chips, lay brush aside.					

EACH PIECE 3.593 Min.   TOTAL 3.593

SET-UP _____   HRS. PER C 5.988

FOREMAN W. H. Armstrong   INSPECTOR C.A. Anderson

OBSERVER George Thuning   APPROVED BY BWM.

FIG. 14-5. Completed time study form (back of form).

ting such factors as delays, foreign elements, and transposed elements, erroneous values will prevail in the readings accepted.

One of the objections to the snapback method that has received considerable attention, particularly from labor groups, is the time that is lost while the hand is being snapped back to zero. Lowry, Maynard, and Stegemerten state: "It has been found that the hand of the watch remains stationary from 0.00003 to 0.000097 hour at the time of snapback, depending upon the speed with which the button of the watch is pressed and released."[2] This would mean an average loss of time of .0038 minute per element which would be a 3.8 per cent error in an element, .10 of a minute in duration. Of course, the shorter the element, the greater the per cent of error introduced, and the longer the element, the smaller the error. Although experienced time study men will tend in reading the watch to allow for the "snapback time" by reading to the next highest digit, it should be recognized that a sizable cumulative error can develop with the snapback method.

Another disadvantage of the snapback method is the tendency for the observer to become careless once he has established a value for the various elements. He may anticipate what the reading will be and record the corresponding value without close attention to the true elapsed time.

In summary, the snapback procedure has the following disadvantages:

1. Time is lost in snapping back; therefore, a cumulative error is introduced into the study.
2. Short elements (.06 minute and less) are difficult to time.
3. Record of the complete study is not always given in that delays and foreign elements may not be recorded.
4. Carelessness on part of time study man is promoted.

The Continuous Method

The continuous method of recording elemental values is recommended for several reasons. Probably the most significant reason is that this type of study presents a complete record of the entire observation period and, as a result, appeals to the operator and his representatives. The operator is able to see that no time has been left out of the study and that all delays and foreign elements have been recorded. With all the facts clearly presented, it is easier to explain and sell this technique of recording times.

The continuous method is also better adapted to recording very short elements. Since no time is lost in snapping the hand back to zero, accurate values can be obtained on successive elements of .04 minute and on elements of .02 minute when followed by a relatively long element. With practice, a good time study man using the continuous method will be able to catch accurately three successive short elements (less than .04

[2] S. M. Lowry, H. B. Maynard, and G. J. Stegemerten, *Time and Motion Study and Formulas for Wage Incentives* (3rd ed.; New York: McGraw-Hill Book Co., Inc., 1940).

minute), if they are followed by an element of about .15 minute or longer. He does this by remembering the watch readings of the terminal points of the three short elements and then recording their respective values while the fourth longer element is taking place.

Of course, as previously pointed out, more clerical work is involved in calculating the study when using the continuous method. Since the watch is read at the breaking point of each element while the hands of the watch continue their movements, it is necessary to make successive subtractions of the consecutive readings in order to determine elapsed elemental times. For example, the following readings might represent the terminal points of a ten-element study: 4, 14, 19, 121, 25, 52, 61, 76, 211, 16, and the elemental values of this cycle would be 4, 10, 5, 102, 4, 27, 9, 15, 35, and 5.

Recording the Time Consumed by Each Element

When recording the watch readings, the analyst notes only the necessary digits and the decimal point is not indicated, thus giving as much time as possible to observe the performance of the operator. Thus, if a decimal minute watch should be used and the terminal point of the first element occurred at .08 minute, the analyst would record only the digit 8 in the "R" (reading) column of the time study form. If the decimal hour watch is in use and the end point of the first element is .0052, the recorded reading would be 52. The following table illustrates the procedure of using a decimal minute watch:

Consecutive Reading of Watch in Decimal Minutes	Recorded Reading
.08	8
.25	25
1.32	132
1.35	35
1.41	41
2.01	201
2.10	10
2.15	15
2.71	71
3.05	305
3.17	17
3.25	25

The small hand on the watch will indicate the number of elapsed minutes so the observer can refer to it periodically to verify the correct first digit to record after the large hand sweeps past the zero. For example, after 22 minutes have passed in taking a given study, the observer may not recall whether the value to record after the termination of the element he is observing should be prefixed by "22" or "21." By glancing at the small hand of his watch, he will note that it has moved past the 22, thus letting him know that 22 is the correct prefix of the reading to be recorded.

All watch readings are recorded in consecutive order in the "R" column until the cycle is completed. Subsequent cycles are studied in a similar manner, and their elemental values are recorded.

Difficulties Encountered

During the course of the time study, the observer will encounter variations from the sequence of elements that he originally established, and occasionally he himself will miss specific terminal points. These difficulties tend to complicate the study, and the less often they occur, the easier it will be to calculate the study.

When the observer misses a reading, he should immediately indicate an "M" in the "R" column of the time study form. In no case should he make an approximation and endeavor to record the missed value, because this practice can destroy the validity of the standard established for the specific element. If the element were used as a source of standard data, appreciable discrepancies in future standards may result. Occasionally, the operator will omit an element, and this is handled by drawing a horizontal line through the space in the "R" column. This variation should happen infrequently, as it is a sign of an inexperienced operator or else an indication of lack of standardization of method. Of course, the operator can inadvertently omit an element such as forgetting to "vent cope" in making a bench mold or omitting the element "apply parting dust." If elements are repeatedly omitted, the analyst should stop the study and investigate the necessity of performing the omitted elements at all. This should be done in co-operation with the foreman and the operator so that the best method can be established. The observer is expected to be constantly on the alert for determining better ways to perform the elements; as ideas come to his mind, he should jot them down in the "note" section of the time study form for future study and possible development.

Another variation in sequence with which the observer will be faced is the performance of elements out of order. This may happen fairly frequently when studying a new or inexperienced employee on a long-cycle job made up of many elements. To avoid as many of these disturbances as possible is one of the prime reasons for studying a competent, fully trained employee. However, when elements are performed out of order, the observer should immediately go to the element that is being performed and draw a horizontal line through the middle of its "R" space; directly below this line is shown the time the operator began the element, and above it, the completion time is recorded. This procedure is repeated for each element performed out of order and for the first element that is performed back in the normal sequence. Figure 14–4 illustrates a typical study, and elements 2, 3, and 4 on Cycle 6 show how the analyst handled the elements performed out of order.

During the course of the time study, the operator may encounter unavoidable delays such as being interrupted by a clerk or a foreman or tool breakage. Furthermore, the operator may intentionally cause a change in the order of work by going for a drink or stopping to rest. Interruptions of this nature occurring in the work cycle are referred to as "foreign elements."

Foreign elements can occur either at the breaking point or else during the course of an element. The majority of foreign elements, particularly if they are controlled by the operator, occur at the termination of one of the elements comprising the study. When a foreign element occurs during an element, the observer will signify the event by an alphabetical designation in the "T" column of this element. If the foreign element took place at the breaking point, the alphabetical designation will be recorded in the "T" column of the work element which follows the interruption. The letter "A" is used to signify the first foreign element and "B" the second, and so on.

As soon as the foreign element has been properly designated with an alphabetical symbol, a short description is made of it in the space provided immediately after the corresponding reference letter. The time that the foreign element begins is shown in the lower part of the "R" block of the foreign element section, and the watch reading at the termination of the foreign element is recorded in the upper part. These values can then be subtracted at the time the study is calculated, in order to determine the exact duration of the foreign element. This value is then shown in the "T" column of the foreign element section. Figure 14–4 illustrates the correct handling of several foreign elements.

Sometimes elements occur during the course of a study which may be treated as foreign elements, but investigation reveals that they have a definite relation to the job being studied. In cases like this, the element should be considered as irregular and the elapsed time should be leveled, the proper allowance added, and the result properly prorated to the cycle time so that a fair standard can be achieved.

Occasionally, a foreign element will occur that will be of such short duration that it will be impossible to record it in the fashion outlined. Typical examples of this would be dropping a wrench on the floor and quickly picking it up, wiping one's brow with a handkerchief, or turning to speak briefly to the foreman. In cases similar to these examples where the foreign element may be .06 minute or less, the most satisfactory method of handling the interruption is to allow it to accumulate in the element where it occurs and immediately circle the reading, indicating that a "wild" value has been encountered. A short comment should also be made in the "note" section of the time study form across from the element where the interruption occurred, thus justifying the circling procedure.

Number of Cycles to Study

The number of cycles to be studied in order to arrive at an equitable standard is a subject that has caused considerable discussion among time study analysts. Since the activity of the job, as well as its cycle time, directly influences the number of cycles that can be studied from an economic standpoint, one cannot be completely governed by the sound statistical practice that demands a certain size sample based on the dispersion of the individual element readings.

The General Electric Company has established the following table as a guide to the number of cycles to be observed:

Cycle Time in Minutes	Recommended Number of Cycles
.10	200
.25	100
.50	60
.75	40
1.00	30
2.00	20
4.00– 5.00	15
5.00–10.00	10
10.00–20.00	8
20.00–40.00	5
40.00–above	3

Source: Information taken from the Time Study Manual of the Erie Works of the General Electric Company, developed under the guidance of Albert E. Shaw, Manager of Wage Administration.

The Westinghouse Electric Corporation has given consideration to activity as well as cycle time and has evolved the values shown in the accompanying table as a guide for their time study men.

WHEN THE TIME PER PIECE OR CYCLE IS OVER:	MINIMUM NUMBER OF CYCLES TO STUDY		
	Activity: Over 10,000 per Year	1,000 to 10,000	Under 1,000
8.000 hours	2	1	1
3.000 hours	3	2	1
2.000 hours	4	2	1
1.000 hours	5	3	2
.800 hours	6	3	2
.500 hours	8	4	3
.300 hours	10	5	4
.200 hours	12	6	5
.120 hours	15	8	6
.080 hours	20	10	8
.050 hours	25	12	10
.035 hours	30	15	12
.020 hours	40	20	15
.012 hours	50	25	20
.008 hours	60	30	25
.005 hours	80	40	30
.003 hours	100	50	40
.002 hours	120	60	50
under .002 hours	140	80	60

The mean of the sample of the observations should be reasonably close to the mean of the population. Thus the analyst should take sufficient readings so that when their values are recorded a distribution of values with a dispersion characteristic of the population dispersion is obtained.

Some concerns,[3] in their training programs for time study analysts, have the observer take readings and plot the values to obtain a frequency distribution. Although there is no assurance that the population of elemental times is normally distributed, still experience has shown that the variation of performance of a given operator will approximate the normal bell-shaped curve (see Figure 14–6).

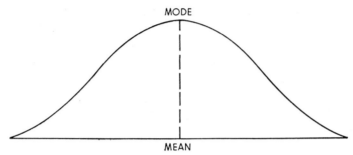

FIG. 14–6. The normal frequency distribution.

The number of cycles to be studied in order to assure a reliable sample may be determined mathematically, and this value, tempered with sound judgment, will give the analyst a helpful guide in deciding the length of observation.

Statistical methods may be utilized as an aid in the determination of the number of cycles to study. It is known that sample averages $\bar{x}$ drawn from a normal distribution of observations are distributed normally about the population mean μ. The variance of $\bar{x}$ about the population mean μ equals $\dfrac{\sigma^2}{n}$ where $n =$ the sample size.

The above normal curve theory leads to the following confidence interval equation:

$$(1) \qquad \bar{x} \pm z\,\frac{\sigma}{\sqrt{n}}.$$

When $z = 1$ there is 68.25 per cent confidence that the interval defined contains μ, likewise 95.46 per cent confidence when $z = 2$ and 99.73 per cent confidence when $z = 3$ (Table XXXIII, Appendix).

When $N \geqq 30$, σ may be estimated by the following equation:

$$(2) \qquad \sigma = \sqrt{\sum_{i=1}^{i=n} \frac{(x_i - \bar{x})^2}{n}}$$

[3] For example, the Kurt Salmon Company.

where

x_i = individual reading of an element
$\bar{x}$ = mean or average of all readings of an element
n = number of readings of an element or sample size
Σ = the sum of terms from $i = 1$ to $i = n$.

For computational purposes, the above equation may be expressed as

(3)
$$\sigma = \sqrt{\frac{\Sigma x_i^2}{n} - \left(\frac{\Sigma x_i}{n}\right)^2}.$$

Consequently, any desired confidence interval may be computed for each element of the study; that is, if 36 readings for a given element showed $\bar{x} = .30$ and $\sigma = .09$, there would be 95 per cent confidence that μ would be contained in the interval .27 to .33 or that $\bar{x}$ is within ± 10 per cent of μ:

$$\bar{x} + \frac{2\sigma}{\sqrt{n}} = .30 + \frac{2(.09)}{\sqrt{36}} = .33$$

$$\bar{x} - \frac{2\sigma}{\sqrt{n}} = .30 - \frac{2(.09)}{\sqrt{36}} = .27 .$$

If the accuracy is deemed unsatisfactory when equation (1) is utilized in the above manner, it is possible to solve for N, the required number of readings for a given accuracy by equating $z\dfrac{\sigma}{\sqrt{N}}$ to a percentage of $\bar{x}$:

(4)
$$z\frac{\sigma}{\sqrt{N}} = k\bar{x}$$

$$N = \left(\frac{\sigma z}{k\bar{x}}\right)^2$$

$$N = \left(\frac{z\sqrt{\dfrac{\sum_{i=1}^{i=n} x_i^2}{n} - \dfrac{\left(\sum_{i=1}^{i=n} x_i\right)}{n}}}{k\bar{x}}\right)^2$$

$$N = \left(\frac{\dfrac{z}{n}\sqrt{n\Sigma x_i^2 - (\Sigma x_i)^2}}{\dfrac{k\Sigma x_i}{n}}\right)^2$$

$$N = \left(z\frac{\sqrt{n\Sigma x_i^2 - (\Sigma x_i)^2}}{k\Sigma x_i}\right)^2$$

where k = an acceptable percentage of $\bar{x}$, that is, in the above example if $\bar{x}$ is required within ± 5 per cent of μ with 95 per cent confidence

$$N = \left[\frac{2(.09)}{(.05)(.30)}\right]^2.$$

When $n \leq 30$, the statistic "t" as explained in most elementary statistic texts should be used instead of z and σ computed taking into account degrees of freedom. Although, the above theory assumes the population of elemental time values normally distributed, sample means may be considered approximately normally distributed even if the distribution of elemental time values is not normally distributed; hence, the above theory will still be approximately valid in a practical sense.

If n readings have been taken on a time study, the selection of the most appropriate element for computing the desired number of readings may be a problem. It is recommended that the element having the greatest coefficient of variation $\frac{\sigma}{\bar{x}}$ be selected for this purpose. It is also possible to solve for N in advance of taking the time study by interpreting historical data of similar elements or by actually estimating $\bar{x}$ and σ from several snapback readings of certain elements to be studied.

One concern[4] has equated the number of observations in terms of the range of the cycle time and the average cycle time. This has been expressed as:

$$N = 205\frac{R}{\bar{x}} - 42$$

where

N = number of observations required
R = range of cycle time
$\bar{x}$ = mean cycle time.

This has been derived as follows:

$R = K\sigma$ where:
K = average ratio between the range and the
    standard deviation in a succession of samples
σ = the standard deviation of the sample taken.

To conform to the limits desired of 95 per cent probability and 3 per cent permissible error, the possible error, $A\sigma$ and the permissible error, $.03\bar{x}$ are assumed to be equal.
Therefore:

$$A\sigma = .03\bar{x}$$
$$\sigma = \frac{.03\bar{x}}{A}$$

where

A = probability factor at 95 per cent.

[4] A. C. Spark Plug Division, General Motors Corporation.

Substituting for σ in the range formula:

$$R = \frac{(K)(.03\bar{x})}{A}.$$

The values of K and A vary with the number of observations (N) taken.

Substituting in the formula

$$R = \frac{(K)(.03\bar{x})}{A}$$

the representative values in the accompanying table are shown.

N	$K*$	$A\dagger$	$\bar{x} = .10$ Minute	$\bar{x} = .20$ Minute
40	4.3216	.3222	.0402	.0805
50	4.4982	.2859	.0472	.0944
75	4.8060	.2310	.0624	.1248
100	5.0152	.1990	.0756	.1512
125	5.1727	.1774	.0875	.1749
150	5.2985	.1617	.0983	.1967
175	5.4029	.1494	.1085	.2169
200	5.4921	.1396	.1180	.2360

* K values obtained from *Biometrika* by L. H. C. Tippett.
† A values obtained from *Statistical Methods for Research Workers* by R. A. Fisher.

On graph paper, plotting R (range), against $\bar{x}$ (average time), for various samples (N), we find a straight-line relationship from the formula, $R = M\bar{x} + B$. Therefore, for sample sizes of 40, 150, 200, we get slope M:

$$N = \ \ 40 \qquad M = \ \ .402 \qquad B = 0$$
$$N = 150 \qquad M = \ \ .983 \qquad B = 0$$
$$N = 200 \qquad M = 1.180 \qquad B = 0$$

To introduce N into the above formula, N was plotted against M for various sample sizes and the resulting straight line formula is:

$$N = M_1 M + B$$
$$N = 205M - 42 \text{ (approximate)}.$$

From the formula, $R = M\bar{x} + B$, since $B = 0$, we get M in terms of R and $\bar{x}$ as:

$$M = \frac{R}{\bar{x}}.$$

Substituting this expression from M in the formula: $N = M_1 M + B$, we get

$$N = 205\frac{R}{\bar{x}} - 42 .$$

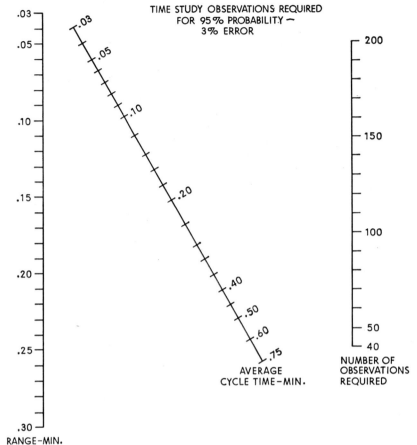

FIG. 14–7. N type alignment chart for determining the time study observations required (above 40) for 95 per cent probability and 3 per cent error.

Having an equation involving N, number of observations, R, range of cycle time, and $\bar{x}$, average cycle time, an alignment chart may be designed to facilitate the solution of N. The N alignment chart illustrated in Figure 14–7 is evolved as follows:

Rearranging the equation to conform to the general N chart equation:

$$\frac{205R}{\bar{x}} - N = 42$$

N varies from 0 to 240
R varies from 0 to .30
$\bar{x}$ varies from 0 to .75 .

Comparing with the general alignment chart equation:

$$Af(u) + Bf(v) = Cf(w) + CK .$$

Then:

$$R = f(u)$$
$$N = f(v)$$
$$O = f(w)$$
$$A = \frac{205}{\bar{x}}$$
$$B = -1$$
$$C = 1$$
$$K = 42 .$$

Selected chart width 8 inches, chart height 12 inches.
Develop scale modulus:

$$M_x = \frac{\text{Length of Scale}}{\text{Range of } f(u)} = \frac{12}{.30} = -40$$
$$\text{(when } B \text{ is negative, } M_x \text{ is negative)}$$
$$M_y = \frac{\text{Length of Scale}}{\text{Range of } f(v)} = \frac{12}{240} = .05 .$$

Calculate A:

$$A = \frac{BDM_x}{AM_y + BM_x} = \frac{(-1)(8)(-40)}{\frac{205}{\bar{x}}(.05) + (-1)(-40)} = \frac{320}{\frac{10.25}{\bar{x}} + 40} .$$

Calculate E:

$$E = \frac{CM_xM_y(f(w) + K)}{AM_y + BM_x} = \frac{(1)(-40)(.05)(42)}{\frac{205}{\bar{x}}(.05) + (-1)(-40)}$$

$$E = \frac{-84}{\frac{10.25}{\bar{x}} + 40} .$$

The scale equations:

$$X = M_x f(u) = -40R$$
$$Y = M_y f(v) = .05N .$$

Values are then developed in tabular form.

Sample

R	$x = -40R$	N	$y = .05N$	$\bar{x}$	$A = \dfrac{320}{\dfrac{10.25}{\bar{x}} + 40}$	$E = \dfrac{-84}{\dfrac{10.25}{\bar{x}} + 40}$
0	0	0	0	0	. . . .	. . . .
.05	-2	40	2	.05	1.306	-.343
.20	-8	150	7.5	.40	4.876	-1.280
.30	-12	240	12.0	.75	5.963	-1.565

Using these values, the N chart is laid out and plotted.

As has been pointed out, these mathematical derivations represent only a guide to the analyst and do not replace common sense and good judgment, which are still fundamental if the time study analyst is to do a good job in a practical manner.

Rating the Operator Performance

Before the observer leaves the work station, he should have given a fair performance rating to the study. On short cycle, repetitive work, it is customary to apply one rating to the entire study. However, where the elements tend to be of long duration and entail diversified manual movements and motions, it is more practical to evaluate the performance of each element as it occurs during the course of the study. The time study form illustrated in Figures 14–4 and 14–5 makes a provision for both the over-all rating and the individual element rating.

Since the actual time that was required to perform each element of the study was dependent to a high degree on the skill and effort of the operator, it is necessary to adjust the time of the good operator up to standard and the time of the poor operator down to standard.

In the performance rating or leveling system, the observer evaluates the effectiveness of the operator in terms of his conception of a "normal" man performing the same element. This effectiveness is given a value expressed as a decimal or percentage and assigned to the element observed. A "normal" operator is defined as a qualified, thoroughly experienced operator who is working under conditions as they customarily prevail at the work station, at a pace that is neither too fast nor too slow but representative of average. The normal man exists only in the mind of the time study analyst and has developed as a result of thorough and exacting training and experience in the technique of measuring wide varieties of work.

The basic principle of performance rating is to adjust the actual observed mean time for each acceptable element performed on the study to the time that would be required by the normal man to perform the same work. In order to do a fair job of rating, the time study man must be able to disassociate himself from personalities and other varying factors and consider only the amount of work being done per unit of time as compared to the amount of work that the normal man would produce. Chapter 15 explains more fully the performance rating or leveling techniques in common use.

Apply Allowances

It would be impossible for an operator to maintain an average pace for every minute of the working day, just as it would be impossible for a football game to entail 60 minutes of actual, continuous play time. Three classes of interruptions take place occasionally for which extra time must be provided. The first of these is personal interruptions, such as trips to the rest room and drinking fountain; the second is fatigue, which, as we all know, affects the strongest individual even on the lightest type of work. Lastly, unavoidable delays take place for which some allowances must be made, such as tool breakage, interruptions by the foreman, and slight tool trouble.

Since the time study is taken over a relatively short period of time and since foreign elements have been removed in determining the normal time, an allowance must be added to the leveled or base time in order to arrive at a fair standard that can be achieved by the normal operator when exerting average effort. Chapter 16 outlines in detail means of arriving at realistic allowance values.

Calculate the Study

Once the analyst has properly recorded all necessary information on the time study form, has observed an adequate number of cycles, and has properly performance rated the operator, he should thank the operator and proceed to the next step, which is computation of the study. In some plants, clerical help is used to compute the study, but in most cases the analyst himself does the work. The analyst usually prefers to analyze his own study because he is vitally interested in the resulting standard and does not care to let other individuals tamper with his calculations. Then, too, less chance of error will be risked if the analyst computes his own study, in that he will encounter no difficulty in interpreting his own notes and reading his own recorded values.

The initial step in computing the study is to verify the final stopwatch reading with the over-all elapsed clock reading. These two values should check within plus or minus a half minute, and if a sizable discrepancy is noted, the analyst should check the study stop-watch readings for error.

When using the continuous method, a subtraction is made between the watch reading and the preceding reading, giving the elapsed time, and this is recorded in ink or red pencil. This procedure is followed throughout the study, each reading being subtracted from the succeeding one. It is important that the analyst be especially accurate in this phase. Carelessness at this point can completely destroy the validity of the study. If elemental performance rating has been used, a supplementary work sheet will be required to record the elapsed elemental time, and these values, after being multiplied by the leveling factor, will be recorded in ink or red pencil in the "T" spaces of the time study form.

Elements that have been missed by the observer are signified by placing an "M" in the "R" column as previously explained. When computing the study, the analyst must disregard both the missed element and the succeeding one, as the subtracted value in the study will include the time for performing both elements.

Elements that have been missed by the operator may be disregarded, since they have no effect on the preceding or succeeding values. Thus, if the operator happened to omit element 7 of cycle 4 in a 30-cycle study, the analyst should have but 29 values of element 7 with which to calculate the mean observed time.

To determine the elapsed elemental time on out-of-order elements, it is merely necessary for the analyst to subtract the value appearing in the lower half of the "R" block from the value in the upper half for the element that was performed out of order.

For foreign elements, it is necessary to deduct the time required for the foreign element from the cycle time of the element in which it occurred. The time taken by the foreign element is obtained by subtracting the lower reading in the "R" space of the foreign element section of the time study form from the upper reading.

After all elapsed times have been calculated and recorded, they should be carefully studied for abnormality. There is no set rule for determining the degree of variation permitted in order to keep the value for calculation. If variations are broad on certain elements and can be attributed to some influence that was too brief to be handled as a foreign element, yet long enough to effect substantially the time of the element, such as dropping a tool or blowing the nose, or if the variation may be attributed to errors in reading the stop watch, then these values should be immediately circled and excluded from further consideration in working up the study. However, if wide variations are due to the nature of the work, then it would not be wise to discard any of the values.

Elements that are "paced" by the facility or process will have little variation from cycle to cycle, whereas considerably wider variation in "operator controlled" elements would be expected. When variations in time occur that are not explainable, the analyst should be quite careful before circling any such values. He must be aware that this is not a performance rating procedure, and by arbitrarily discarding high values or low values, he may end up with an incorrect standard. A good rule is, "When in doubt do not discard the value."

If elemental rating is being used, then after the elemental elapsed time values have been computed, the normal elemental time is determined by multiplying each elemental value by its respective performance factor. This normal time is then recorded for each element in the "T" columns. The mean elemental normal value is next determined by dividing the number of observations into the total of the times in the "T" columns.

If the over-all study is leveled, then the means of the elapsed elemental times are computed and the performance factor is applied to these values in the space provided so as to determine the various normal elemental time values.

After the normal elemental times have been evolved, the percentage allowance is added to each element to determine the allowed time. The nature of the job will determine the amount of allowance to be applied, as will be shown in Chapter 16. Suffice to say at this point that 15 per cent is an average allowance for effort elements and 10 per cent is representative of the allowance applied to mechanically controlled elements.

Upon determination of the allowed time for each element, the analyst should then summarize these values in the space provided on the reverse side of the time study form so as to obtain the allowed time for the entire job. This is commonly referred to as the "standard" or the "rate" for the job.

Summary of Computing the Study

To summarize the steps taken in computation of a typical study with continuous watch readings and over-all performance rating, the following procedure in chronological sequence would be observed:

1. Make subtractions of consecutive readings to obtain elemental elapsed times.
2. Circle and discard all abnormal or "wild" values where assignable cause is evident.
3. Summarize remaining elemental values.
4. Determine mean of the observed values of each element.
5. Determine elemental normal time by multiplying the performance factor by the mean elapsed time.
6. Add the appropriate allowance to the elemental normal values to obtain the elemental allowed times.
7. Summarize the elemental allowed times on the reverse side of the time study form to obtain the standard time. (Elements occurring more than once per cycle need be shown but once with the number of occurrences and the resulting product.)

If elemental leveling has been used on a continuous study, then the series of events in computing the study would be:

1. Make subtractions of consecutive readings to obtain elemental elapsed times.
2. Circle and discard all abnormal or "wild" values where assignable cause is evident.
3. Determine normal times of each individual element by multiplying performance factor by elapsed time value and record in red pencil in the "T" column.
4. Determine mean of the elemental normal times.
5. Add the appropriate allowance to the elemental normal values to obtain the elemental allowed times.
6. Summarize the elemental allowed times on the reverse side of the time study form to obtain the standard time. (Elements occurring more than once per cycle need be shown but once with the number of occurrences and the resulting product.)

TEXT QUESTIONS

1. Define time study.
2. What are the principal responsibilities of the time study observer?
3. What are some of the qualifications for the successful time study analyst?

4. How does the time study analyst "directly effect the pocketbook of the worker"?

5. Explain the statement that all foremen are "management's representatives throughout the plant."

6. Why does the foreman require fair time standards in his department?

7. What are the main responsibilities of the foreman in relation to time study work?

8. What is the significance of the foreman's signature on the time study?

9. What is a fair day's work?

10. Explain how an appreciation course in the elements of time study made available to all employees will promote good labor relations.

11. What considerations should be given to choice of operator to be studied?

12. Of what use is the operator process chart on the time study form?

13. Why is it essential to record complete information as to tools and facility on the time study form?

14. Why are working conditions important in identifying the method being observed?

15. Why would a time study analyst who is hard of hearing have difficulty in recording his stop-watch readings of terminal points?

16. Differentiate between constant and variable elements. Why should they be kept separate when dividing the job into elements?

17. Explain how repeating elements may be recorded on the time study form.

18. What advantages does the continuous method of watch recording offer over the snapback?

19. Why is the time of day recorded on the time study form?

20. What variations in sequence will the observer occasionally encounter during the course of the time study?

21. Explain what a foreign element is and how foreign elements are handled under the continuous method.

22. What factors enter into the determination of the number of cycles to observe?

23. Why is it necessary to performance rate the operator?

24. When should individual elements of each cycle be rated?

25. Define a "normal" operator.

26. For what reasons are allowances applied to the normal time?

27. What is the significance of a "circled" elapsed time?

28. What are the steps taken in computation of a time study conducted by the continuous over-all performance rating procedure?

29. What would be the required number of readings if the analyst wanted to be 87 per cent confident that the mean observed time is within ±5 per cent of the true mean and he established the following values for an element after observing 20 cycles:
.09, .08, .10, .12, .09, .08, .09, .12, .11, .11, .12, .09, .10, .12, .10, .08, .09, .10, .12, .09 .

30. Based upon the Westinghouse guide sheet, how many observations should be taken on an operation whose annual activity is 750 pieces and the cycle time is estimated at 15 minutes? What would be the number of observations needed according to the General Electric guide sheet?

GENERAL QUESTIONS

1. Why are time study procedures the only known techniques for supplying reliable information relative to standard times?
2. To what positions of importance does time study work lead?
3. In what way can "loose" time standards result in poor labor relations?
4. Why are poor time standards a "headache" to union officials?
5. How would you approach a belligerent operator if you were the time study analyst?
6. If you were using the General Electric guide sheet to determine the number of observations to study and it developed that 10 cycles were required, and after taking the study you used the standard error of the mean statistic to estimate the number of observations needed for a given confidence level and the resulting calculation indicated 20 cycles should be studied, what would be your procedure? Why?

CHAPTER 15

Performance Rating

WHILE THE TIME STUDY OB-
server is taking the study, he will carefully observe the performance of
the operator during the entire course of the study. Seldom will the performance being executed conform to the exact definition of "normal,"
often referred to as "standard." Thus, it is essential that some adjustment
be made to the mean observed time in order to derive the time required
for the normal man to do the job when working at an average pace. The
actual time taken by the above-standard operator must be increased to
that required by the normal worker, and the time taken by the below-
standard operator must be reduced to the value representative of normal
performance. Only in this manner can a true standard be established in
terms of a normal operator.

Definition

Performance rating is a technique for equitably determining the time
required to perform a task by the normal operator after the observed
values of the operation under study have been recorded. In Chapter 12,
a "normal" operator was defined as a qualified, thoroughly experienced
operator who is working under conditions as they customarily prevail
at the work station, at a pace that is neither fast nor slow, but representative of average.

There is no one universally accepted method of performance rating,
although the majority of the techniques are based primarily on the
judgment of the time study man. For this reason, the time study analyst
must have the high personal characteristics discussed earlier in this text.
No other component of the time study procedure is subject to as much
controversy and criticism as the performance rating phase. Regardless of

whether the rating factor is based on the speed or tempo of the output or based upon the performance of the operator when compared to that of the normal worker, judgment is still the criterion for the determination of the rating factor. Some attempts have been made to accumulate fundamental motion data and compare these values to the mean observed values so as to arrive at a factor that can be used for evaluation of the entire study. This technique known as "synthetic rating"[1] will be discussed later in this chapter.

Concept of Normal

Just as there is no one universal method of performance rating, so there is no one universal concept of normal performance. In general, industries engaged in the manufacture of low-cost, highly competitive products will have a "tighter" conception of normal performance than that expected by a company producing a line of products protected by patents.

In defining what is meant by "normal" performance, it is helpful to enumerate benchmark examples that are familiar to all. When this is done, care must be taken that method and work requirements are carefully defined. Thus, if the benchmark of dealing 52 cards in .45 minute is established, complete and specific description relative to distance of the four hands dealt, with respect to the dealer and the technique of grasping, moving, and disposing of the cards should be given. Likewise, if the benchmark of .35 minute is established for walking 100 feet (3.25 miles per hour), it should be clearly explained whether this is walking on level ground or not, whether this is walking with or without load, and if with load, how heavy the load. Supplementing the benchmark examples should be a clear description of the characteristics of an employee carrying out a normal performance. A representative description of such an employee might be:

A workman who is adapted to the work, and has attained sufficient experience to enable him to perform his job in a workmanlike manner with little or no supervision. He possesses co-ordinated mental and physical qualities which enable him to proceed from one element to another without hesitation or delay, in accordance with the principles of motion economy. He maintains a good level of efficiency by his knowledge and proper use of all tools and equipment related to his job. He co-operates and performs at a pace best suited for continuous performance.

The more clear-cut and specific the definition of normal, the better it will be. It should clearly describe the skill and effort involved in the performance, so that all workers in the plant will have a comprehensive understanding of the concept of normal that prevails in the plant.

---

[1] Robert Lee Morrow, *Time Study and Motion Economy* (New York: Ronald Press Co., 1946).

Uses and Effects

Even though personnel departments endeavor to provide only "normal" or "above normal" employees for each position within the company, still individual differences do exist. These differences among a given group of employees within the plant can become more pronounced as time goes on. Differences in inherent knowledge, physical capacity, health, trade knowledge, physical dexterity, and training will cause one operator consistently and progressively to outperform another. The degree of variation in the performance of different individuals has been estimated to approximate the ratio of 1 to 2.25.[2] Thus, in a random selection of 1,000 employees, the frequency distribution of the output would approximate the normal curve with less than three cases on the average falling outside the three sigma limits (99.73 per cent of the time). If 100 per cent should be taken as normal, then based on a ratio of the slowest operator to the fastest as 2.25 to 1, $\bar{x} - 3\sigma$ could equal .61, and $\bar{x} + 3\sigma$ would then equal 1.39. This would mean that 68.26 per cent of the people would be within plus or minus one sigma limit or between performance rating values of .87 and 1.13. Graphically, the expected total distribution of the 1,000 people would appear as shown in Figure 15–1.

Since employees are usually carefully screened by personnel departments before being assigned to specific jobs, the mean of any selected group may exceed the 100 per cent figure representative of a sample taken arbitrarily from the population, and the dispersion of their output will probably be considerably less than 2.25 to 1 ratio. In fact, by careful testing programs, some concerns feel that their selection of the right person for the job, supplemented by intensive training in the correct method of performance, will result in similar output within close limits by different operators assigned to the same job.

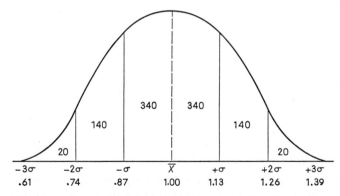

FIG. 15–1. Normal distribution curve of the output of 1,000 people selected at random.

---

[2] Ralph W. Presgrave, *The Dynamics of Time Study* (2nd ed.; New York: McGraw-Hill Book Co., Inc., 1945).

In the majority of cases, significant differences in output will prevail among those assigned to a given class of work, and it is necessary to adjust the performance of the operator being studied to a predetermined concept of normal.

Characteristics of a Sound Rating System

The first and most important characteristic of any rating system is accuracy. Since the majority of rating techniques rely on the judgment of the time study observer, perfect consistency in rating cannot be expected.

However, rating procedures that readily permit the different time study analysts, within a given organization, to study different operators employing the same method, to arrive at standards that are not more than 5 per cent in deviation from the average of the standards established by the group are considered adequate. The rating plan that carries variations in standards greater than the plus or minus 5 per cent tolerance should be improved or replaced.

Other factors being similar, the rating plan that gives the most consistent results will be the most useful. Inconsistency in rating will do more than any other one thing to destroy the operator's confidence in the time study procedure. For example, if a standard should be developed through stop-watch study that allowed 7.88 hours to mill 100 castings, and at some later date a similar casting entailing a slightly longer cut should be studied, and a standard of 7.22 hours be established, considerable complaint would be registered by the operator, even though both studies were within the plus or minus 5 per cent criterion of accuracy.

A rating plan that achieves consistency when used by the various time study analysts within a given plant and yet is outside the accepted definition of normal accuracy can be corrected. A rating procedure that gives inconsistent results when used by the different time study men will be sure to end in failure. Time study men who find difficulty in rating consistently after proper and thorough training will be better off if they seek some other means of livelihood. It is not difficult to correct the rating habits of an analyst who rates consistently high or consistently low, but it is most difficult to instill rating ability in the mind of the analyst who today is rating considerably too high and tomorrow may be rating considerably too low.

The rating system that is simple, concise, easily explained, and keyed to well-established benchmarks will be more successful than complex techniques that require involved adjusting factors and similar mathematical computation techniques that confuse the average shop employee.

In view of the aforementioned accuracy limitations, every company will have, as time goes on, a number of standards which will be referred to as "tight" by the production floor, as well as those that will be known as "loose." If these inequities are within the 5 per cent tolerance range, few grievances will develop. However, if it becomes possible for an operator to earn as much as 50 per cent premium on one job, and he finds it difficult even to make standard on another, then general dissatisfaction can be anticipated for the whole rate program. At this point, it might be well to mention that inequalities in different rates are not necessarily entirely due to poor performance rating. Loose rates frequently are due to methods improvements inaugurated over a period of time without restudy of the job from the time study point of view.

Rating at the Work Station

There is only one time when the performance rating should be done and that is during the course of the observation of the elemental times. As the operator progresses from one element to the next, the analyst carefully evaluates his speed, dexterity, freedom from false moves, rhythm, co-ordination, effectiveness, and all other factors influencing output by the prescribed method. It is at this time, and this time only, that the performance of the operator in comparison to normal performance is most clearly evident to the observer. Once the performance has been judged and recorded, it should not be changed. This does not imply that faulty judgment on the part of the observer is not possible. In case the leveling is questioned, the job or operation should be restudied to prove or disprove the recorded evaluation.

Immediately after completing the study and recording the final performance factor, the observer should advise the operator as to his performance rating. Even if elemental rating is used, the analyst will be able to approximate the operator's performance and so advise him. This practice will permit the analyst to defend his standard prior to its calculation, and will give the operator an opportunity to express his opinion as to the fairness of the performance factor directly to the man responsible for its development. Thus, an understanding can be achieved prior to computation of the standard. Where this procedure is practiced, time study men will find that they receive greater respect from the operators and will also find that they tend to be more conscientious in their rating of the operator's performance. Also, considerably fewer rate grievances will be submitted because most rates will have been agreed upon, or at least satisfactorily explained and sold, before they are issued.

Rating Elements Versus Over-all Study

The question as to how frequently should the performance be evaluated during the course of a study often comes up. Although no set rule can be established as to the interval limit that permits concise rating, generally it can be said that the more frequently the study is rated, the more accurate the evaluation of the true normal performance will be.

On short-cycle repetitive operations, little deviation in operator per-

formance will be realized during the course of the average length study
(15 to 30 minutes). In cases like this, it will be perfectly satisfactory to
evaluate the performance of the entire study and record the rating factor
for each element in the space provided. Of course, power-fed or ma-
chine-controlled elements will be rated normal or 1.00, as their speed
cannot be changed or modified at will by the operator. In short-cycle
studies, if the observer endeavors to performance rate each successive
element of the entire study, he will be so busy recording values that he
will be unable to do an effective job of observation, analysis, and evaluation of the true performance.

When the study to be taken is relatively long (over 30 minutes) or is
made up of several long elements, then operator performance may be
expected to vary during the course of the time study. In such studies,
it is important that performance be periodically evaluated and rated.
Elements longer than .10 minute in duration can be consistently and
accurately rated as they occur. However, if a study is made of a series
of elements shorter than .10 minute, then no effort should be made to
evaluate each element of each cycle of the study, as time will not permit
this operation. It will be satisfactory to rate the over-all time of each
cycle or perhaps each group of cycles.

METHODS OF RATING

Westinghouse System

One of the oldest and very widely used systems of rating is the one
developed by the Westinghouse Electric Corporation and outlined in
detail by Lowry, Maynard, and Stegemerten.[3] In this method, four factors are considered in evaluating the performance of the operator. These
are skill, effort, conditions, and consistency.

Skill is defined as "proficiency at following a given method" and can
be further explained by relating it to craftmanship, demonstrated by
proper co-ordination of mind and hands.

The skill of an operator is determined by his experience and inherent
aptitudes such as natural co-ordination and rhythm. Practice will tend
to develop skill, but it cannot entirely compensate for deficiencies in
natural aptitude. All the practice in the world could not make major
league baseball pitchers out of most male athletes.

A person's skill increases on a given operation over a period of time
because increased familiarity with the work brings speed, smoothness of
motions, and freedom from hesitations and false moves. A decrease in
skill is usually caused by impairment of ability brought about by physical or psychological factors such as failing eyesight, failing reflexes, and

[3] S. M. Lowry, H. B. Maynard, and G. J. Stegemerten, *Time and Motion Study
and Formulas for Wage Incentives* (3rd ed.; New York: McGraw-Hill Book Co.,
Inc., 1940).

loss of muscular strength or co-ordination. From this, it can readily be appreciated that a person's skill can vary from job to job and even from operation to operation on a given job.

According to this system of leveling or rating, there are six degrees or classes of skill within which an operator can perform that represent an acceptable proficiency for evaluation. These are: poor, fair, average, good, excellent, and super. The skill displayed by the operator is evaluated by the observer and rated in one of these six classes. Table XIII

TABLE XIII

SKILL

+0.15	A1	Superskill
+0.13	A2	Superskill
+0.11	B1	Excellent
+0.08	B2	Excellent
+0.06	C1	Good
+0.03	C2	Good
0.00	D	Average
−0.05	E1	Fair
−0.10	E2	Fair
−0.16	F1	Poor
−0.22	F2	Poor

Source: Lowry, Maynard, and Stegemerten, *op. cit.*

illustrates the characteristics of the various degrees of skill together with their equivalent numerical values. The skill rating is then translated into its equivalent percentage value, which ranges from plus 15 per cent for superskill to minus 22 per cent for poor skill. This percentage is then combined algebraically with the ratings for effort, conditions, and consistency to arrive at the final leveling, or performance rating factor.

Effort, according to this rating method, is defined as a "demonstration of the will to work effectively." It is representative of the speed with which skill is applied, and can be controlled to a high degree by the operator. The observer when evaluating the effort given must exercise care to rate only the effective effort demonstrated. Many times an operator will apply misdirected effort with high tempo in order to increase the cycle time of the study and yet retain a liberal rating factor. As for skill, six classes of effort can be exhibited that are representative of acceptable speed for rating purposes: poor, fair, average, good, excellent, and excessive. Excessive effort has been assigned a value of plus 13 per cent and this figure diminishes to minus 17 per cent, the value given to poor effort. Table XIV gives the numerical values for the different degrees of effort and also outlines the characteristics of the various categories.

The conditions referred to in this performance rating procedure are those which affect the operator and not the operation. In more than the majority of instances, conditions will be rated normal or average, as conditions are evaluated in comparison with the way in which they customarily are found at the work station. Elements that would affect the working conditions include temperature, ventilation, light, and noise. Thus, if the temperature at a given work station was 60° F. whereas it customarily was maintained at 68° to 74° F., the conditions would be

TABLE XIV

Effort

+0.13.	A1	Excessive
+0.12.	A2	Excessive
+0.10.	B1	Excellent
+0.08.	B2	Excellent
+0.05.	C1	Good
+0.02.	C2	Good
0.00.	D	Average
−0.04.	E1	Fair
−0.08.	E2	Fair
−0.12.	F1	Poor
−0.17.	F2	Poor

Source. Lowry, Maynard, and Stegemerten, *op. cit.*

rated lower than normal. Those conditions which affect the operation, such as poor condition of tools or materials, would not be considered when applying the performance factor for working conditions. Six general classes of conditions have been enumerated with values from plus 6 per cent to minus 7 per cent. These "general-state" conditions are listed as ideal, excellent, good, average, fair, and poor. Table XV gives the respective values for these different conditions.

TABLE XV

Conditions

+0.06.	A	Ideal
+0.04.	B	Excellent
+0.02.	C	Good
0.00.	D	Average
−0.03.	E	Fair
−0.07.	F	Poor

Source: Lowry, Maynard, and Stegemerten, *op. cit.*

The last of the four factors that influence the performance rating is the consistency of the operator. Unless the snapback method is used, or unless the observer is able to make and record successive subtractions as he goes along, the consistency of the operator must be evaluated as the study is being worked up. Elemental time values that repeat constantly would, of course, have a perfect consistency. This situation occurs very infrequently, as there always tends to be dispersion due to the many variables, such as material hardness, tool cutting edge, lubricant, skill and effort of operator, erroneous watch readings, and presence of foreign elements. Those elements that are mechanically controlled would, of course, have near perfect consistency values, but these elements are not rated. There are six classes of consistency: perfect, excellent, good, average, fair, and poor. Perfect consistency has been given the value of plus 4 per cent and poor consistency is rated minus 4 per cent, while the other categories fall in between these values. Table XVI summarizes these values.

TABLE XVI

CONSISTENCY

+0.04	A	Perfect
+0.03	B	Excellent
+0.01	C	Good
0.00	D	Average
−0.02	E	Fair
−0.04	F	Poor

Source: Lowry, Maynard, and Stegemerten, *op. cit.*

No fixed rule can be cited as to the universal application of the consistency table. Some operations that are of short duration and tend to be free of delicate positioning manipulations will give relatively consistent results from one cycle to the next. Thus, operations of this nature would have a more exacting requirement of average consistency than a job of long duration, demanding high skill in view of the positioning, engaging, and aligning elements. The determination of the justified range of variation for a particular operation must be based to a large extent on the time study analyst's knowledge of the work.

The observer should be cautioned against the operator who consistently performs poorly in an effort to deceive the observer. This is easily accomplished by counting to oneself, thereby setting a pace that can be accurately followed. Operators who familiarize themselves with this performance rating procedure sometimes will perform at a pace that is consistent and yet is below the effort rating curve. In other words, they may be performing at a pace that is poorer than poor. In cases like this, the operator cannot be leveled. The study must be stopped and the situation brought to the attention of the operator or foreman, or both.

Once the skill, effort, conditions, and consistency of the operation have been assigned, and their equivalent numerical values established, the performance factor is determined by algebraically combining the four values and adding their sum to unity. For example, if a given job is rated C2 on skill, C1 on effort, D on conditions, and E on consistency, the performance factor would be evolved as follows:

Skill. . . . . .C2   +.03
Effort. . . . . .C1   +.05
Conditions. . . . . .D   +.00
Consistency. . . . . .E   −.02

Algebraic Sum.   +.06
Performance Factor. 1.06

The reader should again be cautioned that the performance factor is applied only to the effort or manually performed elements; all machine controlled elements are rated 1.00.

The Westinghouse method of performance rating is adapted to the leveling of the entire study rather than elemental evaluation. This method would prove quite cumbersome if used to level each element as soon as it took place. In fact, the time study form itself does not provide sufficient space to evaluate skill, effort, conditions, and consistency for each element of every cycle.

Many companies have modified the Westinghouse system so as to include only skill and effort factors entering into the determination of the rating factor. The contention is that consistency is very closely allied to skill, and conditions in most instances are rated average. If conditions would deviate substantially from normal, either the taking of the study could be postponed, or else, the effect of the unusual conditions could be taken into consideration in the application of the allowance (see Chapter 16).

The Westinghouse Company itself in 1949 developed a new rating method which they termed their "performance rating plan" to distinguish it from the leveling procedure just discussed. The performance rating plan is being used in most of the newer Westinghouse plants.

In developing the performance rating plan, in addition to using physical attributes displayed by the operator, the company made an attempt to evaluate the relationship between the physical attributes and the basic divisions of work. The characteristics and attributes that the Westinghouse performance rating technique considers are:

1. Dexterity
2. Effectiveness
3. Physical Application

These three major classifications do not in themselves carry any numerical weight, but have in turn been assigned attributes that do carry numerical weight. Table XVII gives the numerical values of the nine attributes that are evaluated under this system.

The first major classification, dexterity, has been divided into three attributes; the first of which is: *1. Displayed ability in use of equipment and tools and assembly of parts.*

When considering this attribute, the analyst is concerned primarily with the "do" portion of the work cycle after the "get" operations (reach, grasp, move) have taken place.

The second attribute under dexterity is: 2. *Certainty of movement.*

In evaluating this attribute, the analyst is concerned with the number and degree of hesitations, pauses, or roundabout moves. The basic divisions of accomplishment performed by the operator that will tend to give a low rating for this attribute are change direction, plan, and avoidable delay. All of these affect certainty of movement.

The last attribute considered under dexterity is: 3. *Co-ordination and rhythm.*

This attribute is evidenced by the degree of the displayed performance, by the smoothness of motions, and the freedom from spasmodic spurts and lags.

The second major classification, effectiveness, has been defined as efficient, orderly procedure. This classification has been divided into four individual attributes. The first of these is: 1. *Displayed ability to replace continually and to retrieve tools and parts automatically and accurately.*

Here the analyst evaluates the ability of the workman to repeatedly place tools, materials, and parts in specified locations and positions, and to retrieve them with automatism and accuracy by eliminating such ineffective basic divisions of work as searching and selecting.

The second of the individual attributes in effectiveness is: 2. *Displayed ability to facilitate, eliminate, combine, or shorten motions.*

Here the analyst evaluates the proficiency of the basic divisions: position, preposition, release, and inspect. The transport therbligs are predetermined usually by the established method. However, a skilled workman will be able to eliminate or shorten the elements of preposition, position, and inspect because of his manipulative ability.

The third attribute under effectiveness is: 3. *Displayed ability to use both hands with equal ease.* Here the degree of effective utilization of both hands is rated.

The fourth and last attribute under effectiveness is: 4. *Displayed ability to confine efforts to necessary work.*

This attribute is used to rate the presence of unnecessary work that could not be removed when taking the study. It carries only a negative weight, for when the work is confined to the necessary work, no percentage is added because this condition is expected.

The third major classification, physical demand, is defined as demonstrated rate of performance and has two attributes. The first of these is: 1. *Work Pace.*

Work pace is rated by the comparison of the speed of movement to preconceived standards for the particular type of work under consideration.

The second attribute for physical application is: 2. *Attentiveness.*

Attentiveness is rated as the degree of displayed concentration.

Both of the Westinghouse rating techniques demand considerable training in order that the time study analysts recognize the different levels of each of the attributes. Their training entails a 30 hour course of which approximately 25 hours are spent rating films and discussing the attributes and the degree to which each is displayed. The procedure generally followed is:

1. A film is shown and the operation explained.
2. The film is reshown and rated.
3. The individual ratings are compared and discussed.
4. Film is reshown and attributes pointed out and explained.
5. Step 4 repeated as often as necessary to reach understanding and agreement.

TABLE XVII

	+ Above		O Expected	- Below	
DEXTERITY:					
1. Displayed ability in use of equipment and tools, and assembly of parts.	6	3	0	2	4
2. Certainty of movement.	6	3	0	2	4
3. Co-ordination and rhythm.		2	0	2	
EFFECTIVENESS:					
1. Displayed ability to continually replace and retrieve tools and parts with automaticity and accuracy.	6	3	0	2	4
2 Displayed ability to facilitate, eliminate, combine, or shorten motions.	6	3	0	4	8
3. Displayed ability to use both hands with equal ease.	6	3	0	4	8
4. Displayed ability to confine efforts to necessary work.			0	4	8
PHYSICAL APPLICATION:					
1. Work pace.	6	3	0	4	8
2. Attentiveness.			0	2	4

Synthetic Rating

In an effort to develop a method of rating that would not rely on the judgment of the time study observer and would give consistent results, R. L. Morrow established a procedure known as "synthetic leveling."[4]

The synthetic leveling procedure determines a performance factor for representative effort elements of the work cycle by comparing actual elemental observed times to times constructed through the medium of fundamental motion data (see Chapter 10). Thus, the performance factor may be expressed algebraically as:

$$P = \frac{F_t}{O}$$

---

[4] *Op. cit.*, p. 241.

where

$$P = \text{Performance or leveling factor}$$
$$F_t = \text{Fundamental motion time}$$
$$O = \text{Observed mean elemental time for the}$$
$$\text{same elements as used in } F_t \,.$$

The factor thus determined would then be applied to the remainder of the manually controlled elements comprising the study. Of course, machine controlled elements would not be rated, as is the case in all rating techniques.

A typical illustration of the application of synthetic rating would be as follows:

Element No.	Observed Average Time in Minutes	Element Type	Fundamental Motion Time in Minutes	Performance Factor
1	.08	Manual	.096	123
2	.15	Manual	. . .	123
3	.05	Manual	. . .	123
4	.22	Manual	.278	123
5	1.41	Power Fed	. . .	100
6	.07	Manual	. . .	123
7	.11	Manual	. . .	123
8	.38	Power Fed	. . .	100
9	.14	Manual	. . .	123
10	.06	Manual	. . .	123
11	.20	Manual	. . .	123
12	.06	Manual	. . .	123

It will be noted that for element 1,

$$P = \frac{.096}{.08} = 120\%$$

and that for element 4,

$$P = \frac{.278}{.22} = 126\%.$$

The mean of these would be 123 per cent, and this is the factor used for rating all of the effort elements. It can readily be seen that synthetic performance rating is a sampling technique.

Actually, all experienced time study men unconsciously follow the synthetic rating procedure to some extent. The time study man's mind is full of benchmarks that have been established from past experience on similar work. Consequently, he knows that the normal performance of advancing the drill of a 17-inch single-spindle Delta drill is .03 minute, and of indexing the hex turret of a No. 4 Warner & Swasey turret lathe is .06 minute, and of blowing out a vise or fixture with an air hose and laying the finished part aside is .08 minute. These benchmarks and many others, when compared to actual performance, certainly influence and even determine the rating factor given the operator.

Perhaps one of the major objections to the application of the synthetic leveling procedure is the time required to construct a left- and right-hand chart of the elements selected for the establishment of basic motion times. The reader may well consider the desirability of establishing a standard for the entire job synthetically. This would eliminate the laborious task of recording elemental times, making subtractions, determining the mean elapsed time, determining the normal time synthetically for several elements so as to arrive at a performance factor, and applying the performance factor. In order to arrive at synthetic values rapidly and accurately, for aiding in the determination of the performance factor, an alignment chart has been designed, which may be attached to the time study board (see Figure 13–7). The application of this tool by the analyst will be discussed later in this chapter. This technique permits the analyst to utilize synthetic values as a guide toward the establishment of a true performance factor.

Speed Rating

Speed rating is a method of evaluating the performance in which consideration is given only to the rate of accomplishment of the work per unit time. In this method, the observer measures the effectiveness of the operator against the conception of a normal man doing the same work, and then assigns a percentage to indicate the ratio of observed performance to normal performance. Particular emphasis is placed on the observer having complete knowledge of the job before taking the study. It is evident that the pace for machine work in a plant which produces aircraft engine parts would appear considerably slower to the novice than would the pace executed by machine workers who produce farm machinery components. The greater precision requirements of the aircraft work would require such care that the movements of the various operators would appear unduly slow to one who was not completely familiar with work being performed.

In speed rating, 100 per cent is usually considered normal. Thus a rating of 110 per cent would indicate that the operator was performing at a speed 10 per cent greater than normal and a rating of 90 per cent would mean that he was performing 90 per cent of normal. Some concerns using the speed rating technique have chosen to call 60 standard or normal. This is based on the standard hour approach; that is, producing 60 minutes of work every hour. On this basis, a rating of 80 would mean that the operator was working at a speed of 80/60 which equals 133 per cent or 33 per cent above normal. A rating of 50 would indicate a speed of 50/60 or 83⅓ per cent of normal or standard.

Once the rating has been made, calculation of normal time is accomplished from the basic equation:

$$T_n = (P)(O)$$

where

T_n = Computed normal time
P = Speed rating factor
O = Observed mean elemental time .

In the speed rating method, the analyst first makes an appraisal of the performance to determine if it is above or below his conception of normal. He then executes a second judgment in an effort to place the performance in the precise position on the rating scale, which will correctly evaluate the numerical difference between standard and performance being demonstrated.

A form of speed rating referred to as "pace rating" has received considerable attention from the basic steel industry. In effect, pace rating is speed rating. However, in an effort to identify completely a normal pace on different jobs, benchmarks have been provided on a broad range of work. Thus, such effort operations as shoveling sand, coremaking, brick handling, and walking have been clearly identified as to method and have been quantified as to normal rate of production. Once the time study analyst familiarizes himself with a series of benchmarks closely allied to the work that he is going to study, he will be much better equipped to evaluate the true speed being performed.

Objective Rating

The rating procedure known as "objective rating," a method developed by M. E. Mundel,[5] endeavors to eliminate the difficulty of establishing a normal speed criterion for every different type of work. In this procedure, a single work assignment is established to which all other jobs are compared as to pace. After the judgment of pace, a secondary factor is assigned to the job to take care of its relative difficulty. The factors that influence the difficulty adjustment are: (1) amount of body used, (2) foot pedals, (3) bimanualness, (4) eye-hand co-ordination, (5) handling or sensory requirements, and (6) weight handled or resistance encountered.

Numerical values, resulting from experiments, have been assigned for a range of degrees of each factor. The sum of the numerical values for each of the six factors comprises the secondary adjustment. By this method the normal time can be expressed as follows:

$$T_n = (P_2)(S)(O)$$

where

T_n = Computed established normal time
P_2 = Pace rating factor
S = Job difficulty adjustment factor
O = Observed mean elemental time .

---

[5] M. E. Mundel, *Motion and Time Study* (New York: Prentice-Hall, Inc., 1950).

This performance rating procedure will tend to give consistent results since the comparison of pace of the operation under study to an operation that is completely familiar to the observer can more readily be achieved than judging simultaneously all the attributes of an operation to a concept of normal for that specific job. The secondary factor will not effect inconsistency since this factor merely adjusts the rated time by the application of a percentage. This percentage value used is taken from a table that gives values for the effect of various difficulties present in the operation being performed.

OTHER TECHNIQUES

In an effort to eliminate the performance rating step entirely in the calculation of the standard, some concerns select the operators to be studied and then consider the average observed time as the normal time. When this method is utilized, usually more than one operator is studied and enough cycles are observed so that a reliable average time (within plus or minus 5 per cent of the true average) is calculated. Of course, the success of this method is dependent on the selection of the employees who are to be studied and their performance during the study. If the performances of the operators being observed are slower than normal, then too liberal a standard will result; conversely, if the observed operators produce at a pace more rapid than normal, then the standard will be unduly tight. There is always the possibility of having but one or two available operators and the chance that they may differ from normal. Then, in an effort to avoid delay in establishing a standard, the time study observer will make the study; the result will be a poor time standard.

As has been mentioned, some proponents of the Westinghouse system have considered the necessity of utilizing "conditions" and "consistency" as factors that influence the rating. The thought is that consistency is dependent on skill and to some degree effort, and that conditions in reality represent part of the method which should never be leveled. Thus, in the development of the performance factor, consideration need be given only to the skill and effort presented. Since the range of productivity of 2.76 to 1, that is from minus 50 per cent to plus 38 per cent, as developed by the Westinghouse system, seems to be satisfactory for the majority of operations observed by the time study man, the factors of skill and effort would carry a broader range when used alone than when used in combination with conditions and consistency.

One method that has been developed in which only two criteria are considered in the determination of the performance factor is the technique introduced by Hummel.[6] Here the term "tempo" has been assigned

[6] J. O. P. Hummel, Staff Member, Operations Research Office, Johns Hopkins University.

as a synonym for effort, and the word "effectiveness," as a term somewhat comparable to skill.

These terms are defined as follows: (1) "tempo" is the relative rate of performing work, or the speed of doing work; (2) "effectiveness" is the degree of co-ordination or the lack of false, unnecessary or nonproductive movements.

Tempo ratings are made in terms of percentage: 100 per cent is considered as normal. Tempo ratings cover a range from .60 to 1.30 in increments of .05.

Effectiveness is rated as either superior, excellent, good, average, fair, or poor; the values of each of these categories are:

Superior	+.15	Average	+ 0
Excellent	+.10	Fair	−.10
Good	+.05	Poor	−.20

These characteristics, which parallel the Westinghouse system, have been described as follows:

Superior. Operator works with very nearly perfect smoothness of movement and a co-ordination making full use of hands, arms, and body.
Excellent. Operator works with a high degree of smoothness of movement and co-ordination.
Good. Operator works reasonably smoothly. Unbalanced movements and hesitations are present occasionally but are not readily detected.
Average. Operator does not noticeably have excess or unbalanced movements or hesitations.
Fair. There are occasional unbalanced movements indicating unsatisfactory co-ordination. Occasional hesitations.
Poor. Movements of hands, feet or body are poorly co-ordinated. There are frequent hesitations.

In determining the performance factor using the tempo and effectiveness method, the analyst multiplies the tempo assigned value by the effectiveness value algebraically added to unity. For example, if a tempo value of 1.10 be assigned and an effectiveness rating of "good" be given, then the performance factor will be:

$$P = (1.10)(1.05) = 1.155$$

Thus, in this case, the operator would be performing 15.5 per cent faster than the time study analyst's concept of normal.

This leveling technique has a spread of .48 to 1.495, or is based on a range of productivity of 1 to 3.12.

Analysis of Rating

As is true of all procedures requiring the exercise of judgment, the simpler and more concise the plan, the easier it will be to use, and, in general, the more valid the results will be.

The performance rating plan that is the easiest to apply, the easiest to explain, and the one that tends to give the most valid results is straight speed or pace rating augmented with synthetic benchmarks. As has been explained, in this procedure, 100 is considered normal, and performance greater than normal is indicated by values directly proportional to 100. Thus, a rating of 120 would indicate that a performance of 20 per cent higher than normal was being exhibited. A rating of 60 would indicate that the operator was performing at a pace of only .60 of normal. The speed rating scale usually covers a range from .50 to 1.50. Operators performing outside this productivity range of 3 to 1 may be studied, but it is not recommended. The closer the performance is to normal, the better will be the chance of achieving the true normal time.

The time study analyst using speed rating will have three considerations which when properly followed will allow him consistently to establish values not more than 5 per cent above or below the true normal. These are:

1. Experience in the class of work being performed.
2. Synthetic benchmarks on at least two of the elements being performed.
3. Selection of an operator who has from past experience given performances somewhere between 115 and 85 per cent of normal.

Certainly, the most important of these three criteria is experience in the class of work being performed. This does not necessarily mean that the analyst must have at one time been an actual operator in the work being studied, although this would be desirable. He should be sufficiently familiar with the work from his past personal experience, either by observation or operation, that he understands every detail of the method being used. Thus, on a job being performed on a turret lathe, he should recognize the tooling, have knowledge of the correct speeds and feeds, the correct rake and clearance angles, lubricant, horsepower requirements, method of holding the work, and so on. On an assembly job taking place in a fixture, the time study man should be familiar with the difficulty in positioning the components in the fixture; he should know the class of fit between all mating parts and have a clear understanding of the relationship between time and class of fit. He should know the proper sequence of events and the weights of all parts being handled.

It has often been said that experience is the key to accurate performance rating, and this statement certainly is true. An analyst with ten year's experience in the metal trades would find considerable difficulty in establishing standards in a woman's shoe factory, and of course the reverse would be true: a time study man with years of experience in the fabrication of shoes would be unable to establish equitable standards in a machine shop until he had acquired some experience in the line of work being performed.

There is a definite tendency for an experienced operator to maintain a given level of performance from element to element during the course of the time study. In fact, in the majority of cases involving studies of a half-hour duration and less, the operator's performance will not show much variation during the course of the entire study. If the time study analyst has available information that allows him to pre-establish synthetically the normal time required to perform several of the elements involved in the study, he has an indication of the over-all performance being executed.

The alignment chart[7] shown on the time study board (see Figure 13–7) permits the analyst to establish synthetically the normal time for the elements: "pick up pc. & position in fixture, jig, or die," "pick up pc. & bring to work station," "pick up pc. & lay aside." Since very few work assignments can be performed without utilizing at least one of these elements, the time study analyst has at his disposal a useful guide for establishing a true performance factor. For example, if a 10-pound casting is picked up and placed in a 3-jaw chuck of a turret lathe and the element entailed a reach of 30 inches and a move of 20 inches and a class 4 grasp (see Chapter 10 on M.T.M.) and a P3SE position, the synthetic time could be determined graphically. By going from 20 inches on scale 1 vertically to 10 pounds on scale 2 and then moving horizontally to scale 3, a time of .017 minute for the move and release is shown. This point connected to the G4 grasp of .005 minute (scale 4) gives a turning point on scale 5. This turning point on scale 5 connected with a reach of 30 inches on scale 6 gives a time of .04 minute for the reach, grasp, move, and release. This point connected with a P3SE position entailing .025 minute on scale 8 gives the time to perform the complete element .065 minute on scale 9.

It is not intended to infer that the synthetic value will establish a rating that is to have application for every element of each cycle of the study. The analyst through his experience and training in performance rating will be able to evaluate the operator quite precisely; the alignment chart and resulting synthetic standards will provide an additional check and guide to the analyst, giving him more confidence in his ability to establish fair normal times.

Whenever more than one operator is available to be studied, the one who is thoroughly experienced on the job, who has a reputation of being receptive to time study practice, and who consistently performs at a pace near standard or slightly better than standard should be selected. The closer the operator performs to a normal pace, the easier will he be to level. Sizable errors in judgment during rating are invariably a result of improper evaluation of an operator who is performing at either extremity of the rating scale. For example, if .50 minute is considered normal for

---

[7] The data used in the design of this alignment chart were developed in part by the author after analyzing over 600 feet of film. The remainder of the data used was taken from Methods-Time Measurement tables.

dealing a deck of cards into four bridge hands, it will be found that performance within plus or minus 15 per cent of this conception of normal will be fairly easy to identify. However, once the performance runs 50 per cent faster or 50 per cent slower than normal, considerably more difficulty is encountered in establishing an accurate rating factor indicative of the rate of performance being demonstrated.

Performance rating, like any other form of work involving judgment, must be accomplished by competent, well-trained individuals. If this caliber of person is doing the work, and if he is equipped with a background of experience, has access to reliable synthetic time values, and uses sound judgment in operator selection, then reasonably accurate results can be assured.

Training for Rating

To be successful, the time study man must develop a record for setting standards correctly so that they will be accepted by both labor and management. Furthermore, his rates must be consistent so that he will maintain the respect of all parties. In general, the time study analyst is expected to be able regularly to establish standards within plus or minus 5 per cent of the true rate. Thus, if several operators are performing the same job and different time study men establish time standards on the job, each analyst studying a different operator, then the resulting standard from each individual study should be within plus or minus 5 per cent of the mean of the group of studies.

To assure consistency in rating, not only to keep agreement with former rates which he himself has established, but also to maintain accordance with the other time study analysts in his plant, the time study man should continually participate in organized training programs. Of course, the training in performance rating should be more intense with the neophyte time study analyst.

One of the most widely used methods for training in performance rating is the observation of moving-picture films illustrating diversified operations performed at different productivity levels. Each film has a known level of performance, and after it is shown on the screen, the true rating is compared with the values established independently by the various trainees. If any of the time study analysts' values deviate substantially from the correct value, then specific information is given so as to justify the rating. For example, the observer may have been misled because of high performance in the handling of the material to and from the work station, while poor performance prevailed during the cycle at the work station. Then, too, the analyst may have underrated the operator because of his apparently effortless sequence of motions, whereas his smooth, rhythmic blending of movements is really an indication of high dexterity and manipulative ability.

The operations selected should be simple, yet should contain a number of fast motions. The observation of short elements cultivates both speed and concentration in the observer and trains the "second sight."

If a company feels that it can not afford to maintain a film library for training in performance rating, it may make use of the many films available on a rental basis for training purposes. The Pennsylvania State University, the University of Iowa, and the Society for the Advancement of

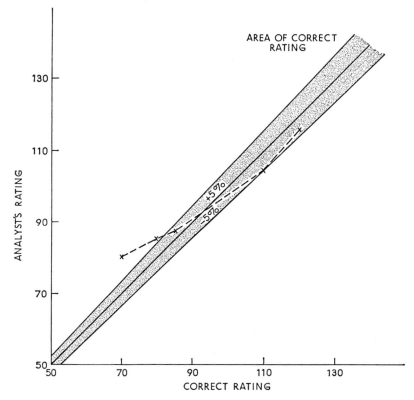

FIG. 15–2. Chart showing record of five studies with analyst tending to rate a little high on studies 1, 2, and 3 and a little low on studies 4 and 5. Studies 1 and 2 were rated outside the 5 per cent criteria of accuracy.

Management have rating films available that are quite helpful in training the new analyst, as well as in maintaining accuracy in the practicing time study man.

As successive films are shown, it is helpful for the analyst to plot his rating against the known values (see Figure 15–2). A straight line would indicate perfection, whereas high irregularities in both directions would indicate inconsistency as well as inability to evaluate performance.

In the example shown, the analyst rated the first film 80, whereas the correct rating was 70. In the second case, he rated 85 while the proper performance was 80. In the third, fourth, and fifth cases, the analyst was within the plus or minus 5 per cent criterion of accuracy.

It is also helpful to plot successive ratings on the X axis and indicate the magnitude of deviation either positive or negative from the known normal on the Y axis (see Figure 15–3). The closer the time study man comes to the X axis with his rating, the more correct he will be.

Today, no known tests are available that can accurately evaluate the ability of a person to rate performance. Experience, however, has shown that unless an analyst shows a tendency toward consistency and proficiency after a brief training in rating, he may never be able to do an acceptable job in rating.

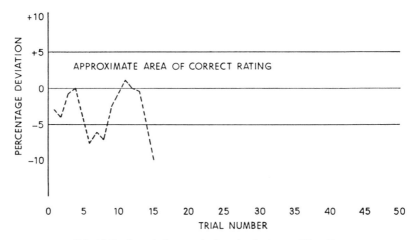

FIG. 15–3. Record of an analyst's rating factors on 15 studies.

A survey made by one large manufacturer disclosed that the industrial engineering employee who was older in point of service did not level any more accurately than the newer man, that those in the higher work classifications did not level better than the lower men, that those in machining areas did no better than those in assembly areas and vice-versa.

Recently, a group of undergraduate engineers were given 15 minutes instruction in rating and then were requested to performance rate a film illustrating a series of heavy labor operations.[8] The students were given no orientation in the class of work, and the operations observed were substantially varied from the operations used in giving them a concept of proper performance. It was interesting to note that the students were extremely successful in adjusting the concepts learned on light operations to those on heavy labor operations.

In another instance, 34 undergraduate engineering students were asked to performance rate five industrial films involving operations rang-

[8] H. A. Lynch, paper given at the Fifth Annual Time Study and Methods Conference, April 20, 1950.

ing from mold making to bench assembly. Four of these films were established as being representative of normal performance and one was rated as 1.15 or 15 per cent above normal. The results are shown in the accompanying table:

Known Rating	Number of Students in Each Rating Bracket					
	85–90	91–95	96–100	101–105	106–110	111–125
1.15...............	0	3	4	12	6	9
1.00...............	4	5	19	2	3	1
1.00...............	2	3	7	12	5	5
1.00...............	7	5	14	8	0	0
1.00...............	1	2	26	4	1	0

It will be noted that the majority of the students did not deviate greatly from the known values.

One division of the General Electric Company upon request checked the validity of the performance rating technique on three different occasions.[9] After brief training in their rating methods, the union steward and the foreman were requested to rate a given operation in conjunction with a time study analyst and the time study supervisor. At the completion of the study, the time study man rated the study without advising the other three men as to the values he used, so that they would not be influenced by his opinion. These three men then went into their respective offices so that they would not be influenced by each other's opinions and independently and secretly rated the operation. The results were as follows: time study man 100; planning and wage payment supervisor 99; foreman 103; union steward 103.

At a later date involving an entirely different class of work, a similar test case was undertaken. These results were: time study man 100; planning and wage payment supervisor 99; foreman 103; union steward 103.

On the third occasion an entirely new set of conditions prevailed and in this instance all four men rated identically—109!

The foregoing studies bring out that (1) a conception of normal performance can be quickly taught, and (2) the concept of normal is transferable to some degree to dissimilar operations.

By actual observation of different work assignments throughout a plant under the guidance of the time study supervisor, it is possible to achieve excellent training in rating. The supervisor will explain in detail the "why" of his values after the trainees have already written their ratings independently. The independent values should be recorded to determine the consistency of the group and the necessity for additional, and perhaps more intensive, training.

It has been proven that companies that have extensive and well-

---

[9] Letter from A. E. Shaw, General Electric Co., Erie, Pennsylvania.

designed programs of training in rating have been successful in largely eliminating the tendency to overrate and underrate.

TEXT QUESTIONS

1. Why has industry been unable to develop a universal conception of "normal performance"?
2. What factors enter into large variances in operator performance?
3. What are the characteristics of a sound rating system?
4. When should the performance rating procedure be accomplished? Why is this important?
5. What governs the frequency of performance rating during a given study?
6. Explain the Westinghouse system of leveling.
7. How does the Westinghouse performance rating method differ from the leveling method?
8. Under the Westinghouse rating system, why are "conditions" evaluated?
9. What is synthetic rating?
10. What is the basis of speed rating and how does this method differ from the Westinghouse system?
11. What is the purpose of the "secondary adjustment" in the objective rating technique? What factors are considered in the "secondary adjustment"?
12. What three criteria are fundamental for doing a good job in speed rating?
13. Why is training in performance rating a continuous process?

GENERAL QUESTIONS

1. Would there be any objection to studying an operator who was performing at an excessive pace? Why?
2. In what ways can an operator give the impression of high effort and yet produce at a mediocre or poor degree of performance?
3. If an operator strongly objected to his performance rating factor upon completion of the study, what would your next step be if you were the time study analyst?

CHAPTER 16

Allowances

AFTER THE CALCULATION OF the normal time, sometimes referred to as the "rated" time, one additional step must be performed in order to arrive at a true standard. This last step is the addition of an allowance to take care of the many interruptions, delays, and slowdowns brought on by fatigue which enter into every work assignment. For example in planning a motor car trip of 1,000 miles, we know that the trip cannot be made in 20 hours when driving at a speed of 50 miles per hour. An allowance to take care of periodic stops for personal needs, for driving fatigue, for unavoidable stops brought on by traffic congestion and stoplights, for possible detours and resulting rough roads, for car trouble, and so forth must be added. Thus we may estimate making the trip in 25 hours since we feel that 5 additional hours would be necessary to take care of all delays. Similarly, an allowance must be provided for the workman in order that the resulting standard will be fair and readily maintainable by the average workman who is performing at a steady, normal pace.

It must be remembered that the watch readings of any time study are taken over a relatively short period of time, and abnormal readings, unavoidable delays, and time for personal needs are removed from the study in the determination of the average or selected time. Therefore, the normal time has not provided for unavoidable delays and other legitimate lost time; consequently, some adjustment must be made to compensate for such losses.

In general, allowances are made to cover three broad areas. These are personal delays, fatigue, and unavoidable delays. The application of allowances in some concerns is considerably broader than in others. For example, a survey of 42 firms relative to what was ordinarily included in their allowances revealed the information shown in the accompanying table.

Allowances are frequently carelessly applied because they have not been established on sound time study data. This is especially true of allowance for fatigue, where it is difficult if not impossible to establish values based on rational theory. Many unions, well aware of this situation, have endeavored to bargain for additional fatigue allowance as if it were a "fringe" issue. (Fringe benefits are those which are expenses to the company but are not proportional to employee output, such as in-

Allowance Factor	No. of Firms	Per Cent
1. Fatigue	39	93
A. General	19	45
B. Rest periods	13	31
Did not specify A or B	7	17
2. Time required to learn	3	7
3. Unavoidable delay	35	83
A. Man	1	2
B. Machine	7	17
C. Both, man and machine	21	50
Did not specify A, B, or C	6	14
4. Personal needs	32	76
5. Setup or preparation operations	24	57
6. Irregular or unusual operations	16	38

Source: J. O. P. Hummel, "Motion and Time Study in Leading American Industrial Establishments" (Master's Thesis, Pennsylvania State University).

surance and pensions.) Allowance must be determined as accurately and correctly as possible; otherwise, all the care and precision that has been put into the study up to this point will be completely nullified.

Allowances are applied to three categories of the study. These are: (1) allowances applicable to the total cycle time, (2) allowances that need be considered on machine time only, and (3) allowances applicable to effort time only.

Allowances applicable to the whole cycle time are usually expressed as a percentage of the cycle time and include such delays as personal needs, cleaning the work station, and oiling the machine. Machine time allowances include time for tool maintenance and power variance, while representative delays covered by effort allowance are fatigue and certain unavoidable delays.

There are two methods of developing standard allowance data that are frequently used. One is the production study which requires an observer to study two or perhaps three operations over a long period of time. The observer records the duration and reason for each idle interval (see Figure 16–1), and upon establishing a reasonably representative sample, summarizes his findings to determine the per cent allowance for each applicable characteristic. The data obtained in this fashion must be adjusted to the level of normal performance as for any time study.

LOST TIME ANALYSIS OF TIME STUDY

Dwg._____ Part _____ Date _____

Operation _____

Symbol _____

A. Personal _____
B. Start work late _____
C. Stop work early _____
D. Talk with foreman or instructor _____
E. Talk with other persons _____
F. Search for tools _____
G. Search for drawings _____
H. Rework fault of operator _____
I. Rework fault of another operator _____
J. Rework fault of machine or fixtures _____
K. Idle-wait for crane (excess over allowed) _____
L. Idle-wait for inspector (excess over allowed) _____
M. Wait in line at tool crib (excess over allowed) _____
N. Wait in line at dispatch office (excess over allowed) _____
O. Wait in line at B/P station _____
P. Tool maintenance _____
Q. Oil machine _____
R. Clean work station _____
S. Circled readings (circled reading minus ave. for ele.) _____
T. Miscellaneous minor delays _____
U. Lost time developing methods during study _____
V. _____
W. _____
X. _____
Y. _____
Z. _____

                                                      Total _____

1. Gross over-all _____ Mins. _____ Hrs.
2. Total lost _____ " _____ "
3. % lost time compared with net actual (2 ÷ 4)   _____
4. Net actual or productive _____ Mins. _____ Hrs.
5. Allowed time   _____ " _____ "

_____
_____
_____

Note--Place lost time symbol alongside description of lost time on study and staple this card
      to study.

FIG. 16–1. Lost time analysis chart.

Since the observer must spend a long period of time in direct observation of one or more operations, this method is exceptionally tedious, not only to the analyst but also to the operator or operators as well. It has further disadvantages in that there is a tendency to take too small a sample, which may result in biased results.

The second technique of establishing allowance percentage is through work sampling studies (see Chapter 20). This method involves the taking of a large number of random observations, thus requiring only part-time, or at least intermittent, services of the observer. In this method, no stop watch is used, as the observer merely walks through the area under study at unscheduled times and makes a brief notation as to what each operator is doing.

The number of delays recorded divided by the total number of observations during which the operator is engaged in productive work will tend to equal the allowance required by the operator to accommodate the normal delays encountered.

In using work sampling studies for the determination of allowances, the observer must practice several precautionary measures. First, the observer must be careful that he does not anticipate his observations and that he records only the actual happenings. Then, a given study should not cover dissimilar work, but should be confined to similar operations on the same general type of equipment. The larger the number of observations and the longer the period of time over which the data were taken, the more valid will be the results. Studies taken by R. L. Morrow indicate that fairly reliable results were obtained with 500 observations while 3,000 observations gave very accurate results.[1] Daily observations should be taken over a span of at least two weeks.

Personal Delays

Under the item of personal delays will come those cessations in work necessary for maintaining the general well-being of the employee. This will include periodic trips to the drinking fountain and the rest room. The general working conditions and class of work will influence the time necessary for personal delays. Thus, working conditions involving heavy work performed at high temperatures, such as that done in the pressroom of a rubber-molding department or in a hot-forge shop, would require greater allowance for personal needs than light work performed in moderate temperature areas. Detailed production checks have demonstrated that a 5 per cent allowance for personal time, or approximately 24 minutes in 8 hours, is appropriate for typical shop working conditions. The amount of time needed for personal delays will, of course, vary to some extent with the person as well as the class of work. The 5 per cent figure cited appears to be adequate for the majority of male and female workers.

Fatigue

Closely associated with allowance for personal needs is allowance for fatigue, although this allowance is usually applied only to the effort portions of the study. Fatigue allowances have not reached the state where their qualifications are based on sound, rational theories, and they probably never will. Consequently, next to performance rating, the fatigue allowance is the least defensible and the most open to argument of all the factors making up a time standard. However, fair fatigue allowances

---

[1] R. L. Morrow, *Time Study and Motion Economy* (New York: Ronald Press Co., 1946).

for different classes of work can be approximated by empirical means. Fatigue is not homogeneous in any respect; it ranges from strictly physical to purely psychological and includes combinations of both the physical and the psychological. It has a marked influence on some people, and apparently has little or no effect on others.

Whether the fatigue that sets in is physical or mental, the results are similar: there is a lessening in the will to work. The major factors that affect fatigue are well known and have been clearly established. Some of these are:

1. Working conditions:
   a) Light.
   b) Temperature.
   c) Humidity.
   d) Air freshness.
   e) Color of room and environment.
   f) Noise.
2. Repetitiveness of work:
   a) Monotony of similar body movements.
   b) Muscular tiredness due to stressing of some muscles.
3. General health of the worker, physical and mental:
   a) Physical stature.
   b) Diet.
   c) Rest.
   d) Emotional stability.
   e) Home conditions.

It is evident that fatigue can be reduced, but can never be eliminated. In general, heavy work is diminishing in industry because of the marked progress in mechanization of both material handling and processing elements. As industry becomes more automated, there will be less muscular tiredness due to stressing of muscles. Thus, we have made real progress toward the decreasing of physical fatigue. The major problem of fatigue today is not physical but psychological, and industry through its scientific selection programs is substantially reducing this factor by putting the right people on the right jobs. A person who has an unfavorable reaction to monotony is not placed on a monotonous job. Since it is not customary to provide fatigue allowance for those general health factors that influence the degree of fatigue that sets in, such conditions as emotional stability, rest, diet, and physical stature are usually considered in employee selection.

Because fatigue cannot be eliminated, proper allowance must be made for working conditions and repetitiveness of work that influence the degree to which it sets in. Experiments have shown that fatigue must be plotted as a curve, not as a straight line. Figure 16–2 illustrates a typical work curve showing the relationship between load in pounds and time for handling each load. Many industrial studies have shown a drop in production toward the end of the working period which is attributable to fatigue alone. Usually, the rate of production tends to increase during the early part of the day and then falls off after the third hour. There is a short period of increased production after the lunch period, but this begins to taper off and output usually continues to decline for the balance of the working day.

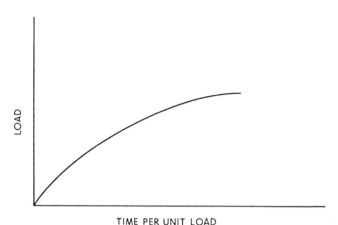

TIME PER UNIT LOAD

Redrawn from *Fatigue Allowances in Industry,* Thesis by J. W. Siphron, The Pennsylvania State College.

FIG. 16–2. Typical work curve.

Perhaps the most widely used method of determining fatigue allowance is that of measuring the decline in production throughout the working period. Thus, the production rate for every quarter of an hour may be measured during the course of the working day. Any decline of production that cannot be attributed to method change or personal or unavoidable delays may be attributed to fatigue and expressed as a percentage. It must be recognized, however, that many outside factors can influence the fatigue factor, such as state of health or outside interference. Thus, many studies should be made in order to obtain a reasonable sample before deciding upon the final fatigue allowance for a given facility. Eugene Brey[2] has expressed the coefficient of fatigue as follows:

$$F = \frac{(T - t)\ 100}{T}$$

where

F = Coefficient of fatigue
T = Time required to perform operation at the end of continuous work
t = Time required to perform operation at beginning of continuous work .

[2] Eugene E. Brey, "Fatigue Research in Its Relation to Time Study Practice," *Proceedings,* Time Study Conference, Society of Industrial Engineers.

Many attempts have been made to measure fatigue, none of which has been completely successful. The tests of fatigue may be classified into three groups: (1) physical, (2) chemical, and (3) physiological.

Physical tests include the various dynamometer tests of changes in the rate of working, such as the hand dynamometer, the mercury dynamometer, the water dynamometer, and the Martin spring balance for registering force exerted by six different sets of large body muscles.

Chemical tests include the various techniques for analysis of the blood and the body secretions, such as the saliva, so as to note changes resulting from fatigue.

The physiological tests of fatigue include pulse count, blood pressure, respiratory rate, oxygen consumption, and production of carbon dioxide. Table XVIII shows the rates of change in physiological reactions due to fatigue.

In recent years, considerable attention has been directed to the physiological requirements of various work assignments. This branch of the scientific study of the worker and his environment is being recognized as "occupational physiology." Here, the effort per unit of time plus the physiological recovery time is measured for the different work assignments within a plant. As these studies progress, more quantitative data will inevitably result for estimating fatigue allowances. It is also expected that laws of physiological economy will result which will supplement and may even supersede some of the laws of motion economy.

Table XVIII

Factor	Per Cent Decrease	Per Cent Increase
1. Pulse count	...	113.5
2. Pulse pressure	...	77.0
3. Respiratory rate	...	60.5
4. CO_2 combining power	41.0	...
5. Metabolism	...	43.0
6. White blood cells	...	57.0
7. Red blood cells	...	6.0
8. Blood pressure; diastolic	28.0	...
9. Blood pressure; systolic	...	20.5
10. Blood sugar	...	12.0

Source: Moss and Roe, *Physiological Reactions Due to Fatigue.*

In the development of equitable fatigue allowances, one of the foremost problems of time study is to determine at which portion of the fatigue curve a time study was made, and then derive a fatigue allowance which can be used as a constant for work performed at the given work station in the future.

For most industrial operations, fatigue allowances have been arbitrarily broken into three elements, each of which has a spread of influence on the total fatigue allowance. These are: operations involving strenuous work, operations involving repetitive work, and operations performed under disagreeable working conditions. Of course, it is possible for more than one of these conditions, in varying degrees, to apply in any specific operation.

By taking controlled production studies from an adequate sample of work it is possible to arrive at fatigue allowance values that will prove equitable for the various degrees of each of the above enumerated factors. The apparent adequacy of fatigue allowances determined by measuring the decline in production through all-day production studies is due to the fact that the fatigue allowance for a given job is not a critical value but may be safely established within a rather broad range.

There are two ways of applying the fatigue allowance. It can be handled as a percentage which is added to the normal time, as has been explained. In this method, the allowance is based on a percentage of the productive time only. As an alternative technique, fatigue allowance can be handled through the establishment of required periodic rest periods.

The former way is preferred because it allows the employee who is physically stronger to participate in greater earnings. If compulsory rest periods are used, the strong employee who is not as subject to fatigue as the average employee, will be restricted in his output.

It should be recognized that rest periods will definitely reduce fatigue. If 10-minute rest periods are introduced in a plant, as they frequently are, the fatigue allowance that formerly prevailed should be proportionally modified. For example, if a bench assembly operation earned a fatigue allowance of 8 per cent and at some later date, through negotiation, a 10-minute rest period was provided in the morning and another 10-minute rest period in the afternoon, the fatigue allowance on this class of work would be diminished

$$\frac{20}{\text{Normal Productive Time}} = \underline{\qquad}\%.$$

The normal daily productive time on this class of work may be 400 minutes. The fatigue allowance accounted for by the 20-minute rest period would then be 20/400 or 5 per cent. Thus future standards in this area will carry a fatigue allowance of 8 per cent minus 5 per cent, or 3 per cent.

Unavoidable Delays

This class of delays applies to effort elements and includes such items as interruptions from the foreman, dispatcher, time study analyst, and others; material irregularities; and difficulty in maintaining tolerances and specifications.

As can be expected, every operator will have numerous interruptions during the course of the working day. These can be due to a wide range of reasons. The foreman or group leader may interrupt the operator to give him instructions or to clarify certain written information. Then the inspector may interrupt him to point out the reason for some defective work that passed through the operator's work station. Interruptions frequently occur from planners, expeditors, fellow workers, production men, time study men, dispatchers, and others.

Unavoidable delays are frequently a result of material irregularities. For example, the material may be in the wrong location or it may be running slightly too soft or too hard. Again, it may be too short or too long, or may have excessive stock on it, as in the case of forgings when the dies begin to wash out, or on castings due to incomplete removal of risers. When material deviates substantially from standard specifications, it may be necessary to restudy the job and establish allowed time for the extra elements introduced by the irregular material, as the customary unavoidable delay allowance may prove to be inadequate.

The heading "maintaining tolerances and specifications" would include time spent in resetting cutting tools, making trial cuts, rechecking work, and other minor delays resulting from difficulty in obtaining and maintaining quality and size.

Avoidable Delays

It is not customary to provide any allowance for avoidable delays which include visits with other operators for social reasons, uncalled-for work stoppages, and idleness other than rest to overcome fatigue. Of course, these delays may be taken by the operator at the expense of his output, but no allowance is provided for these cessations of work in the development of the standard.

Extra Allowances

In typical metal trade and related operations, the percentage allowance for personal, unavoidable, and fatigue delays usually approximates 15 per cent. However, in certain cases, it may be necessary to provide an extra allowance in order to arrive at a standard that is fair. Thus, due to a substandard lot of raw material, it may be necessary to provide an extra allowance to take care of an unduly high generation of rejects caused by the poor material. Again, an operation may develop where, because of breakage of a jib crane, the operator is obliged to place a 50-pound casting in the chuck of his machine. Therefore, an extra allowance must be provided to take care of the additional fatigue brought on by the manual handling of the work.

Whenever practical, allowed time should be established for the additional work of any operation by breaking it down into elements and then including these times in the specific operation. If this is not practical, then an extra allowance must be provided.

Clean Work Station and Oil Machine

The time required to clean and lubricate the operator's machine may be classified as an unavoidable delay. However, this time, when performed by the operator, is usually included as a total cycle time allowance. The type and size of equipment, and the material being fabricated will have considerable effect on the time required to clean the work station and lubricate the equipment. When these elements are included as part of the responsibilities of the operator, applicable allowance must be provided. One concern has established the accompanying table of allowances to cover these items.

CLEAN MACHINE ALLOWANCE CHART

Item	Per Cent Large Machine	Per Cent Medium Machine	Per Cent Small Machine
1. Clean machine when lubricant is used.........	1	¾	½
2. Clean machine when lubricant is not used.....	¾	½	¼
3. Clean and put away large amount of tools or equipment...................................	½	½	½
4. Clean and put away small amount of tools or equipment...................................	¼	¼	¼
5. Shut machine down for cleaning (this percentage for machines equipped with chip pans, which are stopped at intervals to permit sweeper to clean away large chips).................	1	¾	½

MACHINE CLASSIFICATION

Large Machine
1. Turret lathe (20″ ck or over)
2. Boring mill (60″ and over)
3. Punch press (100T and over)
4. Planer (over 48″)

Medium Machine
1. Turret lathe (10″ to 20″ ck)
2. Boring mill (under 60″)
3. Punch press (40T to 100T)

OIL MACHINE ALLOWANCE CHART

Item	Per Cent Large Machine	Per Cent Medium Machine	Per Cent Small Machine
1. Machine oiled or greased by hand...........	1½	1	½
2. Machine oiled automatically................	½	½	½

Frequently, the elements of "clean work station" and "oil machine" are handled by giving the operator 10 or 15 minutes at the end of the day in which to perform this work. When this is done, the standards established of course would not include any allowance for cleaning and oiling the machine.

Power Feed Machine Time Allowance

The allowance required for power feed elements frequently will differ from that required for effort elements. Two factors are usually considered in the application of allowances for power feed: these are power variance and tool maintenance.

Allowances are made for variance in power for reduced speeds brought on by belt stoppage and for shutdowns because of minor repairs. In case a major repair to the facility is needed, then an extra allowance would of necessity be provided. This extra allowance would not be applied within the standard but would be an independent period of time covering the machine repair.

Tool maintenance allowance provides time for the operator to maintain his tools after the original setup. In the setup time the operator is expected to provide first-class tools properly ground. Generally, little tool maintenance takes place during the course of the average production run. Of course, in long runs, tools will have to be periodically sharpened. The percentage allowance for tool maintenance will vary directly with the number of perishable tools in the setup. For example, one manufacturer's tool maintenance allowance table is as follows:

ALLOWANCE FOR TOOL MAINTENANCE

Per Cent

1. One or more tools ground in tool crib............................1
2. One tool sharpened by operator..................................3
3. Two or more tools cutting at one time sharpened by the operator....6

Application of Allowances

The fundamental purpose of allowances is to add enough time to the normal production time to enable the average worker to meet the standard when performing at a normal pace. It is customary to express the allowance as a multiplier so that the normal time, consisting of productive work elements, can be adjusted readily to the time allowed. Thus, if a 15 per cent allowance were to be provided on a given operation, the multiplier would be 1.15.

Care must be exercised when including the allowance with the time study standard. It must be remembered that allowance is based on a percentage of the daily production time and not on the over-all work day. For example, if a study revealed that in an 8-hour working day 50 minutes of delay time are to be allowed during 400 minutes of normal production time, then the percentage allowance applicable would be 50/400 or 12.5 per cent.

Allowance is based on the normal production time, since it is this value that the percentage will be applied to on subsequent studies.

Typical Allowance Values

In an industrial survey comprising 42 different plants, the smallest average total allowance found to be in use was 10 per cent. This was used in a plant producing household electrical appliances. The greatest average allowance found to be in effect was 35 per cent being used in two different steel plants. The average allowance of all plants from which replies were received was 17.7 per cent.

Typical allowances established in a certain plant for standard opera-

TABLE XIX

Time Study Allowances for Standard Operations

Symbol	Facility or Operation	Method	Total Applied to Effort Time	Total Applied to Machine Time	Personal	Clean Work Station	Oil Machine	Power Variance or Shut Down	Tool Maintenance	Unavoidable Delays and Fatigue
21	Anneal	Oven	10	...	5	½	...	...	...	4½
22	Blacksmith	Drop forge	21	...	7	1	...	...	...	13
23	Braze	Electric	14	...	5	½	...	½	...	8
24	Drill, sensitive, single, spindle	Hand feed	14	...	5	½	½	½	2	5½
25	Drill, sensitive, single, sensitive	Power feed	14	12	5	½	½	m–2 e–1½	m–4 e–2	e–5½
26	Engrave	Pantograph	18	..	5	½	½	½	7½	4
27	Engine Lathe	Over 36″	13	15	5	2	1	m–2	m–5	e–5
28	Mold	Machine (cores used)	18	..	6	2	...	...	...	10
29	Punch press	Up to 100 tons	13	...	5	½	1	½	...	6
30	Saw, circular	Hand feed	14	...	5	½	½	½	...	7½

tions appear in Table XIX. These values may or may not apply in other plants.

Summary

In the establishment of time study allowance values, the same care that prevails in taking individual studies should be exercised throughout. It would be folly to divide a job carefully into elements, precisely measure the duration of each element in one-hundredths of a minute, accurately evaluate the performance of the operator, and then arbitrarily assign an allowance that has been picked at random. Practices of this nature will lead to inaccurate standards. If the allowances are too high, obviously manufacturing costs will be unduly inflated, and if the allowances are too low, tight standards will result, which will cause poor labor relations and eventual failure of the system.

TEXT QUESTIONS

1. What three broad areas are allowances intended to cover?
2. To what three categories of the time study are allowances provided? Give several examples of each.
3. What are the two methods used in the development of allowance standard data? Briefly explain the application of each technique.
4. Give several examples of personal delays. What percentage allowance seems adequate for personal delays under typical shop conditions?
5. What are some of the major factors that affect fatigue?
6. Under what groups have the tests of fatigue been classified?
7. What operator interruptions would be covered by the unavoidable delay allowance?
8. What percentage allowance is usually provided for avoidable delays?
9. When are "extra allowances" provided?
10. What fatigue allowance should be given to a job if it developed that it took 1.542 minutes to perform the operation at the end of continuous work and but 1.480 minutes at the beginning of continuous work?
11. Why are allowances based on a percentage of the productive time?
12. What is meant by "occupational physiology"?

GENERAL QUESTIONS

1. Do you feel that the operation or the operator determines the extent to which personal delay time is utilized? Why?
2. Why is fatigue allowance frequently applied only to the effort areas of the work cycle?
3. Should fatigue allowances vary with the different shifts for a given class of work? Why?
4. What are the objections to determining fatigue allowances by measuring the decline of production that are not attributed to method changes or personal or unavoidable delays?

CHAPTER 17

The Standard Time

THE STANDARD TIME FOR A GIVEN operation is the time required for an average operator, fully qualified and trained and working at a normal pace, to perform the operation. It is determined by summarizing the allowed time for all of the individual elements comprising the time study.

Elemental allowed times are determined by multiplying the mean elapsed elemental time by a conversion factor. Thus, we have the expression:

$$T_a = (M_t)(C) ,$$

where:

T_a = the allowed elemental time
M_t = mean elapsed elemental time
C = conversion factor found by multiplying performance rating factor by one plus the applicable allowance .

For example, if the mean elemental time of element number one of a given time study was .14 minute and the performance factor was .90 and an allowance of 18 per cent was applicable, the allowed elemental time would be:

$$T_a = (.14)(.90)(1.18) = (.14)(1.06) = .148 .$$

Allowed elemental times are rounded off to three places to the right of the decimal point. Thus, in the preceding example .1483 minute is recorded as .148 minute. If the result was .1485 minute, then the recording would be .149 minute allowed time.

Expressing the Standard Time

The sum of the elemental allowed times will give the standard in minutes per piece or hours per piece, depending on whether a decimal minute or decimal hour watch was in use. The majority of industrial operations have relatively short cycles (less than five minutes); consequently, it is usually more convenient to express standards in terms of hours per hundred pieces. For example, the standard on a press operation might be .085 hour per hundred pieces. This is a more satisfactory method of expressing the standard than .00085 hour per piece or .051 minute per piece. Thus, if the operator produced 10,000 pieces during the working day, he would have earned 8.5 hours of production, and would have performed at an efficiency of 106 per cent. This is expressed as:

$$E = \left(\frac{He}{Hc}\right)\left(100\right),$$

where:

E = per cent efficiency
He = standard hours earned
Hc = clock hours on the job .

In another instance, the standard time may have resulted in 11.46 minutes per piece. This would be converted into decimal hours per hundred pieces as follows:

$$S_h = 1.667 S_m ,$$

where:

S_h = standard expressed in hours per hundred pieces
S_m = standard expressed in minutes per piece
1.667 = constant developed by converting minutes to decimal hours and multiplying by 100 (100 × 1/60) ,

thus:

$$S_h = (1.667)(11.46)$$
$$= 19.104 \text{ hrs.}/C .$$

If an operator produced 53 pieces in a given working day, the standard hours produced would be:

$$H_e = (.01)(P_a)(S_h) ,$$

where:

H_e = standard hours earned
P_a = actual production in pieces
S_h = standard expressed in hours per hundred ,

or in this example:

$$H_e = (.53)(19.104) = 10.125 \text{ hours} .$$

Once the allowed time has been computed, the standard is released to the operator in the form of an operation card. This card can be run off on a ditto machine, or some other duplicating process can be used. It will serve as the basis for routing, scheduling, instruction, payroll, operator performance, cost, budgeting, and other necessary controls for the effective operation of a business. Figure 17–1 illustrates a typical production operation card.

PRODUCTION OPERATION CARD

DESCRIPTION_____Shower head face_____DWG. NO.____JB-1102____PART NO. J-1102-1
MADE FROM _____2 1/2" diam. 70-30 extruded brass rod

Routing 9-11-12--14-12-18 _____ DATE__9-15-54

OP. NO.	OPERATION	DEPT.	MACHINE AND SPECIAL TOOLS	SET-UP MINUTES	EACH PC. MINUTES
1	Saw slug	9	J. & L. Air Saw	15 min	.077
2	Forge	11	150 Ton Maxi F-1102	70 min	.234
3	Blank	12	Bliss 72 F-1103	30 min	.061
4	Pickle	14	HCL. Tank	5 min	.006
5	Pierce 6 holes	12	Bliss 74 F-1104	30 min	.070
6	Rough ream and chamfer	12	Delta 17" D.P. F-1105	15 min	.334
7	Drill 13/64" holes	12	Avey D.P. F-1106	15 min	.152
8	Machine stem and face	12	#3 W.&S.	45 min	.648
9	Broach 6 holes	12	Bliss 74 1/2	30 min	.167
10	Inspect	18	F-1109, F-1110, F-1112	Daywork	

FIG. 17–1. Typical production operation card.

Temporary Standards

It is common knowledge that time is required to become proficient in any operation that is new or somewhat different.

Frequently, the time study man will be required to establish a standard on an operation that is relatively new and on which there is insufficient volume for the operator to reach his top efficiency. If the analyst bases his grading of the operator upon the usual conception of output, the resulting standard will seem unduly tight, and the operator will in all probability be unable to make any incentive earnings. On the other hand, if he takes into consideration the fact that the job is new and that the volume is low, and establishes a liberal standard, he may find himself in trouble in the event of an increase in the size of the order, or if a new order for the same part is received.

Perhaps, the most satisfactory method of handling situations like this is through the issuance of temporary standards. By doing this the time study analyst will establish the standard giving consideration to the difficulty of the work assignment and the number of pieces to be produced. The resulting standard will be considerably more liberal than if the job were being produced on a mass production basis. The standard, when released to the production floor, will be clearly marked as a "temporary" standard and will show the maximum quantity for which it applies. It is good practice to issue temporary standards on vouchers of a different color than that of permanent standard vouchers, so as to indicate clearly to all affected parties that the rate is temporary and is subject to restudy in the event of additional orders or increase in the volume of the present order.

The analyst must be careful as to the number of temporary standards released, since too many such standards can result in a lowering of the approved conception of normal. Also, the operators may strongly object to the changing of temporary standards to permanent standards, since the tighter permanent standard appears to them as a rate or wage cutting procedure. Only new work that is definitely foreign to the operator and that involves limited quantities of production should be considered as suitable for issuance of temporary standards. When temporary standards are released, they should be in effect for the duration of the contract or for 60 days, whichever period is shorter. Upon their expiration, they should be replaced with permanent standards. Several union contracts specifically state that temporary standards lasting longer than 60 days must become permanent.

Setup Standards

Those elements of work commonly included in setup standards involve all events that take place from the time the previous job was completed to the starting of the first piece of the present job. It is also customary to include in the setup standard, the "tear-down" or "put-away" elements: these include all items of work involved from the completion of the last piece to the setting up of the next job. Typical elements appearing in the setup standard would be:

1. Punching in on job.
2. Getting tools from tool crib.
3. Getting drawings from dispatcher.
4. Setting up the machine.
5. Punching out on the job.
6. Removing tools from machine.
7. Returning tools to crib.

In establishing setup times, the analyst uses the identical procedure followed in establishing standards for production. First, he should be assured that the best setup methods are in effect and that a standardized procedure has been adopted. Then the work is carefully broken down into elements, accurately timed, performance rated, and subjected to the appropriate allowance. The importance of valid setup times cannot be overemphasized, especially in the case of job shops where setup time represents a high proportion of the over-all time.

The analyst must be especially alert when timing setup elements because he will not have the opportunity to get a series of elemental values for determining the mean times. Also, he will not be able to observe the operator perform the elements in advance and, consequently, will be obliged to break the setup down into elements while the study is taking place. Of course, setup elements for the most part are long in duration, and the analyst will find that he has a reasonable amount of time to break the job down, record the time, and evaluate the performance as the operator proceeds from one work element to the next.

There are two ways of handling setup times: first, they can be distributed over a specific manufacturing quantity such as 1,000 pieces or 10,000 pieces. This method is satisfactory only when the magnitude of the production order is standard. For example, industries that ship from stock and reorder on a basis of minimum-maximum inventories are able to control their production orders so as to conform to economical lot sizes. In cases like this, the setup time can equitably be prorated over the lot size. Suppose the economical lot size of a given item was 1,000 pieces and reordering was always done on the basis of 1,000 units. In the event the standard setup time in a given operation was 1.50 hours, then the allowed operation time could be increased by .15 hour per 100 pieces in order to take care of the make-ready and put-away elements.

This method would not be at all practical, if the size of the order were not controlled. In a plant that requisitions on a job-order basis, that is, releases production orders specifying quantities in accordance with customer requirements, it would be impossible to standardize on the size of the work orders issued to the factory. Thus, this week an order may be issued for 100 pieces and next month an order for 5,000 units of the same part. In the example cited above, the operator would be allowed but .15 hour to set up his machine for the 100-unit order, which would be inadequate. On an order for 5,000 pieces, he would be given 7.50 hours, which would be considerably too much time.

It is more practical to establish setup standards as separate allowed times. Then, regardless of the quantity of parts to be produced, a fair standard prevails. In some concerns, the setup is performed by a person other than the operator to do the job. The advantages of having separate setup men are quite obvious. Lower-skilled men can be utilized as operators when they do not have to set up their own facilities. Setups are more readily standardized and methods changes can be more easily introduced when the responsibility for setup rests with but one individual. Also, if sufficient facilities are available, continuous production performance can be achieved by having the next work assignment set up while the operator is working on his present job.

If the setup standard were combined with the production standard, it would be quite difficult to evaluate both the performance of the setup man and the operator. Having production and setup standards separate permits incentive operation of both jobs, since true evaluation of the performance of both the operator and the setup man can be made.

Partial Setups

Frequently, it will not be necessary to set up completely a facility to perform a given operation, because some of the tools of the previous operation are required in the job that is being set up. For example, in hand screw machine or turret lathe setups, careful scheduling of similar work to the same machine will allow partial setups from one job to the next. Instead of having to change six tools in the hex turret, it may be necessary to change only two or three.

Since the sequence of work that is scheduled to a given machine seldom remains the same, it is difficult to establish partial setup times to cover all the possible variations. The standard setup for a given No. 4 Warner & Swasey turret lathe might be .80 hour. However, if this setup is performed after job X, it may take only .45 hour, and if it is performed after job Y, it would require .57 hour, while following job Z, .70 hour would be necessitated, and so on. The possible variations in partial setup time are so broad that the only practical way to establish their values is on the basis of standard data (see Chapter 18) for each job in question.

Common practice is to allow the operator full setup time for each job he performs. This is advantageous for several reasons: first, the operators will be considerably more satisfied because of higher earnings, and they will tend to plan their work to the best possible advantage. This will result in more production per unit of time and lower total costs. Also, considerable time and paper work is saved by avoiding the determination of a standard for the partial setup operations and its application in all pertinent cases. In fact, this saving tends to approach the extra amount paid to the operator resulting from the difference in time required to make the complete setup and the partial setup.

Maintenance of Standard Times

Considerable emphasis has been given to the necessity of establishing time standards that are fair. This means both fair to the worker and fair to the management. Once fair standards have been introduced, it is equally important that they be maintained.

The standard time is directly dependent upon the method used during the course of the time study. Method, in the broad sense, refers not only to the tools and facilities being used, but also to such details as operator motion pattern, work station layout, material conditions, and working conditions. Since method controls the time standard, it is essential, if equitable standards are to be maintained, that method changes and alterations be controlled. If method changes are not controlled, it will only be a short time until inequities develop in standards established and much of the work spent on development of consistent time standards will be undone.

Just as the financial records of a company are periodically subject to audit, so should all established time standards be checked at regular intervals to see if they are in line according to the method being used. The audit of time standards principally involves the investigation of the method currently being used by the operator. Frequently, minor changes will have been made by the operator, the foreman, or even the methods department, and no record of this change will have been given to the time study analyst. It is not uncommon for workers to conceal method changes for which they are responsible, so that they can increase their earnings or diminish their effort while achieving the same production. Of course, changes in method may develop which will increase the amount of time required to perform the task. These changes may be initiated by the foreman or inspector and may be of insufficient consequence, in his opinion, to adjust the standard.

As has been pointed out throughout this text, it is important that the operation being time-studied be analyzed for possible method improvements prior to the establishment of the standard. Operation analysis, work simplification, motion study, and standardization of the method and conditions always precede work measurement. A standard does not get out of line if the method that was time-studied is maintained by the operator. If methods study has developed the ideal method, and if this method is standardized and followed by the operator, then there is less need for maintenance of time standards.

Frequently, however, method changes will be introduced—both favorable and unfavorable. If these changes are extensive, they will be brought to the attention of management. Tight standards will be brought to management's attention by the operator. Standards that become very loose will be brought to management's attention through the payroll department where excessive earnings on the part of a given workman will be reported. However, it is the minor accruing method changes that frequently take place unnoticed and weaken the entire standard structure. In order to maintain standards properly, the time study department should periodically verify the method being used with the method that was studied when the standard was taken. This can readily be done by referring to the original time study where a complete description of the method employed was recorded. If this investigation reveals that the method has been changed adversely, then the reasons for the change should be investigated so that the better method can be employed. If the method has been improved, then the investigation should determine who was responsible for the innovation. If the operator developed the improvement, he should be justly rewarded through a "suggestion plan" or other means. Regardless of where the methods change came from, those elements affected should be restudied and the current standard introduced.

So as to first verify standards that may be out of line, the time study department will enlist the co-operation of the foreman. The foreman, being close to the operators coming under his jurisdiction, will at an early stage be aware of standards that may be either loose or tight. He will be able to advise the time study analyst as to the sequence in the audit of existing standards.

Conclusion

It is common practice to issue standards for setup operations independent of "piece" standards and to specify the allowed time in decimal hours or decimal minutes. Piece standards are expressed in hours per hundred pieces for ease in payroll computation, scheduling, and control. On extremely short-cycle operations, such as punch press work, die-casting, or forging, it may be more desirable to express standards in terms of hours per thousand pieces, since during the course of an eight-hour shift, several thousand pieces can be produced.

Work should be scheduled when feasible to take advantage of partial setups in order to improve delivery dates, decrease total cost, and allow greater remuneration for the operator. Where short setup times prevail and where an extensive variety of small-volume orders are handled daily, no attempt should be made to evaluate partial setup times, but credit for full setup should be given the operators. Where setup times are relatively long, such as setting up a six-spindle automatic screw machine, and where production runs are substantial, then consideration should be given for evaluation of partial setup times. Credit for this time should be given to the operator rather than credit for the complete setup time.

Time standards must be maintained in order to assure a satisfactory rate structure. This calls for a continuing analysis of methods. All standards should be periodically checked to verify that methods being employed are identical with those that were in use at the time the standard was established.

TEXT QUESTIONS

1. Define the term "standard time."
2. How is the conversion factor determined?
3. Why is it usually more convenient to express standards in terms of time per hundred pieces than time per piece?

4. For what reason are temporary standards established?

5. Express the standard of 5.761 minutes in terms of hours per hundred pieces. What would be the operator efficiency if 92 pieces were completed during a working day? What would be his efficiency if he set up his machine (standard for setup = .45 hours) and produced 80 pieces during the 8-hour workday?

6. What elements of work are included in the setup standard?

7. What is the preferred method of handling setup time standards?

8. How is the operator compensated on partial setups on hand screw machines?

9. Determine the conversion factor and the allowed time for a job whose average time was 5.24 minutes and carried a performance factor of 1.15 and an allowance of 12 per cent.

10. Explain why it is necessary that time standards be properly maintained.

GENERAL QUESTIONS

1. For what reasons might it be advantageous to express allowed times in minutes per piece?

2. How can excessive use of temporary standards cause poor labor relations?

3. How does a company effectively maintain standards and avoid the reputation of being a "rate-cutter"?

CHAPTER 18

Standard Data

STANDARD TIME DATA FOR THE most part are elemental time standards taken from time studies that have been proved to be satisfactory. These elemental standards are classified and filed so that they can readily be abstracted when needed. Just as the housewife refers to her cook book to determine how many minutes to cream butter and sugar, how long to beat the mixture, and thus how much time is required to bake the cake, so can the analyst refer to standard data and determine how long it should take the normal operator to pick up a small casting and place it in a jig, close the jig and lock the part with a quick-acting clamp, advance the spindle of the drill press, and perform the remainder of the elements required to produce the part.

The application of standard time data is fundamentally an extension of the same kind of process as that used to arrive at allowed times through the medium of stop-watch time study. The principle of standard data application certainly is not new; many years ago Frederick W. Taylor proposed that each established elemental time be properly indexed so that it could easily be found and used in the establishment of time standards for future work. When we speak of standard data today, we refer to all the tabulated elemental standards, curves, alignment charts, and tables that are compiled to allow the measurement of a specific job without the necessity of a timing device, such as the stop watch. Basic motion times, as discussed in Chapter 10 of this text, are nothing more than a refined form of standard data. Upon completion of this chapter, the reader is urged to reread Chapter 10.

Work standards calculated from standard data will be relatively consistent in that the tabulated elements comprising the data are a result of many proven stop-watch time studies. Since the values are tabulated and

321

it is only necessary to accumulate the required elements in establishing a standard, the various time study men within a given company will arrive at identical standards of performance for a given method. Therefore, consistency is assured for standards established by the different analysts within a plant as well as for the various standards computed by a given time study observer.

Standards on new work can usually be computed more rapidly through standard data than by means of stop-watch time study. The rapidity with which standards are established by means of standard data allows the establishment of standards on indirect labor operations which frequently is impractical if done by stop-watch methods. The use of standard data permits establishment of time standards over a wide range of work. Table XX illustrates the coverage that is possible when standard data elements are determined.

TABLE XX

Operation	Number of Time Studies Taken for Development of Standard Data	Number of Standards Set in One Year from Standard Data Developed	Per Cent of Standards Set That Would Be Covered by Stop-Watch Studies.
Coremaking............	60	7,500	0.8
Snag grinding...........	40	656	6.1
Visual inspection........	53	422	12.6
Turret lathe operation...	100	600	16.7

Source: Phil Carroll, Jr., "Notes on Standard Elemental Data," *Modern Machine Shop*, April, 1950, p. 176.

Development of Standard Time Data

In the development of standard time data, it is necessary to distinguish constant elements from variable elements. A constant element is one for which the allowed time will remain approximately the same for any part within a specific range. A variable element is one for which the allowed time will vary within a specified range of work. Thus, the element "start machine" would be a constant and the element "drill $\frac{3}{8}$-inch diameter hole" would vary with the depth of the hole and the feed and speed of the drill press.

As standard data is developed, it should be indexed and filed. Setup elements should be kept separate from those elements incorporated in the each-piece time, and constant elements should of course be kept separate from the variable elements. Typical standard data would be tabulated as follows:

1. Machine or operation
    A. Setup
        1. Constants
        2. Variables
    B. Each piece
        1. Constants
        2. Variables

DIE-CASTING MACHINE

MACH. NO.

PART NO.——& TYPE————————OPERATOR————————————DATE————
        NO. OF PARTS   METHOD OF PLACING   TOTAL WT. OF FLSH,
OF————IN TOTE PAN————PARTS IN TOTE PAN————PARTS, GATE & SPRUE————
        NO. OF PARTS   LIQUID METAL————
————PER SHOT————PLASTIC METAL————CHILL————SKIM————DRAIN————
CAPACITY IN LBS.   DESCRIBE
HOLDING POT————————GREASING————————————————————————————

DESCRIBE
LOOSENING OF PART————————————————————————————————————

DESCRIBE
LOCATION——

ELEMENTS	TIME	END POINTS
Get metal in holding pot	_____	All waiting time while metal is being poured in pot.
Chill metal	_____	From time operator starts adding cold metal to liquid metal pot until operator stops adding cold metal to liquid metal in pot.
Skim metal	_____	From time operator starts skimming until all scum has been removed.
Get ladleful of metal	_____	From time ladle starts to dip down into metal until ladleful of metal reaches edge of mach. or until ladle starts to tip for draining.
Drain metal	_____	From time ladle starts to tip for draining until ladleful reaches edge of machine.
Pour ladle of metal in machine	_____	From time ladleful of metal reaches edge of mach. until foot starts to trip press.
Trip press	_____	From time foot starts moving toward pedal until press starts downward.
Press time	_____	Complete turnover of press.
Hold plunger down	_____	From time plunger stops downward motion until plunger starts moving upward.
Press button and raise slug	_____	From time plunger stops moving until slug is raised out of cavity.
Remove slug drop slug lift	_____	From time slug is raised out of cavity until slug is pushed into tote pan or pot.
Trip pedal to open dies	_____	From time foot starts moving to pedal until dies start to open.
Wait for dies to open	_____	From time dies start to open until die stops moving.
Remove part from die	_____	From time die stops moving until part is free of die cavity.
Place part in tote pan	_____	From time part is free of die cavity until part is placed in tote pan.

FIG. 18–1.

Standard data are compiled from the different elements that have occurred on the time studies that have been taken on a given process over a period of time. Only those studies that have proven to be valid through use are employed. The analyst should be careful in the tabulation of standard data to define clearly end points. Otherwise, there may be an overlapping of time in the recorded data. For example, in the element "out stock to stop" done on a bar feed No. 3 Warner & Swasey turret lathe, the element could include reaching for the feed lever, grasping the lever, feeding of the bar stock through the collet to a stock stop located in the hex turret, closing the collet, and reaching for the turret handle. Then, again, this element may involve only the feeding of bar stock through the collet to a stock stop. Since standard data elements are compiled from a great number of studies taken by different time study men, care must be exercised in defining limits or end points of each element. Figure 18–1 illustrates a form used to summarize data taken from an individual time study for the purpose of developing standard data on die-casting machines.

In order to fill a specific need in a standard data tabulation, the analyst may resort to work measurement of the particular element in question. This is handled quite accurately by using the "fast" watch (see Chapter 13) which records elapsed times in .001 of a minute. In this type of analysis, the snapback method is used in recording the elapsed elemental time, as usually we are interested in determining allowed time for only a few of the elements comprising the study. Upon completion of the observations, the elemental elapsed times are summarized and the mean determined, as in the case of a typical time study. The average values are then performance rated and an allowance is added so as to arrive at true allowed times.

Sometimes, because of the brevity of individual elements, it is impossible to measure their duration separately. It is possible to determine their individual values by timing groups collectively and using simultaneous equations to solve for the individual elements.

For example, element a might be "pick up small casting," element b might be "place in leaf jig," c might be "close cover of jig," d would be "position jig," e "advance spindle," and so on. These elements could be timed in groups as follows:

1. $a + b + c$ equals Element No. 1 equals .070 min. $= A$
2. $b + c + d$ equals Element No. 3 equals .067 min. $= B$
3. $c + d + e$ equals Element No. 5 equals .073 min. $= C$
4. $d + e + a$ equals Element No. 2 equals .061 min. $= D$
5. $e + a + b$ equals Element No. 4 equals .068 min. $= E$

By adding these five equations:

$$3a + 3b + 3c + 3d + 3e = A + B + C + D + E .$$

Then let

$$A + B + C + D + E = T$$
$$3a + 3b + 3c + 3d + 3e = T = .339 \text{ min.}$$

and

$$a + b + c + d + e = \frac{.339}{3} = .113 \text{ min.}$$

therefore:

$$A + d + e = .113 \text{ min.}$$

and then:

$$d + e = .113 \text{ min.} - .07 \text{ min.} = .043 \text{ min.}$$

since

$$c + d + e = .073 \text{ min.}$$
$$c = .073 \text{ min.} - .043 = .03 \text{ min.}$$

Likewise:

$$d + e + a = .061$$

and

$$a = .061 - .043 = .018 \text{ min.}$$

Substituting in equation 1

$$b = .070 - (.03 + .018) = .022$$

Substituting in equation 2

$$d = .067 - (.022 + .03) = .015 \text{ min.}$$

Substituting in equation 3

$$e = .073 - (.015 + .03) = .028 \text{ min.}$$

In the determination of standard data elements by using simultaneous equations, extreme care must be exercised to be consistent when reading the watch at the terminal points of the established elements. Inconsistency in establishing terminal points will result in erroneous standard data elements.

Calculation of Cutting Times

Through knowledge of feeds and speeds for different types of material, it is a relatively easy matter for the analyst to calculate and tabulate the cutting times for different machining operations. Table XXI tabularizes recommended speeds and feeds for high-speed drills used on various kinds of material. This type of information is available in the various technical handbooks and can readily be obtained from the cutting tool manufacturers.

TABLE XXI

A. RECOMMENDED DRILLING SPEEDS FOR VARIOUS MATERIALS
WITH HIGH-SPEED STEEL DRILLS

Material	Recommended Speed Surface Feet per Minute
Aluminum and its alloys	200–300
Bakelite	100–150
Brass and bronze, soft	200–300
Bronze, high tensile	70–100
Cast iron, soft	100–150
Cast iron, hard	70–100
Magnesium and its alloys	250–400
Malleable iron	80–90
Nickel and monel metal	40–60
Slate, marble, and stone	15–25
Steel, forgings	50–60
Steel, manganese (15% Mn)	15–25
Steel, soft	80–110
Steel, stainless	30–40
Steel, tool	50–60
Wrought iron	50–60
Wood	300–400

NOTE: Carbon Steel Drills should be run at speeds approximately 40% to 50% of those recommended for High Speed Steel.

B. RECOMMENDED FEEDS FOR VARIOUS DIAMETER DRILLS

Diameter of Drill—Inches	Feed Inches per Revolution
Under 1/8	.001 to .002
1/8 to 1/4	.002 to .004
1/4 to 1/2	.004 to .007
1/2 to 1	.007 to .015
1 in. and over	.015 to .025

NOTE: It is best to start with a moderate speed and feed, increasing either one, or both, after observing the action and condition of the drill.
Source: National Twist Drill & Tool Co.

Drill Press Work

A drill, according to the *Tool Engineers Handbook*, is "a fluted end-cutting tool used to originate or enlarge a hole in solid material." In drilling operations on a flat surface, the axis of drill is at 90 degrees to the surface being drilled. When a hole is drilled completely through a part, the lead of the drill must be added to the length of the hole in order to determine the entire distance the drill must travel to make the hole. When a blind hole is drilled, the analyst does not add the lead of the drill to the hole depth, as the distance from the surface being drilled to the furthest penetration of the drill is the distance the drill must travel to make the required depth of hole (see Figure 18–2).

Since the commercial standard for the included angle of drill points is 118 degrees, the lead of the drill may readily be found through the expression:

$$l = \frac{r}{\tan A}$$

where

l = lead of drill
r = radius of drill
$\tan A$ = tangent of ½ the included angle of the drill .

To illustrate, let us calculate the lead of a general purpose drill 1 inch in diameter:

$$l = \frac{.5}{\tan 59°}$$

$$l = \frac{.5}{1.6643}$$

$$l = .3 \text{ inches lead}$$

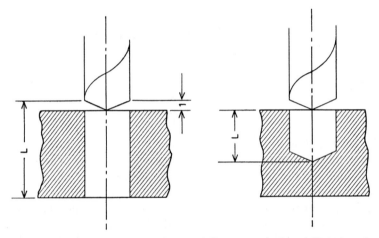

FIG. 18–2. Distance L indicates distance drill must travel when drilling through (illustration at left) and when drilling blind holes (illustration at right). Lead of drill is shown by distance 1.

Once the total length that the drill must move has been determined, then the feed of the drill in inches per minute is divided into this distance in order to determine the drill cutting time in minutes.

Drill speed is usually expressed in terms of feet per minute, and feed is expressed in thousandths of an inch per revolution. To change the feed into inches per minute when the feed per revolution and the speed in feet per minute are known, substitute in the equation:

$$F_m = \frac{3.82 \, (f)(S_f)}{d}$$

where

F_m = feed in inches per minute
f = feed in inches per revolution
S_f = surface feet per minute
d = diameter of drill in inches .

For example, to determine the feed in inches per minute of a 1-inch diameter drill running at a surface speed of 100 feet per minute and a feed of .013 inch per revolution, we should figure

$$F_m = \frac{(3.82)(.013)(100)}{1} = 4.97 \text{ inches per minute}.$$

If we wished to determine how long it would take for this 1-inch drill running at the above-mentioned speed and feed to drill through 2 inches of a malleable iron casting, we should substitute in the equation:

$$T = \frac{L}{F_m}$$

where

T = cutting time in minutes
L = total length drill must move
F_m = feed in inches per minute

and we should have

$$T = \frac{2 \text{ (thickness of casting)} + .3 \text{ (lead of drill)}}{4.97}$$
$$= .464 \text{ minutes cutting time}.$$

The cutting time so calculated does not include any allowance, which of course must be added to determine the allowed time. The allowance will include time for variations in material thickness and tolerance in the setting of stops, both of which affect the cycle cutting time to some extent. Also personal and unavoidable delay allowance must be added in order to arrive at an equitable allowed elemental time.

It must be remembered that all speeds are not available on the machine being used. For example the recommended spindle speed for a given job might be 1,550 R.P.M.; however, the fastest speed that the machine is capable of running may be 1,200 R.P.M. In this case 1,200 R.P.M. would be used and would be the basis of computing allowed times.

Lathe Work

There are many variations of machine tools that can be classified in the lathe group. These would include the engine lathe, turret lathe, automatic lathe (automatic screw machine), and others. In all of these cases, the machine is used primarily with stationary tools or tools that translate over the surface to remove material from the revolving work, which may be in the form of forgings, castings, or bar stock. In some cases, the tool is revolved while the work is held stationary as on certain stations of automatic screw machine work. Thus, a slot in a machine screw head can be machined on the automatic screw machine in the slotting attachment.

Speeds and feeds are altered by many factors, such as condition and design of the machine tool, type of material being cut, condition and design of the cutting tool, coolant used for cutting, method of holding the work, and the method of mounting the cutting tool. Table XXII outlines the approximate cuts, feeds, and speeds for certain metallic and non-metallic turning.

As in drill press work, feeds are usually expressed in terms of thousandths of an inch per revolution and speeds in terms of surface feet per minute.

In order to determine the cutting time for L inches of cut, it is merely necessary to divide the length of cut in inches by the feed in inches per minute or expressed algebraically:

$$T = \frac{L}{F_m}$$

where

$$T = \text{cutting time in minutes}$$
$$L = \text{total length of cut}$$
$$F_m = \text{feed in inches per minute}$$

and

$$F_m = \frac{3.82 \ (S_f)(f)}{d}$$

where

$$f = \text{feed in inches per revolution}$$
$$S_f = \text{speed in surface feet per minute}$$
$$d = \text{diameter of work in inches}.$$

Milling Machine Work

Milling refers to the removal of material with a rotating multiple-toothed cutter. While the cutter rotates, the work is fed past the cutter; thus, the milling machine differs from the drill press where the work usually is stationary. In addition to machining plane and irregular surfaces, the milling machine is adapted for cutting threads, slotting, and cutting gears.

In milling work, as in drill press and lathe work, the speed of the cutter is expressed in surface feet per minute. Feeds or table travel are usually represented in terms of thousandths of inch per tooth.

In order to determine the cutter speed in revolutions per minute from surface feet per minute and the diameter of the cutter, the following expression may be used:

$$N_r = \frac{3.82 \ S_f}{d}$$

where

TABLE XXII
APPROXIMATE CUTS, FEEDS, AND SPEEDS FOR METAL AND NONMETALLIC TURNING*
(Basic engine lathe practice. Tabular values are in fpm)

Class	Material, SAE No.	Cutting tool material	Cut, 0.005 to 0.015; feed, 0.002 to 0.005	Cut, 0.015 to 0.094; feed, 0.005 to 0.015	Cut, 0.094 to 0.187; feed, 0.015 to 0.030	Cut, 0.187 to 0.375; feed, 0.030 to 0.050	Cut, 0.375 to 0.750; feed, 0.030 to 0.090
Free-cutting steels	1112, X-1112 1120 1315, etc.	18-4-1 HSS Cast alloys Sintered carbides	 750-1,500	250- 350 425- 550 600- 750	175-250 315-400 450-600	80-150 215-300 350-450	55- 75 100-210 175-350
Carbon and low-alloy steels	1010 1025	18-4-1 HSS Cast alloys Sintered carbides	 700-1,200	225- 300 375- 500 550- 700	150-200 275-350 400-550	75-125 180-250 300-400	45- 65 100-175 150-300
Medium-alloy steels	1030 1050	18-4-1 HSS Cast alloys Sintered carbides	 600-1,100	200- 275 325- 400 450- 600	125-175 230-300 350-450	70-120 160-225 200-350	40- 60 80-150 125-250
High-alloy steels	1060 1095 1350	18-4-1 HSS Cast alloys Sintered carbides	.... 500- 750	175- 250 250- 350 400- 500	125-175 200-250 300-400	65-100 150-200 200-300	35- 55 65-150 100-300
Nickel steels	2330 2350	18-4-1 HSS Cast alloys Sintered carbides	.... 550- 800	200- 275 300- 375 425- 550	130-180 225-300 325-425	70-110 145-200 225-325	45- 60 85-140 125-225
Chromium nickel-chrome steels	3120, 3450 5140, 52100	18-4-1 HSS Cast alloys Sintered carbides	.... 425- 550	150- 200 230- 315 325- 425	100-125 165-225 250-325	50- 75 110-130 175-250	30- 50 55-110 75-175
Molybdenum steels	4130 4615	18-4-1 HSS Cast alloys Sintered carbides	.... 475- 650	160- 210 250- 325 350- 475	110-140 160-225 275-350	60- 80 120-150 200-275	35- 55 65-100 100-200
Chrome, vanadium, and stainless steels	6120 6150 18 Cr-8Ni 6195	18-4-1 HSS Cast alloys Sintered carbides	.... 375- 500	100- 150 210- 250 300- 375	80-100 170-200 250-300	50- 75 110-165 175-250	30- 50 55-100 75-175
Tungsten steels	7260, 18-4-1 annealed	18-4-1 Cast alloys Sintered carbides	.... 325- 400	120- 150 130- 175 250- 325	75-120 110-130 200-250	40- 75 80-100 150-200	25- 40 35- 80 50-150
Special steels	12-14% Mn	18-4-1 HSS Cast alloys Sintered carbides	200- 250	125- 200	75-125	50- 75	
	Si elect. sheet ingot iron, etc.	18-4-1 HSS Cast alloys Sintered carbides	400- 500 1,000-1,200	300- 400 500- 600 800-1,000	200-300 350-450 600-800	150-200 250-300 500-600	

Source: Firth Sterling, Inc., Pittsburgh, Pa., and *Tool Engineers Handbook* (New York: McGraw-Hill Book Co., Inc.).

TABLE XXII *(Continued)*

APPROXIMATE CUTS, FEEDS, AND SPEEDS FOR METAL AND NONMETALLIC TURNING.*—*(Continued)*

Class	Material, SAE No.	Cutting tool material	Cut, 0.005 to 0.015; feed, 0.002 to 0.005	Cut, 0.015 to 0.094; feed, 0.005 to 0.015	Cut, 0.094 to 0.187; feed, 0.015 to 0.030	Cut, 0.187 to 0.375; feed, 0.030 to 0.050	Cut, 0.375 to 0.750; feed, 0.030 to 0.090
Cast iron	Soft Gray	18-4-1 HSS		120- 150	90-120	75- 90	35- 75
		Cast alloys		225- 300	160-220	125-160	70-125
		Sintered carbides	450- 600	350- 450	250-350	200-250	100-200
	Medium and malleable	18-4-1 HSS		120- 150	90-120	60- 90	30- 60
		Cast alloys		190- 225	150-190	120-150	60-120
		Sintered carbides	350- 450	250- 350	200-250	150-200	75-150
	Hard alloy	18-4-1 HSS		90- 125	60- 90	40- 60	20- 40
		Cast alloys		120- 170	80-120	55- 80	35- 55
		Sintered carbides	250- 300	150- 250	100-150	75-100	50- 75
	Chilled	18-4-1 HSS		10- 30			
		Cast alloys	10- 15				
		Sintered carbides	30- 50				
Copper-base alloys	Leaded, free-cutting, soft brass, and bronze	18-4-1 HSS		300- 400	225-300	150-255	100-150
		Cast alloys		500- 600	400-500	325-400	200-325
		Sintered carbides	1,000-1,250	800-1,000	650-800	500-650	300-500
	Normal brass, bronze low alloy	18-4-1 HSS		275- 375	225-275	150-225	75-150
		Cast alloys		375- 600	325-375	250-325	175-250
		Sintered carbides	700- 800	600- 700	500-600	400-500	200-400
	Tough copper, high tin, manganese, and aluminum bronzes, gilding metal	18-4-1 HSS		100- 150	75-100	50- 75	35- 50
		Cast alloys		225- 300	180-225	125-180	75-125
		Sintered carbides	500- 600	400- 500	300-400	200-300	100-200
Light alloys	Magnesium	18-4-1 HSS	500- 750	350- 500	275-350	200-275	125-200
		Cast alloys	700-1,000	500- 700	400-500	300-400	200-300
		Sintered carbides	1,250-2,000	800-1,250	600-800	500-600	300-500
	Aluminum	18-4-1 HSS	350- 500	225- 350	150-225	100-150	50-100
		Cast alloys	450- 650	300- 450	225-300	150-225	75-150
		Sintered carbides	700-1,000	450- 700	300-450	200-300	100-200
Plastics	Thermoplastic, thermosetting	18-4-1 HSS					
		Cast alloys	650-1,000	400- 650	250-400	150-250	
		Sintered carbides					
Abrasives	Glass, hard rubber, green ceramics, marble, slate	18-4-1 HSS					
		Cast alloys	150- 250	75- 150			
		Sintered carbides					

N_r = cutter speed in revolutions per minute
S_f = cutter speed in feet per minute
d = outside diameter of cutter in inches .

To determine the feed of the work in inches per minute into the cutter, use the expression

$$F_m = fn_tN_r$$

where

F_m = feed of the work in inches per minute into the cutter
f = feed in inches per tooth of cutter
n_t = number of cutter teeth
N_r = cutter speed in revolutions per minute .

The number of cutter teeth suitable for a particular application may be expressed as:

$$n_t = \frac{F_m}{F_t \times N_r}$$

where

$$F_t = \text{chip thickness} .$$

Table XXIII gives suggested feeds and speeds for milling under average conditions.

In computing cutting time on milling operations, the analyst must take into consideration the lead of the milling cutter when determining the total length of cut under power feed. This can be determined by triangulation as illustrated in the example of slab-milling a pad shown in Figure 18–3.

In this case, the lead BC must be added to the length of the work (8 inches) in order to arrive at the total length that must be fed past the cutter. Clearance for removal of the work after the machining cut will, of course, be handled as a separate element because greater feed under rapid table traverse will be used. By knowing the diameter of the cutter, the analyst determines AC as being the cutter radius, and calculates the height of the right triangle ABC by subtracting the depth of cut BE from the cutter radius AE:

$$BC = \sqrt{AC^2 - AB^2} .$$

Let us assume, in the example above, that the cutter diameter is 4 inches, and that it has 22 teeth. The feed per tooth is .008 inch and cutting speed is 60 feet per minute. The cutting time is computed by using the equation

$$T = \frac{L}{F_m}$$

where

T = cutting time in minutes
L = total length of cut under power feed
F_m = feed in inches per minute

then L would be equal to 8 inches + BC and

TABLE XXIII

FEEDS AND SPEEDS FOR MILLING
(Average Conditions)

			\(\frac{1}{4}\)	\(\frac{1}{2}\)	\(\frac{3}{4}\)	1	1\(\frac{1}{4}\)	1\(\frac{1}{2}\)	2	2\(\frac{1}{2}\)	3	4	5	6	7	8	10	12
			width of cut															

WIDTH OF CUT IN INCHES

DEPTH OF CUT IN INCHES			¼	½	¾	1	1¼	1½	2	2½	3	4	5	6	7	8	10	12
	¼	Feed	4.5	4.5	4	4	4	3.5	3.5	3.5	3	3	3	2.5	2.5	2.5	2.25	2.25
		Speed	110	110	105	105	100	100	100	95	95	95	90	90	90	85	85	85
	½	Feed	4.5	4	4	4	3.5	3.5	3.5	3	3	3	2.5	2.5	2.25	2.25	2	2
		Speed	105	105	100	100	95	95	95	90	90	90	85	85	85	80	80	80
	¾	Feed	4	4	3.5	3.5	3.5	3	3	3	2.5	2.5	2.25	2.25	2	2	1.75	1.75
		Speed	100	100	95	95	90	90	90	85	85	85	80	80	80	75	75	75
	1	Feed	4	3.5	3.5	3.5	3	3	3	2.5	2.5	2.25	2.25	2	2	1.75	1.5	
		Speed	95	95	90	90	85	85	85	80	80	80	75	75	75	70	70	
	1¼	Feed	3.5	3.5	3.5	3	3	3	2.5	2.5	2.25	2	1.75	1.5	1.5	1.25		
		Speed	90	90	85	85	80	80	80	75	75	75	70	70	70	65		
	1½	Feed	3.5	3.5	3	3	3	2.5	2.5	2.25	2	1.75	1.5	1.25	1			
		Speed	85	85	80	80	75	75	75	70	70	70	65	65	65			
	2	Feed	3.5	3	3	3	2.5	2.5	2.25	2	1.75	1.5	1.25	1				
		Speed	80	80	75	75	70	70	70	65	65	65	60	60				
	2½	Feed	3	3	2.5	2.5	2.25	2	1.75	1.5	1.25	1						
		Speed	80	75	75	70	70	65	65	65	60	60						
	3	Feed	2.5	2.5	2.25	2	1.75	1.5	1.25	1								
		Speed	75	75	70	70	65	65	60	60								
	4	Feed	2.5	2	1.75	1.5	1.25	1										
		Speed	75	70	70	65	65	60										
	5	Feed	2	1.5	1.25	1												
		Speed	70	70	65	65												
	6	Feed	1.75	1.5	1													
		Speed	70	65	65													

Correction Factors

S.A.E. 1020	= 1.00
S.A.E.1035—Annld.	= .80
Tool Steel—Annld.	= .60
Alloy Steels:	
Free Machining	= .80
Medium	= .65
Tough	= .50
Cast Steel	= .40
Cast Irons:	
Hard	= .70
Medium	= .95
Soft	= 1.20
Malleable Iron	= .80
Brass and Bronze:	
Free Machining	= 2.50
Medium	= 1.60
Hard	= .80
Monel Metal	= .70
Magnesium Alloys	= 3.00
Aluminum	= 2.00

Feeds are given in Inches per Minute.
Speeds are given in Surface Feet per Minute.

To obtain the proper Feed and Speed for a given material, multiply both Feed and Speed figures given in table by the correction factor for that material.

Source: National Twist Drill & Tool Co.

$$BC = \sqrt{4 - 3.06} = .975$$

therefore:

$$L = 8.975$$
$$F_m = f n_t N_r$$
$$F_m = (.008)(22)N_r$$

or

$$N_r = \frac{3.82S_f}{d} = \frac{(3.82)(60)}{4} = 57.3 \text{ revolutions per minute}$$

then

$$F_m = (.008)(22)(57.3) = 10.1 \text{ inches per minutes}$$

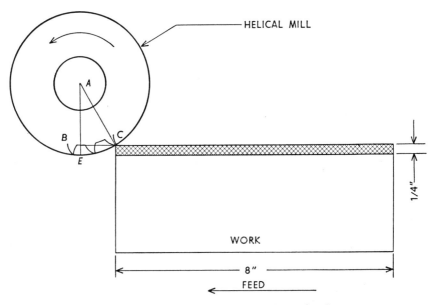

FIG. 18–3. Slab-milling a casting 8 inches in length.

and

$$T = \frac{8.975}{10.1} = .888 \text{ minutes cutting time}.$$

Through a knowledge of feeds and speeds, the time study analyst can determine the required cutting or processing time for various types of work that will be performed in his plant. The illustrations cited in drill press, lathe, and milling work are representative of the techniques used in establishing raw cutting times. To these values must be added the necessary applicable allowances so that true elemental allowed values can be determined.

Determining Horsepower Requirements

When developing standard data times for machine elements, it is advisable to tabulate horsepower requirements for the various materials in relationship to depths of cut, cutting speeds, and feeds. The analyst will frequently use standard data for the planning of new work. So that he does not overload existing equipment, it is important that he have information as to the work load being assigned to each machine for the conditions under which the material is being removed. For example, in the machining of high alloy steel forgings on a lathe capable of a developed horsepower of 10, it would not be feasible to take a ⅜-inch depth of cut while operating at a feed of .011 inch per revolution and a speed of 200 surface feet per minute. Table XXIV indicates a horse-

TABLE XXIV

HORSEPOWER REQUIREMENTS FOR TURNING HIGH-ALLOY STEEL FORGINGS FOR ⅜″ AND ½″ DEPTH OF CUTS OF VARYING SPEEDS AND FEEDS

SURFACE FEET	⅜″ DEPTH CUT						½″ DEPTH CUT					
	Feeds, In./Rev.						Feeds, In./Rev.					
	.009	.011	.015	.018	.020	.022	.009	.011	.015	.018	.020	.022
150.........	6.5	8.0	10.9	13.0	14.5	16.0	8.7	10.6	14.5	17.3	19.3	21.3
175.........	8.0	9.3	12.7	15.2	16.9	18.6	10.1	12.4	16.9	20.2	22.5	24.8
200.........	8.7	10.6	14.5	17.4	19.3	21.3	11.6	14.1	19.3	23.1	25.7	28.4
225.........	9.8	11.9	16.3	19.6	21.7	23.9	13.0	15.9	21.7	26.1	28.9	31.8
250.........	10.9	13.2	18.1	21.8	24.1	26.6	14.5	17.7	24.1	29.0	32.1	35.4
275.........	12.0	14.6	19.9	23.9	26.5	29.3	15.9	19.4	26.5	31.8	35.3	39.0
300.........	13.0	16.0	21.8	26.1	29.0	31.9	17.4	21.2	29.0	34.7	38.6	42.5
400.........	17.4	21.4	29.1	34.8	38.7	42.5	23.2	28.2	38.7	46.3	51.5	56.7

power requirement of 10.6 for these conditions. Consequently, the work would need to be planned for a feed of .009 inch at a speed of 200 surface feet, since in this case the required horsepower would be but 8.7. (See Table XXIV for horsepower requirements.)

Plotting Curves

Because of space limitations, it is not always convenient to tabularize values for variable elements. By plotting a curve or system of curves in the form of an alignment chart, the analyst can express considerable standard data graphically on one page. There are, however, some distinct disadvantages to using curves. First, it is easy to introduce an error in reading from the curve because of a certain amount of interpolation that is usually required. Then, there is always the chance of outright error through incorrect reading or misalignment of intersections on the various scales.

When we refer to the plotting of curves to show the relationship between time and those variables that affect time, our solution may take the form of a single straight line, a curved line, a system of straight lines as in the ray chart, or a special arrangement of lines characteristic of an alignment chart or nomogram. In the plotting of simple, one-line curves, the analyst should observe certain standard procedures. First, it is standard practice to plot time on the ordinate axis of the charting paper and the independent variable on the abscissa. If practical, all scales should begin at zero so that their true proportions can be seen. Lastly, the scale selected for the independent variable should have a sufficient

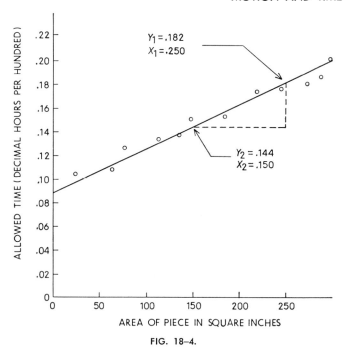

FIG. 18–4.

range to utilize fully the paper on which the curve is being plotted. Figure 18–4 illustrates a chart expressing "forming" time in hours per hundred pieces for a certain gage of stock over a range of sizes expressed in square inches.

Each point in this chart represents a separate time study. Thus, 12 time studies were used in compiling data for this curve. Inspection of the plotted points revealed a straight-line relationship between the various studies. The equation for a straight line is:

$$Y = mx + b$$

(Equation of straight-line frequently expressed as: $Y = a + bx$)
where

Y = ordinate (hours per hundred pieces)
x = abscissa (area of piece in square inches)
m = slope of the straight line, or the proportional change of time on Y axis for each unit change on the X axis
b = intercept of the straight line with the Y axis when $x = 0$.

The curve drawn by inspection shows an intercept value of .088 on the Y (ordinate) axis and the slope can be calculated by the equation:

$$m = \frac{y_1 - y_2}{x_1 - x_2} \text{ where } x_1 y_1 \text{ and } x_2 y_2 \text{ are specific points on the curve}$$

$$= \frac{.182 - .144}{250 - 150} = .00038 .$$

The Least Squares Method

It is also possible to solve for m and b using the method of least squares. In this technique, the resulting slope and y axis intercept will give a straight line whose sum of squares of vertical deviations of observations from this line is smaller than the corresponding sum of squares of deviations from any other line. The two equations that are solved simultaneously are:[1]

$$\text{Equation 1: } \Sigma y = Nb + m\Sigma x$$
$$\text{Equation 2: } \Sigma xy = b\Sigma x + m\Sigma x^2 .$$

The derivations of these equations are available in most mathematical texts.

In the example cited, we can solve for m and b using the least squares method as follows:

Study	x or Area	y or Time	xy	x^2
1...............	25	.104	2.60	625
2...............	65	.109	7.09	4,225
3...............	77	.126	9.70	5,929
4...............	112	.134	15.01	12,544
5...............	135	.138	18.63	18,225
6...............	147	.150	22.05	21,609
7...............	185	.153	28.31	34,225
8...............	220	.174	38.28	48,400
9...............	245	.176	43.12	60,025
10...............	275	.182	50.05	75,625
11...............	287	.186	53.38	82,369
12...............	300	.202	60.60	90,000
	2073	1.834	348.82	453,801

Substituting in Equation 1 and 2:

$$\text{Equation 1: } 12b = 1.834 - 2073m$$
$$\text{Equation 2: } 2{,}073b = 348.82 - 453{,}801m$$

multiplying equation 1 by 2,073 and equation 2 by 12:

$$24{,}876b = 3{,}801.882 - 4{,}297{,}329m$$
$$24{,}876b = 4{,}185.840 - 5{,}445{,}612m$$
$$0 = -383.958 + 1{,}148{,}283m$$

or

$$m = \frac{383.958}{1{,}148{,}283} = .000334$$

and substituting in equation 1:

$$12b = 1.834 - .692$$
$$b = \frac{1.142}{12} = .095 .$$

---

[1] These equations are frequently expressed: $\Sigma y = na + b\Sigma x$ and $\Sigma xy = a\Sigma x + b\Sigma x^2$.

Solving by Regression Line Equations

As shown, the least squares method calls for solving simultaneous equations. These equations can get unwieldy. By solving these equations for the slope m and the y intercept b, direct substitution can be employed. Identical totals, as in the least squares solutions are used which include:

$$\Sigma x, \ \Sigma x^2, \ \Sigma y, \ \Sigma y^2, \ \Sigma xy,$$

and N, the number of data. The regression line equation to solve for the constant b is:

$$b = \frac{(\Sigma x^2)(\Sigma y) - (\Sigma x)(\Sigma xy)}{(N)(\Sigma x^2) - (\Sigma x)^2}$$

and the slope m is computed as follows:

$$m = \frac{(N)(\Sigma xy) - (\Sigma x)(\Sigma y)}{(N)(\Sigma x^2) - (\Sigma x)^2} .$$

Solving for b and m in the foregoing example we get:

$$b = \frac{(453,801)(1.834) - (2,073)(348.82)}{(12)(453,801) - (2,073)^2}$$

$$= \frac{109,168}{1,148,283} = .095$$

and

$$m = \frac{(12)(348.82) - (2,073)(1.834)}{(12)(453,801) - (2,073)^2}$$

$$= \frac{383.96}{1,148,283} = .000334 .$$

Using Standard Data

Constant standard data elements are tabularized and filed under machine or process, for ease of reference. Variable data can be tabularized or may be expressed in terms of a curve or an equation, and are also filed under the facility or operation class.

Where standard data are broken down so as to cover a given machine and class of operation, it may be possible to combine constants with variables and tabularize the summary, thus allowing quick reference data that will express the allowed time to perform a given operation completely. Table XXV illustrates welding data in which the constants "change electrode" and "arc" have been combined with the variables "weld cleaning" and "welding," and the result has been expressed in man-hours required to weld one inch for various sizes of welds.

TABLE XXV

CLASSIFICATION

KIND___Fillet_____

TYPE___Flat Position_____

ELECTRODE___E-6020   D.H._____

WELDING PROCEDURE GENERAL

PROCESS OF WELDING_____Shielded Metallic Arc_____POSITION ___Flat_____

MATERIAL____Mild Steel to Mild Steel_____P.D.S._1550, 1555___S.A.E.___1010____

ELECTRODE ___E-6020_____ D.H._____Convex_____ ____Heavy_____

             A.W.S. CLASS   TYPE   SHAPE OF WELD   COATING

POWER SOURCE (A.C. OR D.C. – AND POLARITY IF D.C.)_____D.C. Straight_____

BACKING____None_____PEENING____None_____CHIPPING _____None____

PREHEAT _____None_____

STRESS RELIEVING_____None_____

WELDING PROCEDURE—DETAILS

SIZE OF WELD	SIZE OF ELECTRODE	THICKNESS OF PLATE	NUMBER OF PASSES	WELDING CURRENT (AMPERES)	WELDING VOLTAGE (@ ARC)	*MAN HOURS PER INCH WELD	*WELDING SPEED FT./HR.
1/8	1/8	1/8	1	160-190	26-28	.0025	33.3
3/16	5/32	3/16	1	160-190	26-28	.0028	29.8
1/4	3/16	1/4	1	180-230	32-36	.0033	25.3
3/8	1/4	3/4	1	280-330	32-36	.0050	16.7
1/2	1/4	3/4	2	280-330	32-36	.0078	10.7
5/8	1/4	1"	2	280-330	32-36	.0123	6.8
3/4	1/4	1 1/2	4	280-330	32-36	.0196	4.3
1	1/4	1 1/2	6	280-330	32-36	.0318	2.6

*NOTE: INCLUDES CHANGE ELECTRODE TIME, ARC TIME, WELD CLEANING TIME AND WELDING TIME.

Table XXVI illustrates standard data for a given facility and operation class where again, elements have been combined so that it is necessary only to identify the job in question as to distance that the strip of sheet stock is moved per piece, in order to determine the allowed time for the complete operation.

Setup elements also can frequently be combined or tabularized in combinations so as to diminish the time required for summarizing a series of elements. Table XXVII illustrates standard setup data for No. 5 Warner & Swasey turret lathes applicable to a specific plant. In order to determine the setup time with this data, it is only necessary to visualize the tooling in the square and hex turret and refer to the table. For example, if a certain job required a chamfering tool, turning tool, and facing tool in the square turret, and needed two boring tools, one reamer,

TABLE XXVI

STANDARD DATA FOR BLANKING AND PIERCING STRIP STOCK HAND
FEED WITH PIECE AUTOMATICALLY REMOVED ON
TOLEDO 76 PUNCH PRESS

L (Distance in Inches)	T (Time in Hours per Hundred Hits)
1	.075
2	.082
3	.088
4	.095
5	.103
6	.110
7	.117
8	.123
9	.130
10	.137

TABLE XXVII

STANDARD SETUP DATA FOR NO. 5 TURRET LATHES

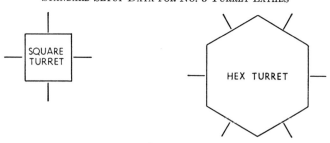

BASIC TOOLING

No.	SQUARE TURRET	HEX TURRET						
		Partial	Chamfer	Bore or turn	Drill	S. Tap or ream	C. Tap	C Die
1	Partial	31.5	39.6	44.5	48.0	47.6	50.5	58.5
2	Chamfer	38.2	39.6	46.8	49.5	50.5	53.0	61.2
3	Face or cut off	36.0	44.2	48.6	51.3	52.2	55.0	63.0
4	Tn bo grv rad	40.5	49.5	50.5	53.0	54.0	55.8	63.9
5	Face and chf	37.8	45.9	51.3	54.0	54.5	56.6	64.8
6	Fa & Cut off	39.6	48.6	53.0	55.0	56.0	58.5	66.6
7	Fa & tn or tn and cut off	45.0	53.1	55.0	56.7	57.6	60.5	68.4
8	Fa, tn, and chf	47.7	55.7	57.6	59.5	60.5	69.7	78.4
9	Fa, tn, and cut off	48.6	57.6	58.5	60.0	62.2	71.5	80.1
10	Fa, tn, and grv	49.5	58.0	59.5	61.5	64.0	73.5	81.6

11	Circled basic tooling from above	_____
12	Each additional tool in square .... 4.20x_____ =	_____
13	Each additional tool in hex .... 8.63x_____ =	_____
14	Remove and setup 3 jaws 5.9	_____
15	Set up subassembly or fixture 18.7	_____
16	Set up between centers 11.0	_____
17	Change lead screw 6.6	_____

Total Setup_____Min.

and a collapsible tap in the hex turret, the setup standard time would be
determined as 69.70 minutes plus 25.89 minutes or 95.59 minutes. The
value is established by finding the relevant tooling under the "square
turret" column (line 8) and the most time-consuming applicable tooling
in the "hex turret" section, in this case, tapping. This gives a value of
69.7 minutes. Since three additional tools are located in the hex turret
(1st bore, 2nd bore, and ream), we multiply 8.63 by three and get 25.89
minutes. The adding of the 25.89 minutes and the 69.70 minutes gives
us the required setup time.

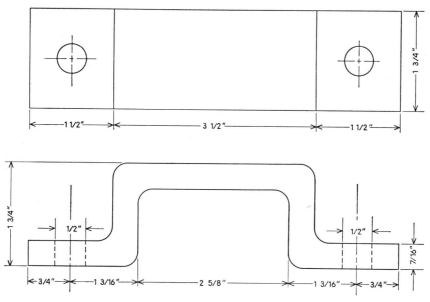

FIG. 18–5. Cast-iron housing.

More frequently, standard data are not combined but left in their
elemental form, thus giving greater flexibility in the development of
time standards. Representative standard data applicable to a given
plant would appear as shown in Table XXVIII.

The data shown include the applicable personal delay and fatigue
allowance. Let us see how this standard time data would be used to
establish allowed setup and piece times to drill the two hold-down bolt
holes in the grey iron housing casting illustrated in Figure 18–5.

The allowed setup time would equal

$$B + C + D + F + G + H + I = 8.70 \text{ minutes} .$$

Element A is not included in the setup time because of the simplicity of
the job. The drawing is not issued to the operator because the operation
card provides him with necessary information relative to drill jig number,
drill size, plug gage number, feed and spindle speed to be used. Element

E is not included in the setup since first-piece inspection is not in this case performed by the inspector. According to the operation card issued, the operator will periodically inspect his own work with the Go-No-Go gage provided. It is recommended that he check every tenth piece drilled.

TABLE XXVIII

Standard Data

Application: Allen 17-inch Vertical Single Spindle Drill
Work Size: Small work—up to four pounds in weight and such that two or more parts can be handled in each hand

Setup elements:

		Minutes
A.	Study drawing	1.25
B.	Get material and tools and return and place ready for work	3.75
C.	Adjust height of table	1.31
D.	Start and stop machine	.09
E.	First piece inspection (includes normal wait time for inspector)	5.25
F.	Tally production and post on voucher	1.50
G.	Clean off table and jig	1.75
H.	Insert drill in spindle	.16
I.	Remove drill from spindle	.14

Each piece elements

1.	Grind drill (prorate)	.78
2.	Insert drill in spindle	.16
3.	Insert drill in spindle (quick change chuck)	.05
4.	Set spindle	.42
5.	Change spindle speed	.72
6.	Remove tool from spindle	.14
7.	Remove tool from spindle (quick change chuck)	.035
8.	Pick up part and place in jig	
	a) Quick-acting clamp	.070
	b) Thumb screw	.080
9.	Remove part from jig	
	a) Quick-acting clamp	.050
	b) Thumb screw	.060
10.	Position part and advance drill	.042
11.	Advance drill	.035
12.	Clear drill	.023
13.	Clear drill, reposition part, and advance drill (same spindle)	.048
14.	Clear drill, reposition part, and advance drill adjacent spindle	.090
15.	Insert drill bushing	.046
16.	Remove drill bushing	.035
17.	Lay part aside	.022
18.	Blow out jig and part and lay part aside	.081
19.	Plug gage part	.12 per hole

Since the casting in question would weigh less than four pounds, and two parts can easily be handled in one hand, the data outlined would be applicable.

After the analyst investigates the design of the drill jig to be used and makes an analytical motion study of the job in order to determine the elements required to perform the operation, he will make his elemental summary. This would appear as shown in the accompanying table.

Element Number	Element	Allowed Time (Minutes)
8.............	Pk. pt. pl. jig (quick acting clamp)	.070
9.............	Rem. pt. jig (quick acting clamp)	.050
10............	Pos. pt. & adv. dr.	.042
13............	Cl. dr. rep. pt. & adv. dr.	.048
12............	Cl. dr.	.023
17............	Lay pt. aside	.022
19............	Plug gage pt. (10%)	.012
1.............	Gr. dr. (once per hundred pcs.)	.008
2.............	Insert dr. in sp. (once per 100 pcs.)	.002
6.............	Rem. tool from sp. (once per 100 pcs.)	.001
		.278 Minute

To this .278-minute time must be added the actual drilling time to drill the two holes. This can readily be determined as previously outlined. For a one-half-inch diameter drill used for drilling cast iron, we should use a surface speed of 100 feet per minute and a feed of .008 inch per revolution.

One hundred surface feet per minute would equal 764 revolutions per minute.

$$\text{R.P.M.} = \frac{12S_f}{\pi d}$$

where

S_f = surface feet per minute
π = 3.14
d = diameter of drill in inches .

However, investigation of the drill press for which this work has been routed reveals that 600 R.P.M. or 900 R.P.M. are the closest speeds that are available to the recommended 764 R.P.M. The analyst proposes to use the slower speed in view of his knowledge of the condition of the machine, and determines the drilling time as follows:

$$T = \frac{L}{F_m} \times 2$$

$$L = .437 + \frac{.25}{\tan 59°} = .588 \text{ inches}$$

$$F_m = (600)(.008)$$
$$= 4.8 \text{ inches per minute}$$

$$T = \left(\frac{.588}{4.8}\right) 2 = .244 \text{ minute .}$$

To this .244 minute cutting time must be added an appropriate allowance. If 10 per cent allowance on the actual machining time is used, we should have a cutting time of .268 minute and a handling time of .278 minute or a total time of .546 minute to drill complete one casting on the single-spindle press available. This standard, supplemented with the setup time of 8.70 minutes, would be released as:

Setup...................... .145 hours
Each piece................. .91 hours per hundred .

Thus if an operator set up this job, and ran 1,000 pieces in an 8-hour working day, he would be performing at an efficiency of 116 per cent:

$$\frac{(.91)(10) + .145}{8} = 116 \text{ per cent .}$$

Conclusion

Standard data, when properly applied, permit the establishment of accurate time standards in advance of the time that the job is to be performed. This feature makes its use especially attractive when estimating the cost of new work for quotation purposes and for subcontracting work.

Time standards can be achieved much more rapidly by using standard data, and the consistency of the standards established can be assured. Standards developed from standard data tend to be completely fair to both the worker and management in that they are the result of already proven standards. It can be pointed out that the elemental values used in arriving at the standards have proven satisfactory as components of established and acceptable standards in use throughout the plant.

The use of standard data simplifies many managerial and administrative problems in plants having a union which operates as a bargaining agent. Union contracts contain many clauses pertaining to such matters as the type of study to be taken (continuous or snapback), the number of cycles to be studied, who shall be studied, and who shall observe the study. These restrictions frequently make it difficult for the analyst to arrive at a standard that is equitable to both the company and the operator. By using the standard data technique, the analyst may avoid restrictive details. Thus, not only is the determination of a standard simplified, but the sources of tension between labor and management are alleviated.

In general, the more refined the elemental times, the greater the coverage possible for the data. Consequently, in job shop practice, it is practicable to have individual elemental values as well as grouped or combined values, so that the data for a given facility will have the flexibility that will allow the setting of rates for all types of work scheduled to the machine.

The use of fundamental motion data for establishing standards, in particular on short-cycle jobs, is becoming more widespread. This data, by nature, is so basic that it allows the predetermination of standards on practically any class or type of manual elements. Of course, the "objective" or "do" basic divisions, such as "use," must be handled as variables, and tabularized data, curves, or algebraic expressions established.

From the illustrative examples cited, it is evident that the application of standard data is an exacting technique. Careful and thorough training in methods and shop practice is fundamental before an analyst can accurately establish standards using standard data. It is essential that the analyst know and recognize the need for each element in the class of work for which he is setting rates. Supplementing this background, it is necessary that the man working with standard data be analytic, accurate, thorough, conscientious, and completely dependable.

TEXT QUESTIONS

1. What do we mean by "standard data"?
2. What advantages are there to establishing time standards through the medium of standard data rather than by taking individual studies?
3. What would the time for the element "mill slot" depend upon?
4. Of what use is the "fast" watch in the compilation of standard data?
5. Compute the times for elements a, b, c, d, and e when elements $a + b + c$ were timed as .057 minute and $b + c + d$ were found to equal .078 minute, $c + d + e = .097$ minute, $d + e + a = .095$ minute, and $e + a + b = .069$ minute.
6. What would be the lead of a ¾-inch diameter drill with an included angle of 118 degrees?
7. What would be the feed in inches per minute of a ¾-inch drill running at a surface speed of 80 feet per minute and a feed of .008 inch per revolution?
8. How long would it take the above drill to drill through a casting 2¼ inches thick?
9. How are feeds usually expressed in lathe work?
10. How long would it take to turn 6 inches of 1-inch bar stock on a No. 3 W. & S. turret lathe running at 120 feet per minute and feeding at the rate of .005 inch per revolution?
11. A plain milling cutter 3 inches in diameter with a width of face of 2 inches is being used to mill a piece of cold-rolled steel 1½ inches wide and 4 inches long. Depth of cut is ⁹⁄₁₆ inch. How long would it take to make the cut if the feed per tooth is .010 inch and a 16-tooth cutter running at a surface speed of 80 feet per minute is in use?
12. What are some of the disadvantages of using curves to tabulate standard data?
13. What standard procedures should be followed in the plotting of simple curves?
14. What would be the horsepower requirements of turning a mild steel shaft 3 inches in diameter if a cut of ¼ inch with a feed of .022 inch per revolution at a spindle speed of 250 R.P.M. were established?

GENERAL QUESTIONS

1. What do you think is the attitude of labor toward establishing standards through the use of standard data?
2. Using the drill press standard data shown in the text, preprice a drilling job with which you are familiar. How does this standard compare with the present rate on the job? (Be sure that identical methods are compared.)
3. Does complete standard data supplant the stop watch? Explain.

CHAPTER 19

Formula Construction

FORMULA CONSTRUCTION AS APplied to time study involves the design of an algebraic expression or system of curves that allows the establishment of a time standard in advance of the beginning of production by substituting known values peculiar to the job for the variable elements. A time study formula represents a simplification of standard data and has particular application in the nonrepetitive type of work where it is impractical to establish standards on the basis of an individual time study for each job.

Application of Formulas

Time formulas are applicable to practically all types of work. They have been successfully used in office operations such as typing, in foundry work, maintenance work, painting, machine work of all types, forging, coil winding, grass cutting, window washing, floor sweeping, welding, and many others. If sufficient time studies are collected to give a reliable sample of data, it is possible to design a formula for a given range of work no matter what type of job is in question.

It is important to recognize that the formula should be applied only to those jobs that fall within the limits of the data used in developing the formula expression. If the boundaries of the formula are extended without supporting proof of individual time studies, erroneous standards, with all the resulting dangers brought about through inequitable rates, may result.

Once a formula has been built to cover a given operation, it should be immediately applied to all pertinent jobs within the range for which it was designed that do not already carry time standards.

Advantages and Disadvantages of Formulas

The advantages of using formulas rather than individual time studies for setting standards parallel those of using standard data. They may be summarized as follows:

1. More consistent time standards are established.
2. The duplication of time study effort on similar operations is eliminated.
3. Standards may be established much more rapidly.
4. A less experienced, less trained man may be used for establishing time standards.
5. Accurate, rapid estimates for labor costs in advance of beginning actual production may be made.

Probably the most significant advantage of the formula over the standard data method is that a less valuable man is needed to work with formulas than with standard data. Any high-school graduate who is proficient in algebra will be able to work out a time study formula and solve for the allowed time required to perform the task. Then, too, standards are established more rapidly by formula than by accumulating standard data elements. Since columns of figures must be added in the standard data method, there is a greater chance for omission or arithmetic error in setting a standard than when using a formula.

In the development of formulas, caution must be exercised in the treatment of constants. There is a natural tendency to treat more elements as constants than should be. Thus, errors can creep into the formula design. It is true that a formula will give consistent results, and so it is also true that if it is not accurate, it will give standards that are consistently wrong.

Another disadvantage of the formula lies in its application. Sometimes, in the interests of arriving at a standard at the earliest possible time, industry will use formulas in instances where the variables are beyond the range of the data used in developing the formula. Thus, the formula may be used where it has no application and the resulting value will be far from valid.

Characteristics of the Usable Formula

A time study formula first must be completely reliable, and secondly, must be practical if it is to be used with confidence. For the expression to be reliable, it must always give accurate results. If the developed formula is accurate, it should verify the individual standards used in its development within plus or minus 5 per cent. The greater the number of studies that can be used in the development of the formula, the better the chance for ending up with a reliable formula. At least ten independent studies should be available for a given class of work before design of a formula is attempted. If tabularized standard data are available, these standards can be used for derivation of the formula. Frequently, when a formula is built, prevailing standard data, existing individual time studies, and new individual time studies will comprise the basic data used in its construction. Of course, it is understood that all mathematical calculation must be free from error before complete confidence can be vested in a formula.

The formula will give as accurate results as the data that entered into its derivation. The studies being used and the elements comprising them must show consistency in their end points and also in the method used, if the formula is to give constantly valid results.

For a formula to be practical, it should be clear, concise, and as simple as possible. The formulas best understood and most easily applied are the simplest expressions. Cumbersome expressions involving the taking of terms to powers should be avoided. Symbols of unknowns should not be repeated throughout the formula but should appear only in one place with their applicable suffixes, prefixes, or coefficients. Each symbol should be specifically identified as to the area of work it represents. Liberal substantiating data should be included in the formula report so that any qualified, interested party can clearly identify the derivation of the formula. It is important that the limitations of the formula be noted by describing in detail its applicable range. Formulas so constructed will allow their users to apply them rapidly and accurately with little difficulty in obtaining the required information.

Steps to Follow in Formula Construction

The first step in formula construction is to determine what class of work is involved and what range of work is to be measured. For example, a formula may be developed for the curing of bonded rubber parts between two and eight ounces in weight. The class of work covered by the formula would be "curing of molded parts," and the range of work involved would be two to eight ounces. After this general over-all analysis has been made and a clear understanding of what is required has been determined, the next step will be the collecting of the formula data. This step involves gathering former studies and standard data elements that have proven to be satisfactory and the taking of new studies in order to obtain a sufficiently large sample to cover the range of work for which the formula is needed. It is important that like elements in the different studies are consistent in their end points. This is essential in determining the variables that influence time, as well as in determining an accurate value for constant elements.

The elemental time study data are then posted on a work sheet for analysis of the constants and variables. The constants are combined and the variables are analyzed so that the factors influencing time can be expressed either algebraically or graphically.

Once the constant values have been selected and the variable elements equated, then the expression is simplified by combining constants and unknowns where possible. The next procedure is to develop the synthesis in which the derivation of the formula is fully explained, so that the person using it, and any other interested party, will be fully cognizant of its application and development.

Before the formula is put into use, it should be thoroughly checked for accuracy, consistency, and ease of application. Once this is done and the formula report has been completely written up, describing the method used, working conditions, limitations of its application, and so forth, then the formula is ready for installation.

In collecting the individual time studies to be used for constructing the formula, it is perfectly satisfactory for the observer to use existing time studies if they have been proven to be satisfactory, if the constant and variable elements in the studies have been properly separated, and if the studies were taken under prevailing conditions and methods. When taking new studies for formula work, the analyst should use the same exacting care, principles, and procedures as when taking a study for an individual standard. However, when taking studies for a time formula, the observer should break the various studies into like elements, with end points terminating at identical places in the work cycle. Also, studies should be made of different operators to get as large a cross section as possible, and those jobs selected should cover the entire range of the proposed formula.

The number of studies that are needed to construct a formula will be influenced by:

1. The range of work for which the formula is to be used.
2. The relative consistency of like constant elements in the various studies.
3. The number of factors that influence the time required to perform the variable elements.

As has been stated, at least ten studies should be available before a formula is constructed. If less than ten are used, the accuracy of the formula may be impaired through incorrect curve construction and data that are not representative of typical performance. Of course, the more studies that are used, the more data there will be available and the more the normal conditions that prevail will be reflected.

Analyzing the Elements

After a sufficient number of time studies has been gathered, it is helpful to summarize the data for analysis purposes on one work sheet. Figure 19-1 illustrates a "Master Table of Detail Time Studies" form which has been designed for this purpose. In addition to the information called for on the form, any specific information, such as surface area, volume,

SHEET NO. __1__
OF __1__ SHEETS

MASTER TABLE O

	S-1	S-2	S-3	S-4

FORMULA __73__
DATE __June 10, 1955__

PART __Cylindrical Core__
OPERATION __Make core from oil sand mix__
PERFORMED ON __Bench__

COMPILED BY __J. Bodesky__

JOB CHARACTERISTICS

STUDY OPERATOR	Petrecca	Winters	Eker	Kump
Performance Factor	110	110	90	110
Diameter of Core	$1\frac{1}{2}$	$2\frac{1}{2}$	$1\frac{1}{2}$	$2\frac{3}{4}$
Length of Core	$7\frac{1}{2}$	$6\frac{1}{2}$	$9\frac{1}{2}$	$4\frac{1}{2}$
Number of Clamps	1	2	1	2
L/D Ratio	4.2	2.89	4.93	1.55
Area	2.76	3.97	2.18	5.93
Volume	21.7	25.8	25.6	25.2
Cl + Dl + Fl	1.242	1.244	1.499	.89

SYMBOL	OPERATION DESCRIPTION	TIME ALLOWED (Hours) minutes	REFERENCE	Operation Class				
A-1	Close core box	.046	Average	C	.049	.041	.050	.05
B-1	Clamp core box (C-clamps)	.112 N	Time vs. No. Cl.	V	.110	.111	.143	.12
C-1	Fill partly full of sand	YX CT	Time vs. Vo vs. Vol.	V	.085	.094	.093	.11
D-1	Ram	YX CT	Time vs. Vo vs. Vol.	V	.225	.255	.242	.24
E-1	Place rod and wire	.0153 L+.03	Time vs. Length	V	.150	.103	.168	.0
F-1	Fill and ram	YXCT	Time vs. Vo vs. Vol.	V	.735	.668	.900	.2
G-1	Strike off with slick	.0157A+.07	Time vs. Area	V	.116	.135	.120	.1
H-1	Remove vent wire	.047	Average	C	.048	.050	.048	.0
J-1	Rap box	.043	Average	C	.039	.042	.045	.0
K-1	Remove clamps	.061 N	Time vs. No. Cl	V	.057	.062	.116	.1
M-1	Open box	.046	Average	C	.046	.040	.038	.0
N-1	Roll out core	.0057 L+.095	Time vs. length	V	.098	.082	.102	.0
P-1	Clean box	V.0067+.0000KV	Time vs. Volume	V	.107	.112	.120	.1

FIG. 19–1.

length, diameter, hardness, radius, and weight, that has an effect on the variable elements should be posted under its corresponding study number in the "job characteristics" section of the form.

Here the name of the operator studied, his rating factor, and the part number of the job are also shown. A separate column has been assigned for each time study for the recording of all this pertinent information.

In the column, on the left-hand side of the work sheet, headed "symbol," an identifying term is placed for each element. The letters of the alphabet followed by a suffix number are frequently used. Thus, we should have the symbols A1, B1, C1, and so on. When more than 26 elements are involved, then the alphabet is repeated, only this time the suffix 2 is used. These symbols are employed for identification and reference from the Master Table to elements grouped in the synthesis.

Under the operation description, every element that has occurred on the individual time studies is recorded. The element description should be expressed clearly, so that any interested person in the future will be able to visualize exactly the work content of the element. After each element description in the column headed "Operation Class" indicate with a "C" or a "V" whether the element is a constant or a variable.

DETAIL TIME STUDIES

S-5	S-6	S-7	S-8	S-9	S-10	S-11	S-12	S-13	S-14	S-15	S-16	S-17
Plasan	Markley	Noyes	Kinachon	Winters	Kumpf	Pettrecca	Judd	Judd	Geiger	Plasan	Ekey	Noyes
105	105	105	98	120	100	108	95	102	117	85	95	100
$1\frac{3}{4}$	2	$1\frac{7}{8}$	$1\frac{1}{8}$	1	$1\frac{3}{4}$	$1\frac{1}{4}$	$1\frac{1}{4}$	$1\frac{1}{4}$	$\frac{7}{8}$	$1\frac{1}{8}$	2	$1\frac{7}{8}$
$9\frac{1}{2}$	8	$4\frac{1}{4}$	10	$13\frac{1}{8}$	$5\frac{1}{8}$	$6\frac{3}{4}$	$7\frac{5}{8}$	$4\frac{1}{8}$	$8\frac{1}{4}$	$6\frac{1}{4}$	10	$12\frac{5}{8}$
2	1	1	2	2	1	1	1	1	1	1	2	2
5.43	4	2.27	8.89	13.13	2.73	5.40	6.10	3.30	9.43	5.56	5.0	6.31
2.40	3.14	2.78	.99	.78	2.40	1.23	1.23	1.23	.60	.99	3.14	2.78
2.8	25.1	11.8	9.90	10.3	12.3	8.27	9.33	5.05	4.96	6.19	31.4	35.1
1.557	1.316	.733	1.489	2.138	.804	1.159	1.181	.797	1.277	1.032	1.740	2.299
045	.042	.047	.050	.041	.043	.042	.047	.048	.049	.046	.043	.048
250	.109	.087	.232	.218	.098	.114	.097	.128	.091	.099	.229	.240
121	.141	.082	.129	.206	.073	.102	.079	.062	.133	.100	.107	.195
272	.245	.160	.344	.436	.194	.281	.252	.090	.342	.162	.285	.480
171	.142	.093	.180	.222	.110	.125	.140	.090	.142	.120	.182	.210
932	.725	.258	.889	1.290	.392	.665	.850	.432	.802	.626	1.089	1.390
109	.120	.104	.078	.079	.098	.089	.084	.086	.074	.085	.119	.106
047	.042	.041	.052	.051	.043	.042	.042	.044	.040	.051	.052	.045
035	.041	.045	.047	.048	.040	.039	.042	.041	.050	.038	.047	.041
.120	.039	.062	.116	.120	.071	.059	.056	.070	.058	.058	.140	.146
.038	.041	.045	.054	.046	.066	.038	.065	.045	.040	.035	.038	.052
.109	.091	.068	.108	.120	.080	.082	.090	.066	.090	.071	.110	.118
.115	.118	.090	.089	.088	.090	.087	.085	.085	085	.088	.138	.150

Next, the allowed elemental times from the individual studies are transposed to the work sheet and are recorded in the appropriate spaces. After these data have been posted, the elemental time values for each element are compared and the reasons for variance are determined. As can be expected, a certain amount of variation will prevail, even in the constant elements, because of inconsistency in performance rating. In general, the constant elements should not deviate substantially, and the allowed time for each constant may be determined by averaging the values of the different studies. This average time should then be posted under the column "Time Allowed," and under the column "Reference" should be shown the word "average."

The variable elements will show a tendency to vary in proportion to some characteristic or characteristics of the work, such as size, shape, or hardness. These elements will have to be studied carefully to determine which factors influence the time, and to what extent. By plotting a curve of time versus the independent variable, it is frequently possible for the analyst to deduce an algebraic expression in terms of time representing the element. This procedure is explained in a later section of this chapter. If an equation can be computed then it should be shown in the

"Time Allowed" column and the curve or curves used in its deduction should be referred to in the adjacent reference column.

Compute Expressions for Variables

If the analysis of the elemental data reveals that one variable characteristic governs the elemental time, then the analyst should construct a simple curve following the procedure outlined in Chapter 18 (see

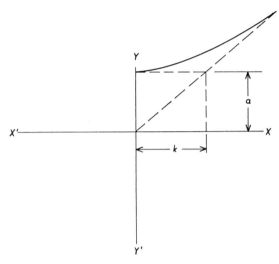

FIG. 19–2. Segment of hyperbolic curve.

Fig. 19–12). If the plotted data take the form of a straight line, the variable element is readily equated in terms of time in the algebraic expression:

$$T = fV + C$$

where

T = time
f = function of the variable (in this case the slope of the line)
V = the variable characteristic governing the elemental time
C = y intercept which is a constant expressed in terms of time .

Not always will the plotted data take the form of a straight line. It may approximate a segment of the hyperbola, ellipse, parabola, or take a shape completely foreign to common geometric forms.

In instances like this, the development of an alignment chart facilitates the computation of the time required to perform the element. The equations of the hyperbola, ellipse, and parabola complicate the formula to such an extent that its use is immediately limited. In order to design an alignment chart that is to become a part of the over-all formula expression, the plotted data of the variable must be equated.

The hyperbolic curve takes the form illustrated in Figure 19–2 and is expressed by the equation:

$$\frac{y^2}{a^2} - \frac{x^2}{k^2} = 1 .$$

If the plotted data take the form of a segment of the hyperbola, k may be computed graphically by drawing a tangent to the curve through the origin and using the resulting line as the diagonal of the rectangle whose height is a, the distance from the origin to the y intercept. Substituting time and the variable characteristic for x and y would give:

$$T = \sqrt{a^2 + \frac{(v^2)(a^2)}{k^2}} .$$

This expression can now be converted to an alignment chart for ease of application.

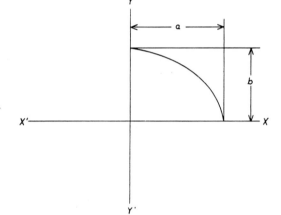

FIG. 19–3. Segment of ellipse.

The ellipse segment shown in Figure 19–3 is expressed by the equation:

$$\frac{x^2}{a^2} + \frac{y^2}{b^2} = 1 .$$

When the plotted time values take the form of the ellipse, a and b may be computed graphically and their values substituted in the expression:

$$T = \sqrt{b^2 - \frac{b^2 v^2}{a^2}} .$$

In other instances, the data may take the form of the parabola as illustrated in Figure 19–4. This curve is expressed by the equation:

$$x^2 = \frac{a^2 y}{b}$$

and after substituting graphic solutions for a and b, we have the equation:

$$T = \frac{bv^2}{a^2}.$$

As in previous illustrations, T is equal to time and v is equal to the variable characteristic governing the elemental time.

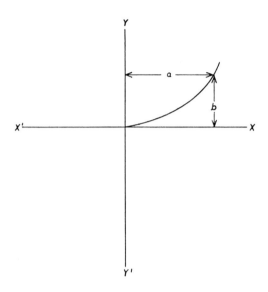

FIG. 19–4. Segment of parabola.

Using Logarithmic and Semilogarithmic Paper

When the plotted curve takes the exponential form it may be plotted on semilogarithmic or logarithmic paper in order to get a straight-line relationship. Sometimes, if the replotting still shows a slight curve, a constant may be added or subtracted from the curved portion of the plotting which will straighten this segment sufficiently to permit using the exponential to express one portion and the exponential plus a constant for the other portion.

For example, the equation $Y = AX^m$ written in logarithmic form becomes:

$$\log Y = \log A + m \log X.$$

It is evident here that $\log Y$ is linear with $\log X$ and when plotted on logarithmic paper a straight-line will be obtained. The equation may take the exponential form of $Y = AB^x$. This equation written in logarithmic form is:

$$\log Y = \log A + X \log B.$$

Inspection of this equation shows that $\log Y$ is linear with X and when plotted on semilogarithmic paper with Y on the log scale a straight line will be obtained. For example, in the element "strike arc and weld" the following data were obtained from ten detailed studies:

Study No.	Size of Weld	Minutes per Inch of Weld
1.	$\frac{1}{8}$	.12
2.	$\frac{3}{16}$	.13
3.	$\frac{1}{4}$	.15
4.	$\frac{3}{8}$	.24
5.	$\frac{1}{2}$	.37
6.	$\frac{5}{8}$	.59
7.	$1\frac{1}{16}$	.80
8.	$\frac{3}{4}$	.93
9.	$\frac{7}{8}$	1.14
10.	1	1.52

When the data were plotted on rectangular coordinate paper, a smooth curve resulted (see Figure 19–5). The data were then plotted on semi-logarithmic paper and the straight line as shown in figure 19–6 was obtained.

This plotting can now be stated in equation form by the following derivation:

Select any two points on the straight line:

$$\text{Point 1} \quad X = 1, \quad Y = \log 1.52$$
$$\text{Point 2} \quad X = \tfrac{3}{8}, \quad Y = \log .24$$

Solving for the slope m:

$$m = \frac{Y_1 - Y_2}{X_1 - X_2}$$
$$= \frac{\log 1.52 - \log .24}{1 - \tfrac{3}{8}}$$
$$= 1.28 .$$

To determine the equation of the line from the equation $Y - Y_1 = m(X - X_1)$ we get:

$$\log Y - \log 1.52 = 1.28 \,(X - 1)$$
$$\log Y - .18184 \;\; = 1.28 \, X - 1.28$$
$$\log Y = 1.28 \, X - 1.10 .$$

From the exponential form

$$Y = AB^x$$
$$\log Y = \log A + X \log B$$

and

$$\log A = -1.10$$
$$A = .07944$$
$$\log B = 1.28$$
$$B = 19.05$$

and

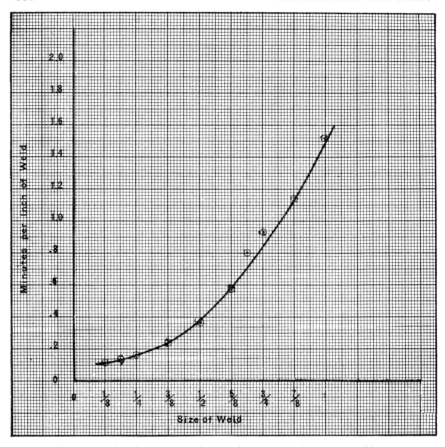

FIG. 19–5. Plotted curve on regular co-ordinate paper takes exponential form.

$$Y = (.07944) (19.05)^x$$

rounding off:

$$Y = (.08) (19)^x.$$

This equation would then be a component of the formula expression and would be less cumbersome than referring to the curve shown in figure 19–6. It can be checked as follows:

With ½″ weld:

$$\text{Time} = (.08) (19)^{.5}$$
$$= .35 \text{ minutes}.$$

This checks quite closely with the time study value of .37 minutes.

Solving for More than One Variable

Sometimes, it will be found that two or more variable characteristics govern the elemental time. It may be possible to combine these variables

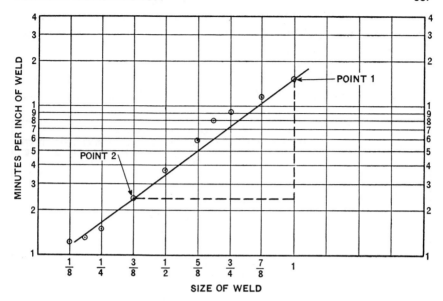

FIG. 19–6. Data plotted on semilogarithmic paper takes the form of a straight line with equation $Y = AB^x$.

into one and then plot the result against time. Thus, the product of length and diameter will give us surface area, which may be plotted against time for various bar stock machining elements. Then radius squared times length will give volume, which may be plotted against time for such operations as welding fillet elements or making green sand cores.

Alignment charts have also been used to express time when two or more variables are involved. The basic principle in construction of alignment charts, frequently called nomograms, is the showing of the relationship between the variables by means of scales along separate axes, in such a way that a straight line will cut the scales and satisfy the equation involving the unknowns. Figure 19–7 illustrates a nomogram used for determining turning and facing time. For example, if the problem is to determine the production in pieces per hour to turn 5 inches of a 4-inch diameter shaft of medium carbon steel on a machine utilizing a .015-inch feed per revolution and having a cutting time of 55 per cent of the cycle time, the answer could be readily determined graphically. By connecting the recommended cutting speed of 150 feet per minute for medium carbon steel shown on scale 1 to the 4-inch diameter of the work shown on scale 2, a speed of 143 R.P.M. is shown on scale 3. The 143-R.P.M. point is connected with the .015-inch feed per revolution that is shown on scale 4. This line extended to scale 5 shows a feed of 2.15 inches per minute being used. This feed point connected with the length of cut shown on scale 6 (5 inches) gives the required cutting time on scale 7. This cutting time of 2.35 minutes when connected with the percentage of cutting time shown on scale 8 (in this case, 55 per cent) gives the production in pieces per hour on scale 9 (in this case, 16).

Frequently, the analyst will find that it is not possible for him to combine variables influencing the time to perform a job. Thus, he would not be able to combine area and hardness, wire gage and length of wire

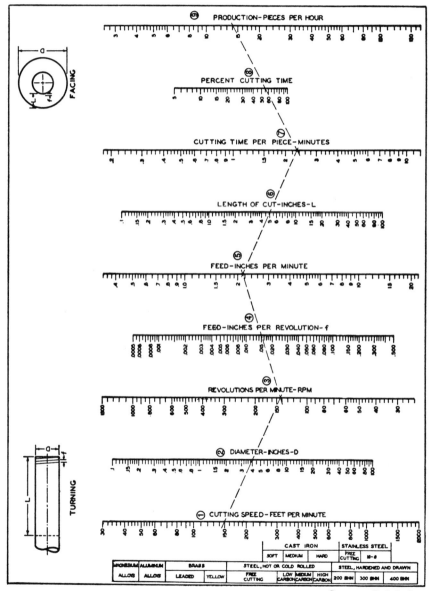

Courtesy: Crobalt, Inc.

FIG. 19–7. Nomogram for determining facing and turning time.

wound, area and slope, and similar groups of variables that would affect the time to perform an element.

It is possible to solve problems like this graphically by constructing two charts. The first will show the relationship between time and one of the variables in selected studies in which the values of the other variables tend to remain constant. The second chart will show the relationship between the second variable and time that has been adjusted so as to remove the influence of the first variable.

Let us look at an example to illustrate the application of this procedure. It is decided to construct a formula for rolling various width and length of .072-inch thick, cold-rolled sheet metal on a bench roll. Element 1 shown on the master table of detail time studies, is "pk. up pc. & pos." and element 3 is "lay aside pc. & pos." Since both of these elements involve handling time of the same amount of stock, their values are combined so as to simplify the final algebraic expression. The values shown in the accompanying table were obtained.

Study No.	Width	Length	Element 1 + Element 3
1......................	2	16	.18
2......................	3	18	.13
3......................	8	1	.09
4......................	10½	32	.14
5......................	7	84	.55
6......................	8½	69	.38
7......................	20	30	.22
8......................	11	55	.26
9......................	10	75	.68
10.....................	20½	41	.66
11.....................	10½	90	1.80
12.....................	16	64	1.44

First inspection seemed to suggest that the time for element 1 plus element 3 would vary with the area of the part handled. However, upon plotting, it was apparent that something else was influencing the time required to perform these elements. Further analysis revealed that the long and narrow pieces required considerably more time than the nearly square parts, even though their respective areas were about the same. It was decided that two variables were affecting time: these were the area of the part and the increased difficulty of handling the relatively longer pieces. The latter may be expressed as a ratio of length to width.

Of the twelve studies appearing on the master work sheet, it was noted that four (studies 5, 6, 7, and 8) were taken on stock having areas of about 600 square inches. It was also apparent that these four studies had a relatively wide spread of "length divided by width" ratio which was apparently responsible for the range in allowed elemental times.

Since these four studies had areas relatively the same, the effect of L/W could be shown by plotting a simple curve. This was done as shown in Figure 19–8. Now, in order to see what the effect of area is on the elemental time, it will be necessary to adjust all the tabularized time study values by the relative amount of time brought about by the influence of the variable L/W. To get a factor that can be used to divide the time study values so as to arrive at an adjusted time that varies with area, we construct a scale parallel to the Y axis and call it "Factor A" (adjustment factor). By extending the lowest point on our L/W curve horizontally to the adjustment axis, we get a distance from the origin that can be evaluated as unity on the adjustment axis. Proportional values can then be constructed so as to get a scale on the adjustment axis.

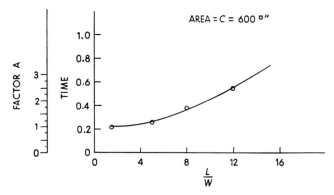

FIG. 19–8. Time plotted against the ratio of length to width for constant areas of about 600 square inches.

Now by taking the L/W value of all the studies appearing on the master table, we can determine adjustment factors graphically for each study by moving horizontally to the Factor A axis from the specific point on the L/W versus Time curve. Once the adjustment values have been determined for each study, then the adjusted time can be computed by dividing the allowed elemental time study values by the adjustment factor. The resulting adjusted times can then be plotted against area (see Figure 19–9).

The system of curves so developed represents the graphic solution and can be used for establishing standards within their range in the following manner. First, the area and the length over width ratio of the sheet is calculated. Using the L/W ratio, we can refer to the first curve to obtain an adjustment factor. Referring to the second curve we can determine an adjusted time. The product of the adjusted time and the adjustment factor will give the allowed time to perform elements 1 and 3.

By extending this procedure, it is possible for the analyst to solve graphically elemental time values when more than two variable characteristics govern the elemental time.

Sometimes variables will remain relatively constant within a specific group. However, once the limits of the specific group are extended, the variable will tend to show a pronounced change in value. For example, the handling of boards of 1-inch white pine to a planer may be classified:

Group	Allowed Time
Small (up to 300 square inches)...................	.070 min.
Medium (300 to 750 square inches)...............	.095 min.
Large (750 to 1,800 square inches)...............	.144 min.

This method of grouping will tend to give erroneous values at the extremities of each group. Thus, in the above example, a board of 295 square inches would be allowed .070 minute handling time while one 305 square inches would be given .095 minute. The chances are that in the first case, .070 minute would represent a tight standard and in the latter case, .095 minute would be somewhat loose.

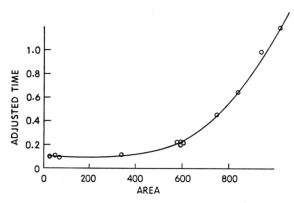

FIG. 19–9. Adjusted time plotted against area.

When elements are grouped in the manner shown, it is important that the grouping be clearly and specifically defined so that there will be no questions as to which category an element belongs.

Develop Synthesis

The purpose of the synthesis in the formula report is to give complete explanation of the derivation of the various components entering into the formula so as to facilitate its use. Furthermore, a clearly developed synthesis will help in explaining and selling the formula in the event questions come up at some later date as to its suitability.

In order that the final expression may be in its simplest form, all constants and symbols should be combined wherever possible, with due respect to accuracy and the flexibility of the formula. Elemental operations may be classified under specific headings as preparation, handling by hand, handling by jib crane, and operation. Constant values will appear under each elemental class. These values can be combined to simplify the final expression of the specific formulas. Details of the combinations are explained in the synthesis. A typical illustration of a synthesis for a constant element would be:

$$A1 + C1 + \text{constant from equation } 4 + H1 = .11 + .17 + .09 + .05 = .42 \text{ minute}.$$

In the treatment of variable elements, a more detailed explanation is usually required due to the added complexities associated with this class of elements. For example, we may wish to combine elements $B1$ and $D1$, in that they have been influenced by the ratio of L/D. The two equations may be:

$$B1 = .1\frac{L}{D} + .08$$

$$D1 = .05\frac{L}{D}$$

and the combination of these would give

$$B1 + D1 = .15\frac{L}{D} + .08 .$$

Thus, the synthesis would clearly show where the .15 L/D came from.

Compute Expression

The final expression may not be entirely in algebraic form. It may have been more convenient to express some of the variables in terms of systems of curves, nomographs, or single curves. Then, too, some of the variable data may have been made up into tables, and these will be referred to by a single symbol in the formula. A typical example of a formula would be:

$$\text{Allowed Time} = .07 + \text{Chart } 1 + \text{Curve } 1 + \frac{.555N}{C}$$

where

$$N = \text{number of cavities per mold}$$
$$C = \text{cure time in minutes}.$$

In applying this formula, the analyst would refer to Chart 1 in order to pick out the applicable tabularized value. He would also refer to Curve 1 to obtain the numerical value of another variable entering into the formula. Knowing the number of cavities in the mold and the cure time in minutes, he would substitute in the latter part of the expression and summarize the values of the three variables with the constant time of .07 minute to get the resulting allowed time.

Check for Accuracy

Upon completion of the formula, the analyst should verify it before releasing for use. The easiest and most rapid way to check the formula is to use it to check existing time studies. This can best be done by tabularizing the results under the following heads: *Part Number, Time Study Value, New Formula Value, Difference,* and *Percentage Difference.*

Any marked differences between the formula value and the time study value should be investigated and the cause determined. It would be expected that the formula show an average percentage difference of less than 5 per cent from the time study values of those studies used in deriving the formula. If at this point, the formula does not appear to have the expected validity, then the analyst should accumulate additional data by taking more stop-watch studies. Once the formula has been satisfactorily tested over a range of work, it will be acceptable to those who are affected directly and indirectly by its application. At this point, it would be time well spent for the analyst to go over the formula with the foreman of the department where it will be used. After the foreman understands its derivation and application and has verified its reliability, the analyst can be assured of his backing on standards resulting from its use.

Write Formula Report

All data, calculations, derivations, and applications of the formula should be consolidated in the form of a complete report prior to putting the formula into use. Then all the facts relative to process employed, operating conditions, and scope of formula will be available for future reference.

The Westinghouse Electric Corporation includes fourteen separate sections in its formula reports. These are:

1. Formula number, division, data, and sheet number
2. Part
3. Operation
4. Work station
5. Allowed time
6. Application
7. Analysis
8. Procedure
9. Time studies
10. Table of detail elements
11. Synthesis
12. Inspection
13. Wage payment
14. Signature of constructor and approver

Formula Number

For ease of reference, all paper work entering into the development of the formula should be identified by the assignment of a number to the formula. The formula number is made up of a prefix which identifies the department or division wherein the formula will be used and a number which gives the chronological arrangement of the formula with reference to other formulas being used in the department. Thus, the formula 11N–56 would infer that it was the fifty-sixth formula designed for use in department 11N. The date that the formula was put into use is also included, so as to connect working conditions in effect at the time the formula was designed with standards established through its application.

Part

The part number or numbers together with drawing numbers should be given, with a concise description of the work, so that the products for which the formula has application are clearly defined. For example: "Parts J–1101, J–1146, J–1172, J–1496, side plates ranging from 12 × 24 inches to 48 × 96 inches" would identify the parts for which the formula may be used.

Operation and Work Station

The operation covered by the formula should be clearly stated, such as "roll radius" or "fabricate inner and outer members" or "broach keyways" or "assemble farm tank." In addition, the work station should be completely described with information as to equipment, jigs, fixtures, gages, and their size, condition, and serial number. A photograph will often help to define the method in effect at the time of compilation of the formula.

Allowed Time

When expressing the formula for the allowed time, use separate equations for the "setup" time and the "each-piece" time. Immediately following the formula should be a key which outlines the meaning of the symbols used in each equation. All tables, nomograms, and system of curves should be included at this point, as well as a sample solution, so that the person using the formula clearly understands it.

Application

After the expressions for the allowed time have been concisely stated, then a clear explanation of the application of the formula should be given. This should give in detail the nature of the work on which the formula may be used and specifically state the limits within which it may be applied. For example, the application of a formula for curing bonded rubber parts may be written as follows: "This formula applies to all curing operations done in 24 × 28-inch platen presses when the number of cavities range between 8 and 100 and the cubic inches of rubber per cavity range between .25 inch and 3 inches.

Analysis

Under the analysis is given a detailed account of the entire method employed, which will include the tools, fixtures, jigs, and gages and their application; workplace layout; methods of material handling; method of obtaining supply materials; and nature of setup with details as to how the operator is assigned the job, distance to the tool crib, and other pertinent data.

In the analysis section of the report is included information as to the breakdown of the allowances used in the formula. The reason for any special or extra allowance should be clearly stated. The allowance for personal time, fatigue, and unavoidable delays should be shown independently so that if any question comes up in the future as to the inclusion of an allowance in the formula, it can be clearly shown what allowances were included and why.

Procedure

After the analysis of the job has been established, the procedure used by the operator in performing the work should be written up in detail. The best way of doing this is to include all the elements appearing on the master work sheet in their correct chronological arrangement. While abbreviations were liberally used on the time studies and on the master table, care should be exercised to avoid their use in writing up the operator's procedure. Individual elements should be written in exact detail. Then all parties will have no doubt as to the work elements included in the scope of the formula.

Time Studies

It is not necessary to include the actual time studies used in compilation of the formula in the formula report, as they are usually available in their own independent files. However, reference should be made to the time studies used. This can be done in tabular form as follows:

Time Study No.	Part	Drawing	Plant	Date Taken	Taken By
S–112.............	J–1102	JB–1102	A	9–15–54	J. B. Smith
S–147.............	J–1476	JA–1476	B	10–24–54	A. B. Jones
S–92..............	J–1105	JB–1105	B	6–11–54	J. B. Smith

Table of Detail Elements

This table is used as a reference source for information as to the allowed element time and its derivation. The information for composing this table is taken from the master table of detailed elements and is recorded in chart form as follows:

Symbol	Element Description	Allowed Time	Reference
Al......................	Close core box	.08 min.	Average
Bl......................	Fill partly full of sand	A × C.T.	All Studies
Cl......................	Rap box	.04 min.	S–4–6–7–8–12

Synthesis

After recording the table of detail elements, the analyst includes the synthesis of the report. The synthesis, as previously explained, tells the manner in which the allowed time was derived.

Inspection, Payment, and Signatures

Upon completion of the synthesis the constructor records the following information in order: the inspection requirements appearing on the drawings of the jobs covered by the formula; the type of wage payment plans where the formula will be used, such as daywork, piecework, and group incentive; and finally his signature and that of his supervisor.

Representative Formula

The following formula report will illustrate and help clarify the procedures discussed in this chapter:

> FORMULA No.: M–11–No. 15
> DATE: September 15, 1954
> SHEET: 1 of 15

PART: Cylindrical oil sand mix cores ⅞″ in diameter to 2¾″ diameter and 4″ long to 13″ long.
OPERATION: Make core complete in wood core box.
WORK STATION: 30″ × 52″ Bench 36″ high.
ALLOWED TIME: Piece time in demical minutes equals:

$$.173N + .0210L + \sqrt{.0067 + .000016V^2} + Y \times C.T. + .0157A + .327$$

Where

$$
\begin{aligned}
N &= \text{number of "C" clamps} \\
L &= \text{length of core in inches} \\
V &= \text{volume of core in cubic inches} \\
Y &= \text{adjustment factor (Curve 1)} \\
CT &= \text{adjusted time (Curve 2)} \\
A &= \text{cross-sectional area of core .}
\end{aligned}
$$

EXAMPLE:

Calculate allowed time to make a green sand core 2″ in diameter and 8″ long. Volume would be 25.1 cubic inches and with 8″ length, only one clamp would be required. L/D would be equal to 8/2 or 4.

THEN:

$$\text{Time} = (.173)(1) + (.0210)(8) + \sqrt{.0067 + (.000016)(25.1^2)}$$
$$+ (1.5)(.76) + (.0157)(3.14) + .327 = 1.987 \text{ minutes .}$$

APPLICATION

This formula applies to all cylindrical cores made of oil sand mix between diameters ranging from ⅞ inch to 2¾ inches and lengths ranging from 4 inches to 13 inches. This work is performed manually in wooden split core boxes.

ANALYSIS

The following hand tools are provided the operator for making cores covered by this formula: C-clamps, slick, and rammer. The work is done at a bench with the operator standing. Oil sand mix for producing the cores is piled on the floor by the move man approximately four feet from the operator. Periodically, the operator replenishes a supply of sand on his bench from the inventory on the floor, through the use of a short-handled shovel. Rods and reinforcing wires are requisitioned from the storeroom by the operator. He usually acquires a full day's supply with each requisition.

The work voucher placed above the operator's work station by the departmental foreman indicates the sequence of jobs to be performed and is the authority for the operator to begin a specific job. Operation cards and drawings must be obtained by the operator from the tool crib.

The standard allowance which must be added when applying this formula is 17 per cent. This involves 5 per cent for personal delays, 6 per cent for unavoidable delays, and 6 per cent for fatigue.

PROCEDURE

The working procedure followed in making oil sand mix cores covered by this formula includes fourteen elements exclusive of setup and put-away elements. These are:

1. Pick up two sections of core box and close together.
2. Clamp core box shut using one clamp for cores less than 9 inches and two clamps for cores greater than 9 inches in length.
3. Fill core box partly full of sand (about one third depending on core).
4. Ram the sand solid in the core box.
5. Place the vent rod and reinforcing wire.
6. Fill the remainder of the core box with sand and ram solid.
7. With slick, strike off sand on both ends of core box so sand core is flush with box.
8. Remove the vent wire from the core and lay aside.
9. Rap box lightly.
10. Remove clamps and lay aside.
11. Open core box.
12. Roll out core on rack beside work station.
13. Clean core box with kerosene rag.

TIME STUDIES

The following summary includes the time studies used in developing this formula:

Time Study No.	Part Number		Plant	Date Taken	Taken By
S–13	P–1472	PB–1472	A	6–15–54	Black
S–111	P–1106	PB–1106	A	12–11–54	Black
S–45	P–1901	PB–1901	A	7–13–54	Hirsch
S–46	P–1907	PB–1907	B	7–14–54	Black
S–47	P–1908	PA–1908	B	7–14–54	Black
S–32	P–1219	PA–1219	A	8–10–54	Black
S–76	P–1711	PA–1711	A	11–12–54	Obe
S–70	P–1701	PB–1701	B	11–9–54	Obe
S–17	P–1311	PB–1311	B	6–16–54	Black
S–18	P–1312	PB–1312	B	6–16–54	Black
S–59	P–1506	PB–1506	A	7–26–54	Hirsch
S–60	P–1507	PB–1507	A	7–26–54	Hirsch
S–50	P–1497	PB–1497	B	7–19–54	Obe
S–51	P–1498	PA–1498	B	7–20–54	Obe
S–52	P–1499	PA–1499	B	7–21–54	Obe
S–53	P–1500	PA–1500	B	7–21–54	Obe
S–54	P–1501	PA–1501	B	7–22–54	Obe

TABLE OF DETAIL ELEMENTS

Symbol	Element Description	Decimal Minute Allowed Time	Reference
A–1........	Close core box	.046	Average
B–1........	Clamp core box	.112N	Time vs. no. clamps
C–1.......	Fill partly full of sand	$Y \times CT$	Time vs. L/D & vol. Time vs. vol.
D–1........	Ram	$Y \times CT$	Time vs. L/D & vol. Time vs. vol.
E–1........	Place rod and wire	.0153L + .03	Time vs. length
F–1........	Fill and ram	$Y \times CT$	Time vs. L/D & vol. Vs. vol.
G–1........	Strike off	.0157A + .07	Time vs. area
H–1........	Remove vent wire	.047	Average
J–1........	Rap box	.043	Average
K–1........	Remove clamps	.061N	Time vs. no. clamps
M–1.......	Open box	.046	Average
N–1........	Roll out core	.0057L + .045	Time vs. length
P–1........	Clean box	$\sqrt{.0067 + .000016 V^2}$	Time vs. volume

SYNTHESIS

Allowed time = Sum of allowed elemental time
= A–1 + B–1 + C–1 + D–1 + E–1 + F–1 + G–1
+ H–1 + J–1 + K–1 + M–1 + N–1 + P–1 .

Since Elements C–1, D–1, and F–1 are all dependent on the variables volume and length/diameter, their values may be combined before plotting on co-ordinate paper. The combined values for these three elements for the seventeen time studies are:

Study No.	*C–1 + D–1 + F–1*
S–13	1.045
S–111	1.017
S–45	1.235
S–46	.647
S–47	1.325
S–32	1.110
S–76	.500
S–70	1.362
S–17	1.932
S–18	.659
S–59	.988
S–60	1.181
S–50	.584
S–51	1.277
S–52	.888
S–53	1.481
S–54	2.065

For reference purposes, the combination of C–1 + D–1 + F–1 will be designated R–1 [see Figures 19–10 and 19–11]. Curves 1 and 2 are used to solve the allowed time for these three elements by first getting adjustment factor from curve 1 and then getting the adjusted time from curve 2. The product of these two values will give the allowed time for C–1 + D–1 + F–1.

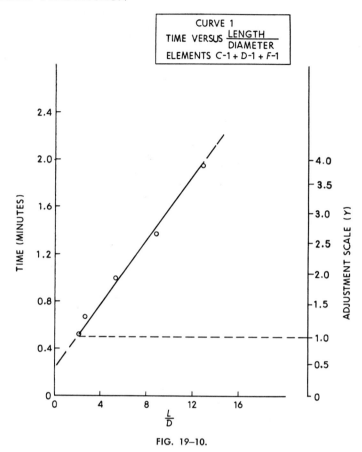

FIG. 19–10.

The time for elemental E–1 (place rod and wire) has been plotted on curve 3 [see Figure 19–12], where its relationship to core length is shown. This curve can be expressed algebraically by the equation:

$$T = fv + C$$

or

$$\text{Time} = (\text{slope})(\text{length}) + y \text{ intercept}.$$

Solving graphically:

$$f = \frac{.210 - .100}{12 - 4.8} = \frac{.110}{7.20}$$
$$= .0153$$
$$C = .03 \text{ (from graph)}.$$

Thus:

$$\text{Time} = .0153L + .03.$$

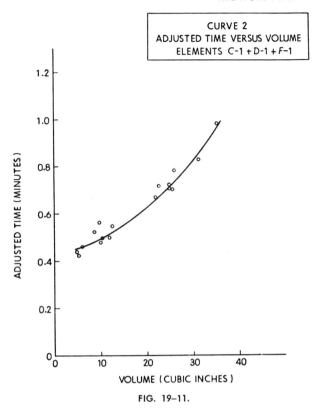

FIG. 19–11.

Element G–1 (strike off) has also been solved as a straight-line relation-ship. Here a cross-sectional area of the core has been plotted against time (see curve 4) [Figure 19–13]. In this case

$$\text{Time} = (f)(\text{area}) + .07$$

and

$$f = \frac{.132 - .08}{4 - .7} = \frac{.052}{3.3}$$

$$f = .0157 \ .$$

Then:

$$\text{Time} = .0157A + .07 \ .$$

Element N–1 (Roll out core) is shown on curve 5 [see Figure 19–14] Here

$$\text{Time} = f(\text{length}) + .045$$

and

$$f = \frac{.125 - .068}{14 - 4}$$
$$= .0057 \ .$$

Then:

$$\text{Time} = .0057L + .045 \ .$$

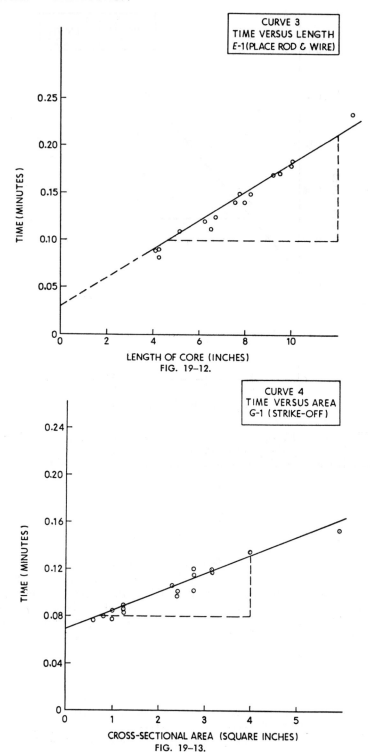

CURVE 3
TIME VERSUS LENGTH
E-1 (PLACE ROD & WIRE)

LENGTH OF CORE (INCHES)
FIG. 19–12.

CURVE 4
TIME VERSUS AREA
G-1 (STRIKE-OFF)

CROSS-SECTIONAL AREA (SQUARE INCHES)
FIG. 19–13.

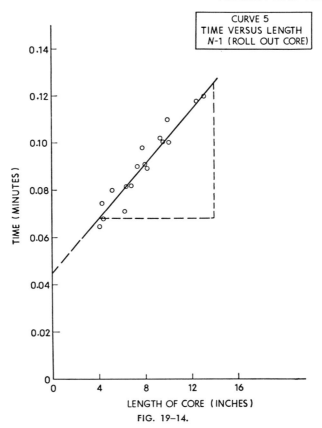

FIG. 19-14.

The time for Element P–1 (Clean Box) when plotted against volume of core, gives a hyperbolic relationship as shown in Curve 6 [Figure 19–15]. This relationship with time can be expressed algebraically as follows:

$$\text{Time} = \sqrt{a^2 + \frac{v^2 a^2}{k^2}}$$

$$= \sqrt{\frac{.082^2}{.082^2} + \frac{(v^2)(.082)^2}{400}}$$

$$= \sqrt{.0067 + .000016v^2}.$$

Elements A–1, H–1, J–1, M–1 were classified as constants with the following respective allowed times determined by taking their average values: .046, .047, .043, .046. When these constants are added to the sum of the y intercept values of equations 3, 4, and 5, a total constant time of .327 minute is determined:

A–1	.046
Curve 3 intercept	.030
H–1	.047
Curve 4 intercept	.070
J–1	.043
M–1	.046
Curve 5 intercept	.045
	$C_T = .327$ minute

Both elements B–1 and K–1 are proportional to the number of clamps N. Thus, these two elements may be combined for simplicity as follows:

$$B–1 = .112N$$
$$K–1 = .061N$$
$$\overline{S–1 = .173N} \,.$$

Since elements E–1 (place rod and wire), and P–1 (roll out core) are proportional to length of core, we may combine their equated relationships with length and designate the combined total by the Symbol T–1.
Thus:

$$E–1 = .0153L$$
$$N–1 = .0057L$$
$$\overline{T–1 = .0210L} \,.$$

Simplifying our initial equation:

$$\text{Allowed Time} = \text{S–1} + \text{T–1} + \text{P–1} + \text{R–1} + \text{G–1} + C_T$$
$$= .173N + .0210L + \sqrt{.0067 + .000016V^2}$$
$$+ Y \times \text{CT} + .0157A + .327$$

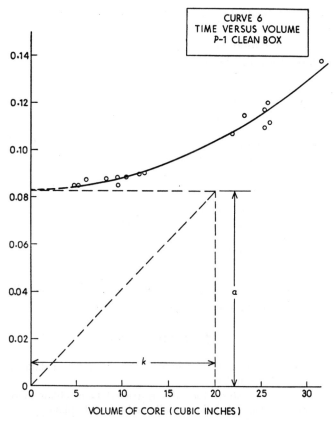

CURVE 6
TIME VERSUS VOLUME
P-1 CLEAN BOX

VOLUME OF CORE (CUBIC INCHES)

FIG. 19–15.

INSPECTION

The only inspection requirement on the cores covered by this formula is visual inspection done by the operator at the time the core is rolled free from the core box.

PAYMENT

This formula is to be used in development of allowed times that will be applied to individual standards in a one-for-one incentive wage payment plan.

APPROVED: *John Purdy*   *Scott Dickinson*
                    Supervisor   Formula Constructor

Conclusion

Through the design of a time study formula, it is possible to establish standards in a fraction of the time required by taking individual studies. However, before a formula is released for use, the mathematics used in its development should be carefully checked to assure that the expression is correct. Then, too, several test cases should be tried to be certain that the formula will establish true, consistent standards. The formula should be clearly identified as to its range of application, and in no case should standards be established with data that are beyond the scope of the formula.

In summary, the following steps represent the chronological procedure in time study formula design:

1. Collect data
    a) Using time studies already available
    b) Using standard data already available
    c) Taking new time studies
2. Compile master work sheet and identify formula
3. Analyze and classify elements
    a) Constants
    b) Variables
4. Develop synthesis
5. Compute the final expression
6. Check mathematics of developed formula
7. Test formula
8. Write formula report
9. Use the formula

By systematically following these nine steps, the analyst will have little difficulty in designing reliable time study formulas.

TEXT QUESTIONS

1. What advantages does the formula offer over standard data in the establishment of time standards?
2. Is the use of time study formulas restricted to machine shop operations where feeds and speeds influence allowed times? Explain.

3. What are the characteristics of a sound time study formula?

4. What is the danger of using too few studies in the derivation of a formula?

5. What is the function of the synthesis in the formula report?

6. Write the equation of the ellipse with its center at the origin and axes along the co-ordinate axes and passing through (2, 3) and (−1, 4).

7. Find the equation of the hyperbola with center at (0, 0) and $a = 4$, $b = 5$, focci on the y axis.

8. What fourteen sections make up the formula report?

9. What nine steps represent the chronological procedure in the design of time study formulas?

10. Explain in detail how it is possible to solve graphically for time when two variables are influential and they cannot be combined.

11. Develop an algebraic expression for the relationship between time and area from the following data:

Study No.	1	2	3	4	5
Time	4	7	11	15	21
Area	28.6	79.4	182	318	589

12. If the data shown in Figure 19–5 were plotted on logarithmic paper, would the plotting be a straight line? Why?

GENERAL QUESTIONS

1. Would the company union prefer standards to be set by means of formulas or standard data? Why?

2. Would it be necessary for the "chart and formula" designer to have a background in time study work? Why?

3. If an operator objected strongly to a rate established through a formula, explain in detail how you would endeavor to prove to him that the rate was fair.

CHAPTER 20

Work Sampling Studies

WORK SAMPLING IS A TECH-
nique for analyzing work for the purpose of finding allowances applicable
to the job, for the determining of machine utilization, and for establishing
standards of production. This same information can be obtained by time
study procedures. Work sampling is a method that frequently will provide the information faster and at considerably less cost than by stop-
watch techniques.

In conducting a work sampling study, the analyst takes a comparatively large number of observations at random intervals. The ratio of the
number of observations of a given state of activity to the total number of
observations taken will approximate the percentage of time that the
process is in that given state of activity. For example, if 10,000 observations at random intervals over a period of several weeks showed that a
given automatic screw machine was turning out work in 7,000 instances,
and in 3,000 instances, it was idle for miscellaneous reasons, then it would
be reasonably certain that the down time of the machine would be 30
per cent of the working day, or 2.4 hours, and the effective output of the
machine would be a matter of 5.6 hours per day. The application of work
sampling was first made by L. H. C. Tippett in the British textile industry.
Later under the name "ratio-delay" study,[1] it received considerable attention in this country. The accuracy of the data determined by work
sampling depends upon the number of observations; unless the sample
size is of sufficient quantity, inaccurate results will occur.

The work sampling method has several advantages over that of acquir-
ing data by the conventional time study procedure. These are:

---

[1] R. L. Morrow, *Time Study and Motion Economy* (New York: Ronald Press Co.,
1946).

1. It does not require continuous observation by an analyst over a long period of time.
2. Clerical time is diminished.
3. The total man-hours expended by the analyst are usually much fewer.[2]
4. Operator is not subjected to long-period stop-watch observations.
5. Crew operations can be readily studied by a single analyst.

The whole theory of work sampling is based on the fundamental laws of probability. If at a given instant an event can either be present or absent, statisticians have derived the following expression, which shows the probability of x occurrences of an event in n observations:

$$(p + q)^n = 1$$
p = the probability of a single occurrence
$q = (1 - p)$ the probability of an absence of occurrence
n = number of observations

If the above expression, $(p + q)^n = 1$, is expanded according to the Binomial Theorem, the first term of the expansion will give the probability that $x = 0$, the second term $x = 1$, and so on. The distribution of these probabilities is known as the Binomial Distribution. Statisticians have also shown that the mean of this distribution is equal to np and the variance is equal to npq. The standard deviation is, of course, equal to the square root of the variance.

One may now logically ask, of what value is a distribution that allows only one event to either occur or not occur? For the answer to this, consider the possibility of taking one condition of the work sampling study at a time. All the other conditions can then be considered as nonoccurrences of this one event. Using this approach we can now proceed with the discussion of binomial theory.

Elementary statistics tell us that as n becomes large the Binomial Distribution approaches the Normal Distribution. Since work sampling studies involve quite large sample sizes the Normal Distribution is a satisfactory approximation of the Binomial Distribution. Rather than use the Binomial Distribution with a mean of np and a standard deviation of $\sqrt{npq}$, we can use the distribution of a proportion with a mean of p (i.e., $\dfrac{np}{n}$) and a standard deviation of $\sqrt{\dfrac{pq}{n}}\left(\text{i.e., } \dfrac{\sqrt{npq}}{n}\right)$. In work sampling studies, we take a sample of size n in an attempt to estimate p. We know according to elementary sampling theory that we cannot expect the p' (p' = the proportion based on a sample) of each sample to be the true value of p. We do however, expect the p' of any sample to fall within the range of $p \pm 2$ sigma approximately 95 per cent of the time. In other words, if p is the true percentage of a given condition, we can expect p' of any sample to fall outside the limits $p \pm 2$ sigma only about 5 times in 100 due to chance alone. This theory will be used to derive the total sam-

---
[2] *Ibid.*, p. 334.

ple size required to give a certain degree of accuracy. It will be used also for sub-sample sizes a little later.

Determining Observations Needed

In order to determine the number of observations needed, the analyst must know how accurate his results must be. The larger the number of observations, the more valid the final answer will be. Three thousand observations will give considerably more reliable results than three hundred. However, if the accuracy of the end result is not the prime consideration, three hundred observations may be ample.

In random sampling procedures, there is always the chance that the final result of the observations will be beyond the acceptable tolerance. These sampling errors will diminish as the size of the sample increases. The standard error of a sample percentage shown in most textbooks on statistics may be expressed by the equation:

$$\sigma_p = \sqrt{\frac{p(1-p)}{n}}$$

where

σ_p = the standard deviation of a percentage
p = true percentage occurrence of the element being sought expressed as a decimal
n = total number of random observations upon which p is based

By approximating the true percentage occurrence of the element being sought and knowing the allowable standard error permitted, it is possible to substitute back in the above expression and compute n.

$$n = \frac{p(1-p)}{\sigma_p^{2}}$$

For example, it is desired to determine the number of observations required with 95 per cent confidence so that the true proportion of personal and unavoidable delay time is within the interval 6–10 per cent. It is expected that the unavoidable and personal delay time encountered in the section of the plant under study is 8 per cent. These assumptions expressed graphically in terms of the normal curve are shown in Figure 20–1.

In this case, p would equal .08 and σ_p would equal 1 per cent or .01. Using these values, we can solve for n as follows:

$$n = \frac{.08\ (1 - .08)}{(.01)^2}$$

$$= 736 \text{ observations}$$

Frequently it is desirable to express the interval of the element being sought as a per cent element tolerance. In the example given, we use a

± 25 per cent element tolerance (.02/.08). To simplify the calculation of n for varying tolerances of the element being sought for a given confidence level, it is possible to construct an alignment chart. Figure 20–2 illustrates such an alignment chart for 95 per cent confidence limits (±2 standard deviations).

After the initial estimate of the number of observations have been obtained, a more accurate estimation of p may be computed. By using the above equation, $n = \dfrac{p(1-p)}{\sigma_p{}^2}$, again the achieved accuracy is computed. If the achieved accuracy is as good or better than the desired accuracy, we

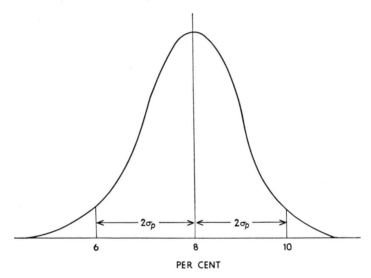

FIG. 20–1.   Distribution of percentage of unavoidable delay allowances required within a given section of a plant.

accept this p' as the true value of the population value p. If the desired accuracy has not been obtained, more observations are taken and the above process is repeated.

Determine the Frequency of the Observations

The frequency of the observations is dependent for the most part on the number of observations required and the time limit that has been placed on the development of the data. For example, if 3600 observations were needed and the study was to be completed in 30 calendar days, we should need to obtain approximately:

$$\frac{3600 \text{ observations}}{20 \text{ working days}} = 180 \text{ observations per working day}$$

Of course, the number of analysts available and the nature of the work being studied will also influence the frequency of the observations. For example, if only one analyst is available and if he is accumulating allowance data on a limited battery of facilities, it may be impractical for him to take 180 observations during one working day. Once the number of observations per day has been determined, then the actual time that the analyst records his observations must be selected. In order

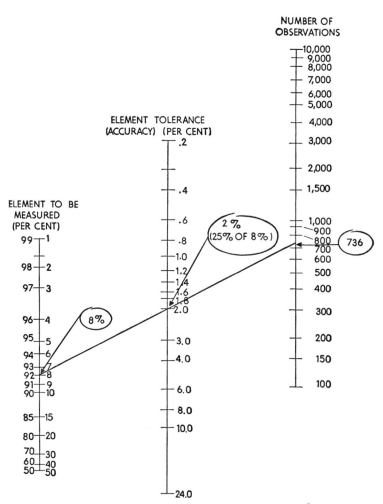

Courtesy: R. P. Heller

FIG. 20-2. Nomogram to determine number of random observations for 95 per cent confidence limits.

to obtain a representative sample, it is important that observations be taken at all times of the working day.

In the example cited, we may assume that one analyst is available and that he is studying a battery of 20 turret lathes in order to determine personal and unavoidable delay allowance. He has calculated that 180 observations per day will be required and since he has 20 machines to observe, he must make 9 random trips to the machine floor every 8-hour working day for a period of 20 days. The time of day selected for these 9 observations should be chosen at random daily. Thus no set pattern should be established from day to day as to the appearance time of the analyst on the production floor.

One method that may be used is to select daily 9 numbers from a statistical table of random numbers, ranging from 1 to 48 (see Appendix 3, Table XLI). Let each number carry a value in minutes equivalent to 10 times its size. The numbers selected can then set the time in minutes from the beginning of the working day to the time for taking the observations. For example, the random number 20 would mean that the analyst should make a series of observations 200 minutes after the beginning of the shift. If the working day began at 8:00 A.M., then at 20 minutes after 11:00 A.M. an inspection of the 20 turret lathe operators (in the example cited above) would be made.

Observing and Recording the Data

So as to record conveniently the necessary information, the analyst should design a chart for posting the frequency of events as they occur. A representative sample form for a shift study is shown in Figure 20–3. Here 6 random observations of each facility were made per shift. A digit designating the particular observation was indicated in the space provided for the state of each facility under study. Since 14 facilities were being studied, a total of 84 observations were made per shift.

As the analyst approaches the work area, he should not anticipate the recording he expects to make. He should walk to a point a given distance from the facility, make his observation, and record the facts. It might be helpful to make an actual mark on the floor on which the analyst must stand before making his observations. If the operator or machine being studied is idle, the analyst should determine the reason for idleness, confirming the reason with the line foreman before making the proper entry. The analyst should learn to take visual observations, making his written entries after leaving the scene of the work area. This will minimize a feeling of being watched on the part of the shop workers and they will perform in their accustomed manner.

To help assure that the operators perform in their usual fashion, it is advisable to inform them of the purpose of the study. The fact that no watch is used tends to relieve the operators of a certain mental tension; little difficulty is experienced in getting their full co-operation.

Application in Establishing Allowances

One of the most extensive uses of work sampling has been in the establishment of allowances to be used in conjunction with normal times so as to determine allowed times. However, the technique is also being used for establishing standards of production, for determining machine utili-

WORK SAMPLING OBSERVATION RECORD

STUDY NO. ___46___ STUDY AREA ___Section C of Heavy Machine Shop___

PLANT ___DuBois___ REMARKS ___Were Producing Three Cylinder Turbines___

DATE ___5/13/58___

OBSERVER ___R. Guild___

MACHINE	DWG.	CUTTING	SETUP	MACHINE IDLE	CRANE WAIT	WAIT-INSPECTION	AID INSPECTION	WAIT-TOOLS NOT AVAILABLE	WAIT-TOOL TROUBLE	CONFER WITH OTHER SHIFT	TOOL HANDLING	GET OR GRIND TOOLS	CONFER WITH FOREMAN, INSP.	WAIT FOR JOB	REMOVE CHIPS, CLEAN TABLE	MISCELLANEOUS	NO OPERATOR
20' VBM	93J967	3 5	4						1	6		2					
16' VBM (S)	98J469 / 90J384	2 5		3									4 6 1				
28' VBM	34E9	2 6	4	3 5	1												
12' VBM	96J961	2 5	4						1	3 6							
16' PLANER	98J184	3 4 5	1														
8' IMM	97J686	3 4		1 6						2							
16' VBM	96J939	1 3 4 6								2		5					
14' PLANER	92J518	1 2 3 4 5 6															
72" E.LATHE	97J43	2 4 5 6	1							3							
96" E.LATHE E-1810	30F307	2 3 4	1 6							5							
96" E.LATHE	36F463	2 3 5 6	1 4														
160" E.LATHE	93J771	2 3	6			5			1	4							
11-1/2' PLNR (S)	90J158 / 96J798	3	2 4 5 6							1							
32' VBM	96J739	1 2 3 4 5 6															
Total		40	13	10	1	2	1		3	9		2	3				= 84

FIG. 20—3. Observation form for recording events on 14 facilities during work sampling study.

zation, for allocation of work assignments, and for methods improvements.

As explained in Chapter 16, the determination of time allowances must be correct if fair standards are to be realized. Prior to the introduction of work sampling, allowances for personal reasons and unavoidable delays were frequently determined by taking a series of all-day studies on several operations, and then averaging the results. Thus, the number of trips to the rest room, the number of trips to the drinking fountain, the number of interruptions, and so forth could be recorded, timed, and

XYZ ELECTRIC PRODUCTS, INC.

PLANT _26_
DEPARTMENT _4_

SUMMARY SHEET (RATIO DELAY)

DATE _4/22/54_

OPERATION	Engineer	Supply	Quality	Mechanic	Supervision	Turning on Light	Miscellaneous	Working		Number of Interferences	TOTAL OBSER.	PER CENT ALLOWANCE
Bench	1	11	1	0	12	1	119	2,750		26	2,895	.95
Bench Machine	0	2	0	0	5	0	69	984		7	1,060	.71
Machine	0	1	6	11	9	0	29	1,172		27	1,228	2.30
Spray	0	0	0	7	36	0	262	1,407		43	1,712	3.06

REMARKS: Summary Sheet for Interference Allowances.
See observation sheet for details of Miscellaneous. Miscellaneous was included in working category because in all cases downtime was credited to the operators.

NOTE: ALL OBSERVATIONS ARE TO BE TAKEN AT RANDOM.

FIG. 20–4. Summary of interruptions on various classes of work taken from work sampling study for determination of unavoidable delay allowance.

analyzed, and a fair allowance determined. Although this method gave the answer, it was a costly, time-consuming operation that was fatiguing to both the analyst and the operator. Through ratio delay study, a great number of observations (usually over 2,000) are taken at different times of the day, and of different operators. Then, if the total number of legitimate occurrences other than work that involve the operators is divided by the total number of working observations, the result will tend to equal the percentage allowance that should be given the operator for the class of work being studied. The different elements that enter into personal delays and unavoidable delays can be kept separate, and an equitable allowance determined for each class or category. Figure 20–4 illustrates a summary of a ratio delay study for determining unavoidable delay allowances on bench, bench machine, machine, and spray operations. It will be noted that in 26 cases out of 2,895 observations made on bench operations, there were interferences. This indicated an unavoidable delay allowance of .95 per cent on this class of work.

Application in Determining Machine Utilization

Machine utilization is readily determined by the work sampling technique in the same manner that was explained in establishing allowances. In order to give the reader a clearer understanding of the steps involved, a case history will be related.

It was desired to gain information as to machine utilization in a section of a heavy machine shop. Management had estimated that actual cutting time in this section should be 60 per cent of the working day in order to comply with quotations being submitted. There were 14 facilities involved in this section of the shop and it was estimated that approximately 3,000 observations should be taken in order to get the accuracy desired.

A work sampling form was then designed (see Figure 20–3) to accommodate the 16 possible states that each of the facilities under study might be in at the time of an observation.

In order to assure random observations, a random pattern of visitation to the shop area was established. Six observations of the 14 facilities were made during each shift. To get the required total number of observations, 36 separate shifts were observed—12 studies on each of the three shifts.

Since there were 14 machines and 6 observations of each per shift, a quick check for 84 separate readings per sheet assured complete coverage of the shift (see Figure 20–3). Each trip took the analyst about 15 to 20 minutes, thus he was occupied on this work only about 2 hours per shift, leaving him free to perform his other work during the remaining 6 hours.

Since it was principally desired to learn the status of the actual cutting time in this section, a cumulative percentage machine cutting chart was kept (see Figure 20–5). At the beginning of each day's study, all previous cutting observations were taken cumulatively as a ratio to the total observations to date. By the end of the tenth day of study, the percentage of machine cutting time began to level off at 50.5 per cent.

After 36 shifts had been studied, the sums of all observations in each category divided by the total number of observations resulted in percentages which represented the distribution of the cutting time, set-up time, and the various delay times listed. Figure 20–6 illustrates the summary sheet of this study. It will be noted that cutting time amounted to 50.7 per cent. The percentage of time required by the various delays indicated areas for method improvement that would help increase the cutting time.

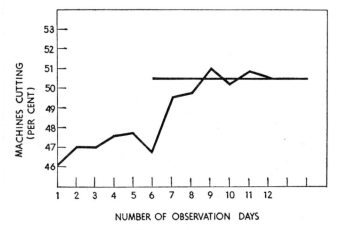

FIG. 20–5. Cumulative percentage machine cutting.

Application in Establishing Indirect Labor Standards

Some companies[3] are finding this tool applicable for the establishment of incentive standards on indirect labor operations. The technique is the same as for allowance determination. A large number of random observations is taken; then the percentage of the number of observations that the facility or operation is working will approximate the percentage time that it is truly in that state.

One company's technique for taking work sampling studies on clerical operations is to take observations on each operator at one-minute intervals. The various elements of work in which the operator may be engaged are assigned identifying numbers, and the analyst, at the time of the observation, merely checks the appropriate number in the space provided on his form. Every five minutes, the analyst rates the performance of the operator in the space provided. At the end of the study, a selective average rating factor is determined.

The normal minutes required for a given element of work may be expressed:

$$T_n = \frac{P \times N}{P_a}$$

where

T_n = Normal minutes to perform the element
P = Selective average rating factor
N = Total observations for the given element
P_a = Total production for period studied

For example, in order to determine the normal time for the element "write report heading on one BM report," the analyst may have prepared

---
[3] Aluminum Company of America and Douglas Aircraft Co.

DATE 7-15-58
OBSERVER R. Guild

MACHINE	DWG.	CUTTING	SETUP	MACHINE IDLE	CRANE WAIT	WAIT-INSPECTION	AID INSPECTION	WAIT-TOOLS NOT AVAILABLE	WAIT-TOOL TROUBLE	CONFER WITH OTHER SHIFT	TOOL HANDLING	GET OR GRIND TOOLS	CONFER WITH FOREMAN, INSP.	WAIT FOR JOB	REMOVE CHIPS CLEAN TABLE	MISCELLANEOUS	NO OPERATOR
20′ VBM		101	7	14	2	3		1		2	37	5	3			6	35	216
16′ VBM		102	34	14	15	3	1		1	1	28	5	7	4				216
28′ VBM		119	34	10	5	5	2			1	18	2	2				18	216
12′ VBM		109	24	12	13	6	1			3	26	6	3	3		2	6	216
16′ PLANER		127	17	6	2	2					22		15			4	12	216
8′ IMM		64	18	17	16	3				2	30	7				28	28	216
16′ VBM		147	19	10	14	3					15	2		1		1	3	216
14′ PLANER		140	8	5	7	2			2	2	17	3	3	3		11	18	216
72″ E. LATHE		99	13	12	7	3			1		32	8	2			3	36	216
96″ E. LATHE		89	9	29	18	11			2		29	8	3	4		3	10	216
96″ E. LATHE		109	14	12	8	10	3	3			32	9	8	2		1	5	216
160″ E. LATHE		72	34	13	14	6	1		4		21	3	3	1	1	4	37	216
11-1/2′ PLNR		106	35	11	10	4			1		11	4	5	3	2	8	16	216
32′ VBM		151	23	8	7	1		3	1		10	2	1	5	2	5		216
		1535	289	173	145	62	8	6	3	19	328	64	34	45	13	76	224	3024 =
%		50.7	9.6	5.9	4.8	2.1	.3	.2	.1	.6	10.8	2.1	1.1	1.5	.4	2.5	7.4	100%

FIG. 20-6. Work sampling summary sheet.

a work sampling study showing 84 observations during which the employee was actually engaged in performing this work element. During the study period, 12 reports were made and it was determined that the

1. SIGHT–VERIFY REPORT TOTAL	11. OBTAIN INFORMATION (DISCUSS, PHONE, ETC.)
2. HEADINGS	12. OBTAIN SUPPLIES (PLUS TRIPS)
3. POSTING FROM REPORT	13. FILING
4. DELIVERY	14.
5. MANUAL REPORT PREPARATION	15.
6. EDITING –ASSIGN NO'S (RECAP NO'S ETC.)	16.
7. CORRECT ERROR CARDS	17.
8. ADDING	18. IDLE TIME
9. TYPING	19. PERSONAL TIME
10. TELEGRAMS —RECEIVING–SENDING	20. MISCELLANEOUS

TABULATING–CLERICAL

FROM 8:00 TO 8:40   DATE 1/12/55 Cavanaugh

MI.	1	2	3	4	5	6	7	8	9	10	11	12	13	14	15	16	17	I	P	M	LEV.	REMARKS
1																				✓		NOT HERE
2																				✓		NOT HERE
3					✓																	
4					✓																	
5					✓																110	
6					✓																	
7			✓																			
8			✓																			
9					✓																	
10					✓																115	
11					✓																	
12					✓																	
13					✓																	
14					✓																	
15					✓																115	
16					✓																	
17					✓																	
18					✓																	
19					✓																	
20					✓																100	
21					✓																	
22					✓																	
23					✓																	
24					✓																	
25																				✓	105	SEARCH FOR STAMP
26																				✓		DATE STAMP
27						✓																
28						✓																
29						✓																
30																				✓	110	OBTAIN CLIPS
31						✓																
32						✓																
33						✓																
34						✓																
35						✓															110	
36						✓																
37						✓																
38						✓																
39						✓																
40						✓															115	
TOTAL			2		20	13														5		

FIG. 20–7. Work sampling time study form for studying clerical operations.

selective average rating factor was 110 per cent. The normal time would then equal:

$$\frac{(110\%)(84)}{12 \text{ reports}} = 7.7 \text{ minutes normal time per report heading}$$

Figure 20–7 illustrates the study form developed for taking a 40-minute study. The columns I, P, and M are to accommodate idle, personal delays, and miscellaneous observations. Under the column headed "Lev" is recorded every 5 minutes the performance factor of the operator. The ac-

companying table illustrates representative standard data developed by
the technique just outlined.

PUNCH AND VERIFY STANDARD ELEMENTS

(Punch and Verify Section of Tabulating Department)

Code	Normal Min./Occ.	Description
P1001	.377	*Get Material from Work Table.* Operator gets up from workplace, walks (4 feet to 22 feet) to obtain material, returns to workplace.
P1002	.356	*Put Program Card on Machine.* Operator selects proper program card from small card file (4 × 7½ inch) at normal arms length on worktable at left. Operator removes program cylinder from machine, attaches program card, and locks cylinder in machine. (Includes remove previous program card.)
P1003	.016	*Remove Cards from Machine; Stamp Copy.* Operator removes cards from machine receptacle at left, stamps copy (invoices, order IBM list, etc.), with operator identification stamp.
P1004	.071	*Tube Code Reference.* Operator refers to reference board to obtain tube type tabulating code (6 digits). Reference board is indexed by RTMA tube type descriptions.
P1005	.065	*Place Cards and Copy in Work Bin.* Operator places copy and cards in slots beneath worktable on left. Normal arm's reach.
P1006	.377	*Give Cards and Copy to Verifier.* Operator gets up, walks (4 to 22 feet), and places cards and copy on worktable of verifier.
P1007	.300	*Punch Group Card.* Operator punches group card containing information common to the group of work (see individual description).
P1008	.300	*Punch Work Card.* Operator punches work card containing information common to the particular unit (order, invoice, bill, etc.) (see individual description).
P1009	.300	*Punch Total Card.* Operator punches card containing common or total information (see individual description).
P1010	Chart	*Punch Detail Card.* Operator punches detail card containing information partially duplicated from group. Work on total card and punches information relevant to the individual item (ex: a particular tube type as an item on an order).
P1011	Chart	*Punch Delivery Date Card.* Operator punches card bearing delivery dates of individual items.

This company's technique can be criticized in that random observations have not been taken. Consequently, biased results could occur. For example, some short cyclic element may be completely omitted by taking observations at regular one-minute intervals. This would not happen if sufficient random observations were taken. The expression used by this company for establishing standards on office work can be modified so as to be applicable on work sampling studies involving random observations rather than regular ones a minute apart. This may be expressed:

$$T_a = \frac{(n)(T)(P)}{(P_a)(N)}$$

Where:

T_a = Allowed elemental time
P = Performance rating factor
P_a = Total production for period studied
n = Total observations of element under study
N = Total observations of study
T = Total operator time represented by study

For example, assume a standard was to be established on the maintenance operation of lubricating fractional horsepower motors. If a work sampling study of 120 hours revealed that, after 3,600 observations, lubrication of fractional horsepower motors on the facilities being studied was taking place in 392 cases and a total of 180 facilities using fractional horsepower motors were maintained and the average performance factor was .90, then the allowed time for lubricating a fractional horsepower motor would be:

$$\frac{(392 \text{ observations}) (7,200 \text{ minutes}) (.90 \text{ performance factor})}{(180 \text{ total production}) (3,600 \text{ total observations})} =$$

$$\frac{(392) (7,200) (.90)}{(180) (3,600)} =$$

3.92 minutes to lubricate one fractional horsepower motor.

It can be seen that this tool has many applications. Machine down time can be determined, the relative amount of setup and put-away elements for all classes of work can be made known, and the relative amount of manual, mental, and delay times for clerical work, direct labor, and administrative work can be studied for establishing the ideal work assignments and methods procedures.

Selling Work Sampling

Before beginning a program of work sampling, it is a good idea for the analyst to sell the use and the reliability of the tool to all members of the organization who are to be affected by the results. If it is to be used for establishing allowances, it should be sold to the union and the foreman, as well as company management. This can be done by having several short sessions with representatives of the various interested parties and explaining examples of the law of probability, thus illustrating why ratio delay procedures will work. Unions as well as workmen look with favor upon work sampling techniques, once the procedure is fully explained, since work sampling is completely impersonal, does not utilize the stop watch, and is based on accepted mathematical and statistical methods.

In the initial session where work sampling is explained, the simple study in tossing unbiased coins may be used. All participants will, of course, readily recognize that a single coin toss stood a 50–50 chance of being heads. When asked how they would have determined the probability of heads versus tails, they undoubtedly will propose tossing a coin a few times to find out. When asked if two times is adequate, they will respond "No." Ten times may be suggested and the response will be "that may not be adequate." When 100 times is suggested, the group will agree: "That should do it with some degree of assurance." This example will firmly plant the principal requisite of work sampling— adequate sample size to insure statistical significance.

The instructor would next discuss the probable results of tossing four unbiased coins. It can be explained that there is only one arrangement in

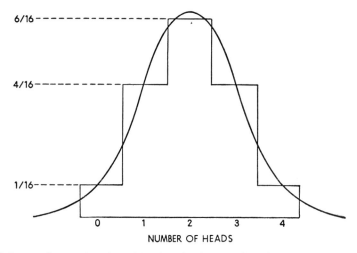

FIG. 20–8.   Distribution of number of heads with infinite number of tosses using four unbiased coins.

which the coins can fall showing no heads, only one arrangement that permits all heads. However, three heads can result from four possible arrangements and likewise one head can result from four possible arrangements. There are six possible arrangements that will give two heads.

With all sixteen possibilities thus accounted for, the group will recognize that if four unbiased coins are tossed continually they will distribute themselves as shown in figure 20–8.

After the above explanation and the demonstration of this distribution by making several tosses and recording the results, it will readily be accepted that a hundred tosses could demonstrate a normal distribution. Furthermore, it will be understood that a thousand tosses would probably approach a normal distribution more closely and a hundred thousand would give a nearly perfect distribution, but not sufficiently more accurate than the thousand toss distribution to be economically worth the extra effort. Here the idea of approaching significant accuracy rapidly at first, and then at a diminishing rate, can be established.

Now it can be pointed out that a machine or operator could be in a heads or tails state. For example, a machine could be running (heads) or idle (tails). An example can be demonstrated where 360 observations are made on a turret lathe. These observations might give the following data:

OPERATION	OBSERVATION	TOTAL	PER CENT
	̄H̄L ̄H̄L ̄H̄L ̄H̄L ̄H̄L ̄H̄L ̄H̄L ̄H̄L ̄H̄L ̄H̄L II		
	̄H̄L ̄H̄L ̄H̄L ̄H̄L ̄H̄L ̄H̄L ̄H̄L ̄H̄L ̄H̄L ̄H̄L		
RUNNING	̄H̄L ̄H̄L ̄H̄L ̄H̄L ̄H̄L ̄H̄L ̄H̄L ̄H̄L ̄H̄L ̄H̄L	252	70
	̄H̄L ̄H̄L ̄H̄L ̄H̄L ̄H̄L ̄H̄L ̄H̄L ̄H̄L ̄H̄L ̄H̄L		
	̄H̄L ̄H̄L ̄H̄L ̄H̄L ̄H̄L ̄H̄L ̄H̄L ̄H̄L ̄H̄L ̄H̄L		
	̄H̄L ̄H̄L ̄H̄L ̄H̄L ̄H̄L		
	̄H̄L ̄H̄L ̄H̄L ̄H̄L III		
IDLE	̄H̄L ̄H̄L ̄H̄L ̄H̄L	108	30
	̄H̄L ̄H̄L ̄H̄L ̄H̄L		
	̄H̄L ̄H̄L ̄H̄L ̄H̄L		
		TOTAL	360	100

A cumulative plot of "running" would level off, giving an indication as to when it would be safe to stop taking readings (see Figure 20-9).

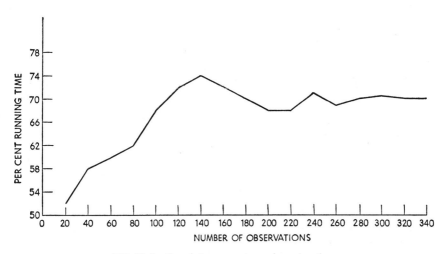

FIG. 20-9. Cumulative percentage of running time.

All those in attendance would understand that "idle" machine time could be broken down into the various types of interruptions and delays and could be accounted for and evaluated.

Once the validity of work sampling has been sold up and down the line, the analyst then should clearly define his problem. If he wishes to establish allowance data, he should make a summary of all elements that customarily are included in the various allowance categories. To do this, he would be wise to make a preliminary survey of the class of work for which the allowances are to be determined. It may be necessary to spend several hours on the production floor observing all types of delays encountered, so that the element listing can be complete.

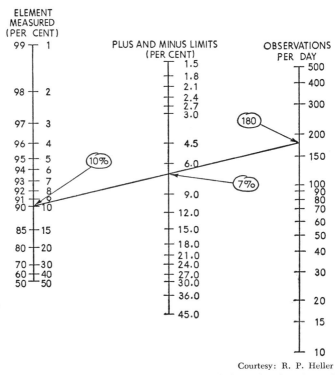

ELEMENT
MEASURED
(PER CENT)

PLUS AND MINUS LIMITS
(PER CENT)

OBSERVATIONS
PER DAY

Courtesy: R. P. Heller

FIG. 20–10. Nomogram for establishing control limits on daily results of work sampling study.

Use of Control Charts

The control chart techniques, used so extensively in statistical quality control work, can be applied readily to work sampling studies. Since work sampling studies deal exclusively with percentages or proportions, the "p" chart is most used.

In order to understand how the "p" chart can be of value in a work sampling study, the reader should have an understanding of the theory behind control charting. While a complete discussion of control chart theory is impractical in a text of this nature, a brief discussion will now be presented so as to enable the reader to see the logic in the use of control charts.

The first problem encountered in setting up a control chart is the choice of limits. In general, a balance is sought between the cost of looking for an assignable cause when there is none present and not looking for an assignable cause when there is one present. As an arbitrary choice the 3 sigma limits will be used throughout the remaining discussion for establishing control limits on the "p" chart.

Suppose p for a given condition is .10 and samples of size 180 are taken each day. By substituting in equation (1), control limits of $\pm.07$ are obtained. The nomogram (Figure 20–10) is designed to give the correct 3 sigma limits for various sample sizes and various values of p. A control chart similar to Figure 20–11 could then be constructed. The p' values for each day would be plotted on the chart.

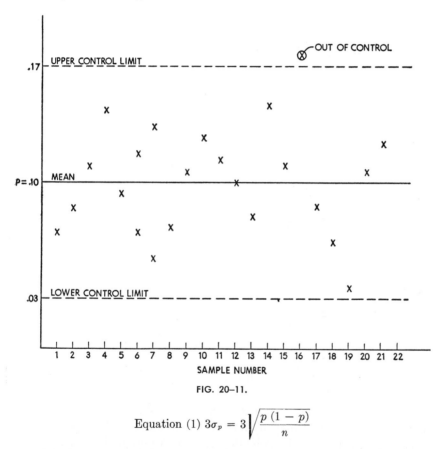

FIG. 20–11.

$$\text{Equation (1)} \quad 3\sigma_p = 3\sqrt{\frac{p(1-p)}{n}}$$

What does a control chart indicate? In quality control work we say that the control chart indicates whether or not the process is in control. In a similar manner, the analyst in work sampling considers points beyond 3 sigma limits of p out of control. Thus, a certain sample that yields a value of p' is assumed to have been drawn from a population with an expected value of p if p' falls within the plus or minus three sigma limits of p. Expressed another way, a sample with a value p' is assumed to be from some different population or the original population has been changed if p' falls outside the 3 sigma limits.

As in quality work, points other than those out of control may be of some statistical significance. For example, it is more likely that a point will fall outside the 3 sigma limits than that 2 successive points will fall between the 2 and 3 sigma limits. Hence, 2 successive points between the 2 and 3 sigma limits would indicate that the population had changed. Series of significant sets of points have been derived. This idea is dis-

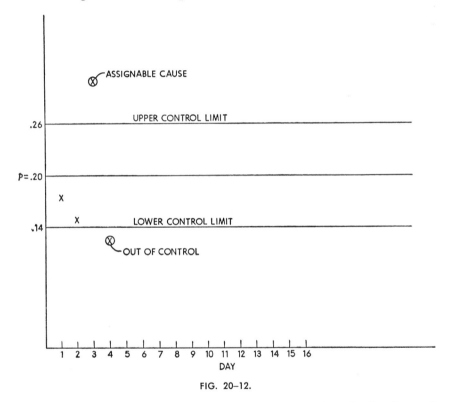

FIG. 20–12.

cussed in most statistical quality control texts under the heading of "Theory of Runs."

A hypothetical example will show how control charts can facillitate a work sampling study. Company XYZ wishes to measure the percentage of machine down time in the lathe department. An original estimate shows down time to be approximately .20. The desired results are to be within ±5 per cent of p with a level of significance of .95. The sample size is computed to be 6,400. It was decided to take the 6,400 readings over a period of 16 days at the rate of 400 readings per day. A p' value was computed for each daily sample of 400. A p chart was set up for $p = .20$ and subsample size $N = 400$ (see Figure 20–12). Readings were taken and p' was plotted each day. On the third day the point for p' went above the upper control limit. An investigation revealed there had been an accident in the plant and several of the men had left their machines to assist the injured employee to the plant hospital. Since an assignable cause of error was discovered, this point was discarded from the study. If a control chart had not been used, these observations would have been included in the final estimate of p.

On the fourth day the point for p' fell below the lower control limit. No assignable cause could be found for this occurrence. The industrial engineer in charge of the project also noted that the p' values for the first two

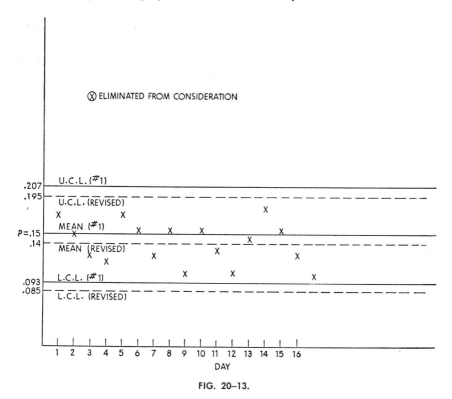

FIG. 20–13.

days were below the mean p. He decided to compute a new value for p using the values from days 1, 2, and 4. The new estimate of p turned out to be .15. To obtain the desired accuracy n is now only 5,700 observations. The control limits also change as shown in Figure 20–13. Observations were taken for 12 more days and the individual p' values were plotted on the new chart. As can be seen, all the points fell within the control limits. A more accurate value of p was then calculated using all 6,000 observations. The new estimate of p was determined to be .14. A recalculation of achieved accuracy showed it to be slightly better than the desired accuracy. As a final check, new control limits were computed using p equal to .14. The dashed lines superimposed on Figure 20–13 showed that all points were still in control using the new limits. If a point would have fallen out of control, it would have been eliminated and a new value of p would have been computed. This process would then be repeated until the desired accuracy is achieved and all p' values were in control.

One may ask, is there any reason to assume that since the per cent down time today is .14 that it will be .14 a year from now? Improvement should be a continuing process and per cent "down" time should diminish. One purpose of work sampling is to determine areas of work which might be improved. After discovering such areas, an attempt is made to improve the situation. Control charts can be used to show progressive improvement of work areas. This idea is especially important if work sampling studies are used to establish standard times, for such standards must be changed whenever conditions change if they are to remain realistic.

Conclusion

The work sampling method is another tool that has been made available to the time and methods study analyst that allows him to get the facts in an easier, faster way. Every person who is in the field of methods, time study, and wage payment should become familiar with the advantages, limitations, uses, and application of this technique. In summary the following considerations should be kept in mind:

1. Explain and sell the work sampling method before putting it to use.
2. Confine individual studies to similar groups of machines or operations.
3. Use as large a sample size as is practical.
4. Take individual observations at random times so that observations will be recorded for all hours of the day.
5. The observations should be taken over a reasonably long period of time (two weeks or more).

TEXT QUESTIONS

1. Where was work sampling first used?
2. What advantages are claimed for the work sampling procedure?
3. In what areas does work sampling have application?
4. How many observations should be recorded in determining the allowance for personal delays in a forge shop if it is expected that a 5 per cent personal allowance will suffice, and this value is to remain between 4 and 6 per cent 95 per cent of the time?
5. How is it possible to determine the time of day to make the various observations so that biased results will not occur?
6. What considerations should be kept in mind relative to the taking of work sampling studies?
7. To get ±5 per cent precision on work that is estimated to take 80 per cent of the workers' time, how many random observations will be required at the 95 per cent confidence level?

8. If the average handling activity during a 10-day study is 82 per cent and the number of daily observations is 48, how much tolerance can be allowed on each day's per cent activity?

GENERAL QUESTIONS

1. Is there an application for work sampling studies in the determination of fatigue? Explain.
2. How can the validity of work sampling be sold to the employee who is not familiar with probability and statistical procedure?

CHAPTER 21

Establishing Standards on Indirect Work

SINCE 1900 THE PERCENTAGE IN-
crease of indirect workers has more than doubled that of direct labor workers. Groups which usually are classified as indirect labor include shipping and receiving, trucking, stores, inspection, office clerical, tool-room, janitorial, and maintenance.

This rapid growth in the number of office workers, maintenance workers, and other indirect employees is due to several reasons. First, the increased mechanization of industry and complete automation of many processes has decreased the need for craftsmen and even for operators. This trend toward mechanization has resulted in a greater demand for electricians, technicians, and other servicemen. Also, the design of complicated machines and controls has resulted in greater demand for engineers, designers, and draftsmen.

Another reason for the rise in the number of indirect employees is that office and maintenance work has not been subjected to methods study and technical advances that have been applied so effectively to industrial processes.

With a large share of most payrolls being earmarked for indirect labor, progressive management is beginning to realize the opportunities for the application of methods and standards in this area.

Automation

The term automation may be defined as "increased mechanization." A manufacturing process that is completely automated is one that is capable of operating for prolonged periods without the use of human effort. Few industries or even processes within an industry are completely automated. However, there is a pronounced tendency toward semi-automation in American and European industry. With the increasing demand for greater production at lower costs, it is anticipated that as much as 20 per cent of American industry will be automated or semi-automated within the next decade.

A program of automation begins with the development of the fully automatic machine (such as the automatic screw machine) integrated with automatic transfer handling devices, so that a series of operations may be performed automatically.

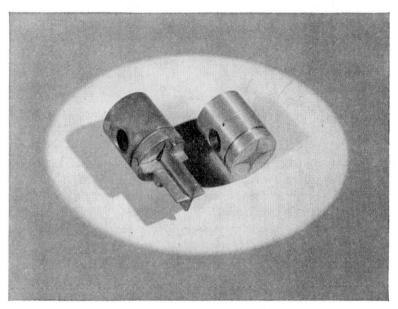

FIG. 21–1. Die casting with fin so that work can be handled in automated type equipment.

In order to determine the extent of automation justified, two factors should be considered: (1) the quantity requirements of the product, (2) the nature or design of the product itself.

If quantity requirements of the product are large, the design engineer will endeavor to design the product so that it lends itself to automation. Frequently, by adding something to a part, such as a lug, fin, extension, or hole, it will be possible to provide means of mechanical handling to and from the work station. Such a redesign can accommodate indexing at a work station for successive production operations. For example, a holding fin was added to the die casting for producing a compressor piston. This permitted mechanical fingers to hold the work while process-ing, as well as to automatically transport the work between production stations (see Fig. 21–1).

As automation equipment is developed, the need for effective preventative maintenance is apparent. A failure of a single minor component may cause the shutdown of a complete process or even the entire plant. This fact, together with the complexity of automated equipment through the use of pneumatic, hydraulic, and electronic controls, brings out the reasons for the growth of indirect workers not only in numbers but in diversification of occupation.

Methods Improvements in Maintenance and Material Handling Operations

A program of establishing standards on indirect labor should be preceded by careful analysis of the existing methods. This in itself invariably will result in the introduction of economies. For example, one large plant with considerable line shafting made a study, prior to the establishment of standards, of the lubrication of the bearings in the shafting that was utilizing the time of 60 men. The result was the setting up of specific routes throughout the plant for each service employee. This reduced the crew for oiling to 29 men.

Frequently, it is advantageous to provide pipe fitters, millwrights and other traveling mechanics with a portable kit of tools that is wheeled right to the job. This eliminates the necessity of the mechanic having to return to the shop to get some tool that he forgot. Supplies such as Allen set-screws, standard fittings, and tape are frequently made a part of the mechanic's kit and transported by hand truck along with his tools, thus making it unnecessary to make several trips to carry material.

A careful analysis should be made as to which jobs require helpers and which do not. Sometimes maintenance men get in the habit of taking a helper along to the job whether he is needed or not.

After good methods have been developed, they must be standardized and taught to the workers who will be using them. This seems apparent, but is too often neglected by management.

By giving the same attention to operation improvement in indirect work that has been exercised in direct labor operations, industry can get good results.

Maintenance, Material Handling, and Toolroom Standards

A time standard can be established on any operation or group of operations that can be quantified and measured. If the elements of work performed by the electrician, blacksmith, boilermaker, sheet metal worker, painter, carpenter, millwright, welder, pipe fitter, material handler, toolmaker, and others performing indirect work, are broken down and studied, it usually will be possible to evolve an equitable standard in the same manner that standards are established for production work. The tools used for establishing standards for indirect work are identical with those used in direct work—time study, predetermined motion time standards, standard data, time formulas, and work sampling.

Thus, a standard can be established for such tasks as hanging a door, rewinding a one-horsepower motor, painting a centerless grinder, sweeping the chips from a department, or delivering a skid of 200 forgings. Standard times for each of these operations can be established by measuring the time required for the operator to perform the job, then performance rating the study and applying an appropriate allowance.

Careful study and analysis will reveal more unavoidable delays in indirect work than on direct work because of crew balance and interference. Crew balance is that delay time encountered by one member of a crew while waiting for other members of the team to perform elements of the job. Interference time is the time that a maintenance or other worker is delayed in waiting for other production workers to do necessary work. Both crew-balance delays and interference delays may be thought of as unavoidable delays; however, they are usually characteristic of indirect labor operations only, such as those performed by maintenance workers.

Because of the high degree of variability characteristic of most maintenance and material handling operations, it will be necessary to conduct a sufficient number of independent time studies of each operation to assure completely that average conditions have been determined and that the resulting standard is representative of the time needed for the normal operator to do the job under these average conditions. For example, if a study indicates that 47 minutes are required to sweep a machine floor 60 feet wide by 80 feet long, it will be necessary to assure that average conditions prevailed when the study was taken. Obviously, the work of the sweeper would be considerably more time consuming if the shop was machining cast iron than if an alloy steel was being cut. Not only is the alloy steel much cleaner, but the chips are easier to handle and the fact that slower speeds and feed would be used would result in fewer chips. If the standard of 47 minutes was established when the shop was working with alloy steel, it would be inadequate when the department was producing cast-iron parts. It would be necessary to take additional time studies to assure that average conditions had been determined and that the resulting standards were representative of those conditions.

In a similar manner, standards can be established for painting. Thus, a standard will be determined for overhead painting based on square footage. Likewise, vertical and floor painting can be measured, and time standards can be developed on a square-footage basis.

When painting cylindrical work such as pipe, it is common practice to establish time standards based on the lineal feet of pipe of a given diameter. Thus, we will have a standard for painting 1-inch pipe, $1\frac{1}{2}$-inch pipe, 3-inch pipe, and other sizes.

Just as the automotive industry has established time standards for common repair jobs such as grinding valves, replacing piston rings, and adjusting brakes, so can standards be determined for typical maintenance and repair operations performed on the machine tools within the plant. Thus, a set of time standards can be determined for rewinding fractional horsepower motors. A standard can be established for the rewinding of $\frac{1}{8}$ HP, $\frac{1}{4}$ HP, $\frac{1}{2}$ HP, $\frac{3}{4}$ HP, and so on.

Toolroom work is very similar to work done in job shops. The method by which such tools as a drill jig, milling fixture, form tool, or die will be made can be predetermined quite closely. Consequently, it is possible by time study and/or predetermined elemental times for the analyst to establish a sequence of elements and measure the normal time required for each element. Work sampling provides an adequate tool to determine the allowances which must be added for fatigue, personal, unavoidable, and special delays. The standard elemental times thus developed can be tabularized in the form of standard data or may be used to design time formulas for pricing future work.

Setting Standards on Office Work

More and more management is recognizing its responsibility to determine accurately the appropriate office forces for a given volume of work. In order to control office payrolls, management must develop time standards, as they are the only reliable "yardstick" for evaluating the size of any task.

As for other work, methods analysis should precede work measurement in all office operations. The flow process chart is the ideal tool for presenting the facts of the present method. Once presented, the present method should be reviewed critically in all of its detail. Such factors as purpose of operation, design of forms, office layout, elimination of delays resulting from poor planning and scheduling, and adequacy of existing equipment, should be considered; the primary approaches to operation analysis should be used.

After the completion of a thorough methods program, standards development can commence. Many office jobs are repetitive in nature; consequently, it is not particularly difficult to set fair standards. Central typing pools, billing groups, file clerks, addressograph operators, punch card operators, and tabulating machine operators are representative groups that readily lend themselves to work measurement either by stop watch or motion picture techniques. In studying office work, the analyst should carefully identify element end points, so that standard data may be established for pricing future work. For example, in the typing of production orders, the following elements of work normally occur on each page of each order typed:

1. Pick up production order from pile and position in typewriter.
2. Pick up sheet to be copied from, and place in Copy Right.
3. Read product order instructions.
4. Type heading on order.
   a. Date

    b. Number of pieces
    c. Material
    d. Department

Once standard data have been developed for most of the common elements used in the office, time standards can be achieved quite rapidly and economically. Of course, many clerical positions within an office are made up of a series of diversified activities that do not readily lend themselves to time study. Such work is not made up of a series of standard cycles that continually repeat themselves and, consequently, is more difficult to measure than direct labor operations. Because of this characteristic of some office routines, it is necessary to take many time studies, each of which may be but one cycle in duration. Then, by calculating all studies taken, the analyst develops a standard for typical or average conditions. Thus, a time standard may be calculated for copy typing based on the page. Granted, some pages of technical typing requiring the use of symbols, radicals, fractions, formulas, and other special characters or spacing will take considerably longer than typing the routine page. But if the technical typing is not representative of average conditions, it will not result in an unfair influence on the operator's performance over a period of time: simple typing and shorter than standard pages will tend to balance the extra time needed to type the complex letter.

It usually is not practical to establish standards on office positions that require creative thinking. Thus jobs such as tool designing and product designing should be carefully considered before a decision is made to establish time standards on the work done by the men filling these positions. If standards are established on work of this nature, they should be used for such purposes as a basis for scheduling, control, or labor budgeting and should not be used for purposes of incentive wage payment. Work demanding creative thinking can be retarded if pressure is put on the employee. The result may lead to inferior designs that can be more costly to the business than the amount saved through greater productivity of the designer.

In setting standards for office workers, the analyst usually will find that, since the white-collar worker is not accustomed to having his work measured, he will not like the practice. Therefore, it is important that the same observance of good human relations practiced in the shop be adhered to in the office.

Supervisory Standards

By establishing standards for supervisory work, it is possible to determine equitable supervisor loads and maintain a proper balance between supervision, facilities, clerical employees, and direct labor.

The work sampling technique is probably the most fruitful tool for the development of supervisory standards. The same information could also be attained through all-day stop watch studies, but the cost usually would be prohibitive before reliable data could be obtained. Supervisory standards can be expressed in terms of "effective machine running hours" or some other benchmark.

For example, one study of a manufacturer of vacuum tubes revealed that .223 supervisory hours were required per machine running hour in a given department (Fig. 21-2). The work sampling study showed that,

INDIRECT LABOR STANDARD

JOB - SUPERVISION   DEPT. - GRID   DATE - 4-16-58

Cost Center	Number of Observations	Per cent of Observations	Prorated Hours	Base Indirect Hours	Effective Machine Running Hours (EMRH)	Direct Labor Hours		Base Indirect Hours Per Machine Running Hour (Includes 6% Personal)
Grid Machines	129	21	130	130	2,461			.223
Inspect Grids	161	26	160	160				
Desk Work	54	9	56	56				
Supply Material	18	3	18	18				
Misc. Allow.	150	24	148	148				
Walking	7	1	6	6				
Out of Dept.	11	2	12					
Idle	86	14	86					
Total	616	100	616	518	2,461			.223

FIG. 21-2.

out of 616 observations, the supervisor was working with the grid machines, inspecting grids, doing desk work, supplying material, walking, or engaged in activity classified as miscellaneous allowances a total of 519 times. This figure converted to prorated hours revealed that 518 indirect hours were required while 2,461 machine running hours took place. When a 6 per cent personal allowance was added, a standard of .223 supervisory hours per machine running hour was computed.

$$\frac{518}{(2461)\ (1.00 - .06)} = .223$$

Thus, if one supervisor handled a department of a given type of facility operating 192 machine running hours during a week's period, his efficiency would be:

$$\frac{192 \times .223}{40 \text{ (hrs./week)}} = 107 \text{ per cent}.$$

Standard Data on Indirect Labor

The development of standard data for purposes of establishing standards on indirect labor operations is quite feasible. In fact, in view of the diversification of indirect labor operations, standard data is, if anything, more appropriate on office, maintenance, and other indirect work than it is on standardized production operations.

As individual time standards are calculated, it is wise to tabularize the elements and their respective allowed times for future reference. As the inventory of standard data is built up, the cost of taking new time studies will decline proportionally.

For example, the tabularizing of standard data for fork lift truck operations is based on only six different elements: travel, brake, raise fork, lower fork, tilt fork, and the manual elements required to operate the truck. Once standard data have been accumulated for each of these elements (through the required range), the standard time to perform any fork truck operation may be determined by summarizing the applicable elements. In a similar manner standard data can readily be established on janitorial work elements such as sweep floor; wax and buff floors; dry mop; wet mop; vacuum rugs; clean, dust, and mop lounge.

Several manufacturers of material-handling equipment have taken detailed studies of their product and make standard data, applicable to the equipment, available when the facility is purchased. This information will save the analyst many hours in the development of material-handling time standards.

Universal Indirect Standards

Where the number of maintenance and other indirect operations is great and diversified, the task of developing standard data and/or formulas to preprice all indirect operations may appear to be more costly than the expected savings brought about by the introduction of time standards. In order to reduce the number of different time standards for indirect operations, there has been an effort by some engineers to develop universal indirect standards.

The principle behind universal standards is the assignment of the major proportion of indirect operations (perhaps as much as 90 per cent) to appropriate groups. Each group will have its own standard which will be the average time for all indirect operations assigned to the group. For example, group A may include the indirect operations of:

1. Replace defective union.
2. Repair door (replace two hinges).
3. Replace limit switch.
4. Replace two sections (14' of 1" pipe).

The standard time for any indirect operation performed in group A may be 20 minutes. This time will represent the mean ($\bar{x}$) of all jobs within the group and the dispersion of the jobs within the group for $\pm 2\sigma$ will be some predetermined percentage of $\bar{x}$ (perhaps ± 10 per cent).

Standards may be established for each group by developing many (several hundred) time standards using standard data, formulas, and stop-watch procedure for typical indirect operations. These standards will be arranged in ascending sequence and then be bracketed in sufficient divisions so that the range of any bracket does not exceed the desired accuracy of any operation included in the bracket. Similar operations, that have not been studied, but have had the method standardized, may be assigned to the bracket that is representative of the work elements of the operation.

This procedure may utilize as few as 100 standards to cover many thousands of different indirect operations. Since the majority of operations will cluster about the mean of their respective brackets, the total average error introduced by such standards will be slight. This will be especially true when indirect employees perform a broad variety of assignments, which is usually the case.

The application of universal indirect standards offers the opportunity to introduce standards on the majority of indirect operations at a moderate cost and also minimizes the cost of maintaining the indirect standard system.

Advantages of Work Standards on Indirect Work

Standards on indirect work offer distinct advantages to both the employer and the employee. Some of these advantages are:

1. Installation of standards will lead to many operating improvements.
2. The mere fact that standards are being established will result in better operation performance.
3. Indirect labor costs can be related to the work load regardless of fluctuation in the over-all work load.
4. Budgeting of labor loads can be achieved.
5. Efficiency of various indirect labor departments can be determined.
6. Costs of such items as specific repairs, reports, and documents can be easily determined. This frequently results in elimination of needless reports and procedures.
7. System improvements can be evaluated prior to installation. Thus, it is possible to avoid costly mistakes by choosing the right procedure.
8. It is possible to install incentive wage payment plans on these positions, thus allowing employees to increase their earnings.
9. All indirect labor work can be planned and scheduled more accurately, with the obvious resulting benefits of getting the job done on time.
10. Less supervision is required, as a program of work standards tends to enforce itself. As long as each employee knows what is required of him, he will not arbitrarily waste or "kill" time.

Conclusion

The nonrepetitive task, characteristic of many indirect labor operations, is more difficult to study and determine representative standard times for than is the repetitive task that is performed over and over again. Since indirect labor operations are difficult to standardize and study, they have not been widely subjected to methods analysis. Consequently, this area usually offers a greater percentage potential for reducing costs and increasing profits through time study than any other.

After good methods have been introduced and operator training has taken place, it is not only readily possible but it is practical to establish standards on indirect labor operations. The usual procedure is to take a sufficiently large sample of stop-watch time studies to assure the representation of average conditions, and then to tabularize the allowed elemental times in the form of standard data. Fundamental motion data also have a wide application for establishing standards on indirect work. Thus, allowed operation times may be established consistently, accurately, and economically.

TEXT QUESTIONS

1. Why has there been a marked increase in the number of indirect workers employed?
2. Why do more unavoidable delays occur in maintenance operations than on production work?
3. What is meant by crew balance? By interference time?
4. Explain how time standards would be established on janitorial operations.
5. What office operations are readily time studied?
6. Why are standard data especially applicable to indirect labor operations?
7. Summarize the advantages of standards established on indirect work.
8. Why is work sampling the best technique for establishing supervisory standards?

GENERAL QUESTIONS

1. Discuss the implications of establishing time standards for a tool designer, for a product engineer, and for a purchasing agent.
2. Explain how productivity should be reported in an office involving clerical work.

CHAPTER 22

Uses of Time Standards

$$W_{\text{E HAVE FOUND THAT TIME}}$$

standards may be determined in a number of ways:

1. By estimate (see Chapter 11)
2. By performance records (see Chapter 11)
3. By stop-watch time study (see Chapter 14)
4. By standard data (see Chapter 18)
5. By time study formulas (see Chapter 19)
6. By work sampling studies (see Chapter 20)

Methods 3, 4, 5, and 6 will give considerably more reliable results than either method 1 or 2. If standards are to be used for purposes of wage payment, it is essential that they be determined as accurately as possible. Consequently, standards determined by estimate and performance records will not suffice. Of course, standards developed through performance records and estimates are better than no standards at all and frequently can be used to exercise controls throughout an organization.

All of these methods have application under certain conditions and all have limitations as to accuracy and cost of installation.

In the operation of any manufacturing enterprise or business, it is fundamental that we have time standards. Time is the one common denominator from which all elements of cost may be evolved. In fact, everyone uses time standards for practically everything he does or wants anyone else to do. A man arising in the morning will allow himself one hour to wash, shave, dress, eat breakfast, and get to work. This surely represents a time standard that has a bearing on the number of hours of sleep he gets. A football game involves but 60 minutes of playing time. This also represents a standard. The student reading this chapter will allow himself so many minutes to cover the assignment. This, too, is a standard which will affect the student's program for the remainder of the day.

We are particularly interested in the use of time standards as applied to the effective operation of a manufacturing enterprise. Several of the results of the application of time study in this way will be discussed.

Basis for Wage Incentive Plans

Time standards are usually thought of in their relation to wage payment. As important as this is, there are many other uses of standards in the operation of an enterprise. However, the need for reliable and consistent standards is more pronounced in connection with wage payment than in any other area. Without true standards, no incentive plan that endeavors to compensate in proportion to output can possibly succeed. If we have no yardstick, how can we measure individual performance? With standardized methods and standard times, we have a yardstick that will form a basis for wage incentive application.

Common Denominator in Comparing Various Methods

Since time is a common measure for all jobs, time standards are a basis for comparing various methods of doing the same piece of work. If, for example, we thought it might be advantageous to install broaching on a close-tolerance inside diameter rather than to ream the part to size as is currently being done, we could make a sound decision as to the practicality of the change, if time standards were available. Without reliable standards, we should be groping in the dark.

To Secure an Efficient Layout of Available Space

Time is the basis for the determination of the amount of each kind of equipment needed. By being able to know exact requirements relative to facilities, we can achieve the best possible utilization of space. If we know that we shall require 10 milling machines, 20 drill presses, 30 turrent lathes, and 6 grinders in a particular machining department, then we can plan for the layout of this equipment to best advantage. Without time standards, we may have overprovided for one facility, and underprovided for another, thereby inefficiently utilizing the space available.

Means for Determining Plant Capacity

Through the medium of time standards, not only machine capacity, but also department and plant capacity are determined. It is a matter of simple arithmetic to estimate product potential once we know the available facility hours and the time required to produce a unit of product. For example, if the bottleneck operation in the processing of a given product required 15 minutes per piece, and if 10 facilities for this operation existed, then the plant capacity based on a 40-hour per week operation on this product would be:

$$\frac{40 \text{ hours} \times 10}{.25 \text{ hours}} = 1,600 \text{ pieces per week}.$$

Figure 22–1 illustrates a weekly graphic analysis of the direct labor requirements for a specific industrial plant. Note how clearly this chart indicates when the plant will be in a position to produce new customer orders.

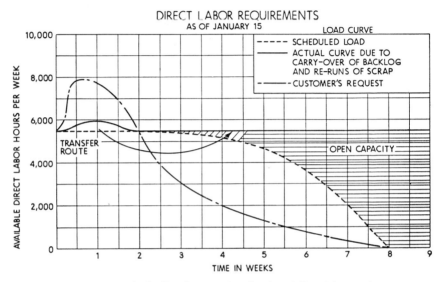

FIG. 22–1. Time standards allow determination of projected direct labor requirements.

Basis for Purchasing New Equipment

Since time standards allow us to determine machine, department, and plant capacity, they also provide the necessary information for determining how many of what type of facilities need be provided for a given volume of production. Accurate comparative time standards also highlight the advantages of one facility over its competitors. For example, we may find it necessary to purchase three additional single-spindle, bench-type drill presses. By reviewing available standards, we shall be able to procure the style and design of drill press that will give the most favorable output per unit of time.

Basis for Balancing Working Force with Available Work

By having concrete information as to required volume of production, as well as amount of time needed to produce a unit of that production, we are able to determine the required labor force. For example, if our production load for a given week is evaluated as 4,420 hours, then we should need: 4,420/40 or 111 operators. This use of standards is especially important in a retrenching market where volume of production is going down. When over-all volume diminishes, if there is no yardstick to determine the actual number of people needed to perform the re- duced load, then there will be a tendency for the entire working force to slow down so that the available work will last. Unless we balance our working force with available volume of work, unit costs will progres- sively rise. It will only be a matter of time, under these circumstances, until production operations will be performed at a substantial loss, thus necessitating increasing selling prices and the facing of further reduc- tions in volume. The cycle will repeat until it becomes necessary to close the plant.

In an expanding market, it is equally important to be able to budget

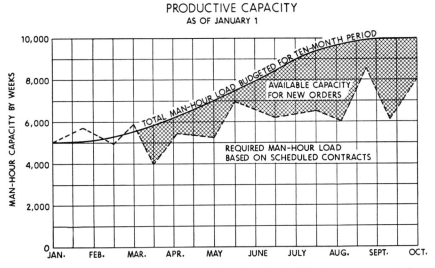

FIG. 22–2. Chart illustrating actual projected man-hour load and budgeted man-hour load.

labor. As customer demands rise, necessitating greater volume of man- power, it is essential that the exact number and type of personnel to be added to the payroll be known so that they can be recruited in suffi- cient time to meet customer schedules. If accurate time standards pre- vail, it is a matter of simple arithmetic to convert product requirements to departmental man-hours.

Figure 22–2 illustrates how over-all plant capacity may be provided in an expanding market. Here the plant anticipates doubling its man- hour capacity in the period between January and November. This budget was based on projecting the scheduled contracts in terms of man-hours and allowing a reasonable cushion (crosshatched section) for receiving additional orders.

In addition to budgeting plant labor requirements, time standards serve in budgeting the labor needs of specific departments. Figure 22–3 illustrates the budgeting of spindle hours in the multiple winding de-

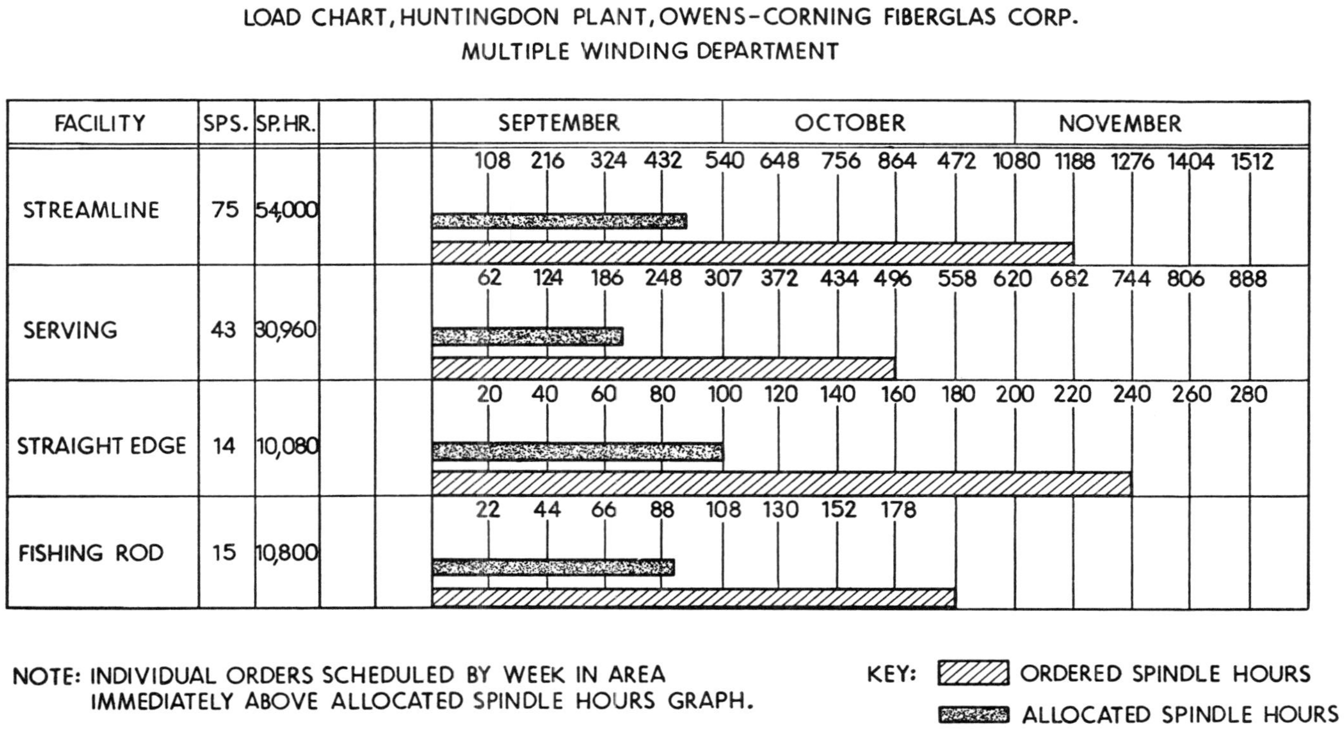

LOAD CHART, HUNTINGDON PLANT, OWENS–CORNING FIBERGLAS CORP.

MULTIPLE WINDING DEPARTMENT

FIG. 22–3.   Chart illustrating the budgeting of spindle hours of a specific department so as to best meet customer needs.

NOTE: INDIVIDUAL ORDERS SCHEDULED BY WEEK IN AREA
IMMEDIATELY ABOVE ALLOCATED SPINDLE HOURS GRAPH.

KEY: ▨ ORDERED SPINDLE HOURS
       ▦ ALLOCATED SPINDLE HOURS

partment of one of the Owens-Corning Fiberglas plants. It will be noted that four product areas are served: "streamline," "serving," "straight-edge," and "fishing rod." In view of present customer requirements, 75 spindles have been allotted for multiple winding of "streamline" products, 42 spindles for "serving," 14 for "straight-edge," and 15 for "fishing rod." Based on this budgeting of spindle and man-hours, the load for "streamline" extends to the end of the first week in November, "serving" to the middle of October, "straight-edge" to the middle of November and "fishing rod" to the last week in October. Although customer requirements fluctuate, it will be possible through the use of time standards to adjust the labor budget of this department to best meet all customer requirements. The solid bar on this chart shows the material that has been allocated to the various product classes as of September 1.

With valid time standards, we are able to keep our working force in proportion to the volume of production required, thus controlling costs and maintaining operation in a competitive market.

Improves Production Control

Production control is that phase of operation that schedules, routes, expedites, and follows up production orders so that operating economies are achieved and customer requirements are best satisfied. The whole function of controlling production is based upon determining where and when the work will be done. This obviously cannot be achieved unless we have a concrete idea as to the "how long."

Scheduling, one of the major functions of production control, is usually handled in three degrees of refinement: (1) long-range or master scheduling, (2) firm order scheduling, and (3) detailed operation scheduling or machine loading.

Long-range scheduling is based on existing volume of production and anticipated volume of production. In this case, specific orders are not given any particular sequence, but are merely lumped together and scheduled in appropriate time periods. Firm order scheduling involves the scheduling of existing orders so as to meet customer demands and still operate in an economical fashion. Here degrees of priority are assigned to specific orders, and anticipated shipping promises are evolved from this schedule. Detailed operation scheduling, or machine loading, is the assignment of specific operations day by day to individual machines. This scheduling is planned to minimize set-up time and machine down time while meeting firm order schedules. Figure 22-4 illustrates the machine loading of a specific department for a period of one week. Note that considerable capacity exists on milling machines, drill presses, and internal thread grinders.

No matter what the degree of refinement in the scheduling procedure, it would be utterly impossible without time standards. The success of any schedule is in direct relation to the accuracy of the time values used

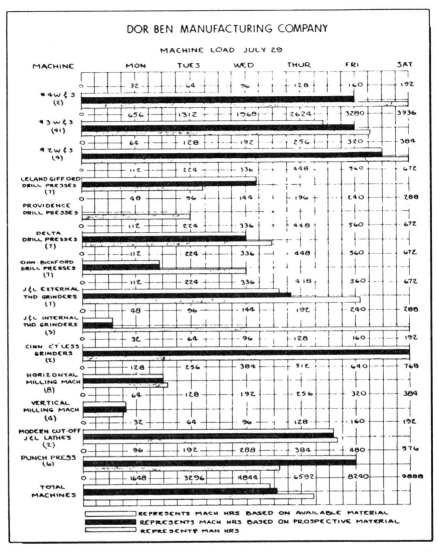

FIG. 22–4. Machine load of a machining department for a one-week period. Notice several schedules are dependent on receiving additional raw material.

in determining the schedule. If time standards do not exist, and schedules are formulated on the basis of judgment only, they cannot be expected to be reliable.

Through the use of time standards, rate of flow of materials and work in progress may be predetermined, thus forming the basis for accurate scheduling.

Accurate Control and Determination of Labor Costs

With true time standards, a plant does not have to be on incentive wage payment in order to determine and control its labor costs. The ratio of departmental clock hours to departmental earned production hours provides information as to the efficiency of the specific department. The reciprocal of the efficiency multiplied by the average hourly rate will give the hourly cost in terms of standard production. For example, the finishing department in a given plant using straight daywork may have had 812 clock hours of labor time, and in this period let us assume that it has earned 876 hours of production. The departmental efficiency would then be:

$$E = \frac{He}{Hc} = \frac{876}{812} = 108 \text{ per cent}.$$

If the average daywork hourly rate in the department was $1.60, then the hourly direct labor cost based on standard production would be:

$$\frac{1}{1.08} \times \$1.60 = \$1.48.$$

Let us look at another example. We might assume in another department that the clock hours were 2,840 and the hours of production earned for the period were only 2,760. In this case, the efficiency would be:

$$\frac{2,760}{2,840} = 97 \text{ per cent}$$

and the hourly direct labor cost based on standard production with an average daywork rate of $1.60 would equal:

$$\frac{1}{.97} \times \$1.60 = \$1.65.$$

In the latter case, management would realize that its labor costs were running $0.05 per hour more than base rates and could take steps with supervision so that total labor costs would be brought into line. In the first example, labor costs were running less than standard, which would allow a downward price revision so as to increase the volume of production, or make some other adjustment suitable both to the management and labor. Figure 22–5 illustrates a direct labor variance report where departmental performance above and below standard is indicated.

Requisite for Standard Cost Methods

Standard cost methods refer to the procedure of accurate cost determination in advance of production. The advantage of being able to predetermine cost is apparent. It is really necessary in many instances today to compute costs and contract work at the predetermined price. By having time standards on direct labor operations, it is possible to preprice those elements entering into the prime cost of the product. (Prime cost is usually thought of as the sum of the direct material and direct labor costs.)

DIRECT LABOR VARIANCE-HOURS
Week Ending June 3

No.	Name	Allowed Direct Labor	Efficiency Variance Week Ending			Weekly Average		Per Cent Total Variance Over-Under Standards				
			%	5/26	5/19	First Qtr.	Apr.	%	Week Ending 5/26	5/19	4 Weeks, April	First Qtr.*
11	Machine shop	892	204	29	110	33	3	22.9%	2.5%	9.2%	0.2%	2.2%
12	Wire brush	178	…	…	…	…	3	…	…	…	4.5	9.1
19	Punch press	41	18	8	…	6	…	43.9	9.5	…	4.5	13.8
20	Rubber milling	21	101	43	124	21	51	481.0	18.1	172.2	57.4	5.2
31	Rubber fabricating	1 183	36	29	12	116	59	3.0	1.5	0.7	3.2	…
35	Pilot plant	53	…	…	…	…	…	…	…	…	…	…
39F	Finishing	339	60	107	27	42	50	17.7	18.5	5.8	10.0	6.6
39P	Paint	23	1	9	12	8	3	4.3	12.7	23.1	11.0	26.4
40	Assembly	13	1	15	15	14	4	7.7	28.3	25.9	6.0	19.9
50	Reclaim	20	…	…	…	…	…	…	…	…	…	…
65	Toolroom	…	…	…	…	…	…	…	…	…	…	…
	Total—This week	2,763	217	148	192	104	59	7.9%	3.7%	4.5%	1.2%	1.9%
	—Last week	4,462										

NOTE: The latest planning and method changes are reflected in all groups.
*First Quarter includes the thirteen weeks beginning January 1, through March 31.

FIG. 22–5. Weekly report illustrating departmental performance in a specific manufacturing plant. Heavy print indicates hours and percentage earned over standard. Light print indicates to what degree standard has not been achieved.

As a Basis for Budgetary Control

Budgeting is the establishment of a course of procedure: the majority of budgets are based on the allocation of money for a specific center or area of work. Thus we may establish a sales budget for a given period of time, a production budget, and so forth. Since money and time are definitely related, any budget is a result of standard times regardless of how the standards were determined.

As a Basis for Supervisory Bonus

Wage incentives will be discussed at length in later chapters of this text. At this time, it will suffice to point out that any type of supervisory bonus that is keyed to workers' earnings will be directly dependent on having equitable time standards. And since workers receive more and better supervisory attention under a plan where the supervisory bonus is related to workers' pay, the majority of supervisory plans give consideration to worker productivity as the principal criteria for bonus. Other factors that are usually considered in the supervisory bonus are indirect labor costs, scrap cost, and method improvements.

Quality Standards Are Enforced

The establishing of time standards forces the maintenance of quality requirements. Since production standards are based on the quantity of acceptable pieces produced in a unit of time, and since no credit is given for defective work turned out, there will be a constant intense effort by all workmen to produce only good parts. If an incentive wage payment plan is in effect, operators are compensated for good parts only, and in order to keep their earnings up, they will keep their scrap down.

If some of the pieces that are produced are found to be defective through subsequent inspection, either the operator that produced the parts will be held responsible for their salvage or else his earnings will be diminished by the number of pieces of scrap produced.

Personnel Standards Are Raised

Where standards are used, there will be a natural tendency to "put the right man on the right job," so that the standards established will be either met or exceeded. Placing employees on work for which they are best suited goes a long way toward keeping them satisfied.

Problems of Management Are Simplified

With time standards go many control measures that it would be impossible to exercise unless time standards were available, such as scheduling, routing, material control, budgeting, forecasting, planning, and standard costs. With tight controls on practically every phase of an enterprise, including production engineering, sales, and cost, the problems of management are minimized. By exercising the "exception principle" where attention is given only to the items deviating from the planned course of events, managerial efforts need be devoted but to a small segment of the total activity of the enterprise.

Governmental operations have found time standards extremely helpful. Added emphasis was given to the need for a standards' program in all governmental agencies when President Truman, by Executive Order 10072, in July of 1949, and the Eighty-First Congress, by Public Law 429, passed in the same year, emphasized the need for continuous examination and review of governmental operations so as to insure the achievement of planned programs in each department. Title X of Public Law 429 makes specific provisions for the establishment of an efficiency awards system in each government agency. Time standards provide means for evaluating the individual or groups of individuals who submit proposals, and also provide the basis for those who submit entries to examine the potential of their ideas.

Service to Customers Is Bettered

With the use of time standards, up-to-date production control procedures can be introduced with the resulting advantage to the customer of getting his merchandise when he wants and needs it. Also, time standards tend to make any company more time and cost conscious; this usually results in lower selling prices to the customer. As has been explained, quality will be maintained under a work standards plan, thus assuring the customer of more parts made to required specifications.

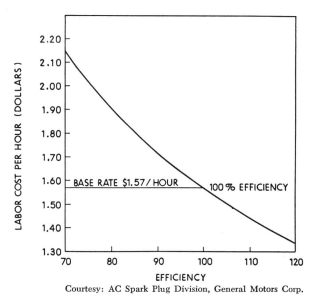

Courtesy: AC Spark Plug Division, General Motors Corp.

FIG. 22–6. Relationship of labor cost to efficiency.

Conclusion

Several of the uses of time standards have been briefly summarized. There are, of course, many more applications in all areas of any enterprise. Probably the most significant result of time standards is maintenance of over-all plant efficiency. If efficiency cannot be measured, it cannot be controlled, and without control it will markedly diminish.

Once efficiency goes down, labor costs rapidly rise and the result is eventual loss of competitive position in the market. Figure 22–6 illustrates the relationship of labor cost to efficiency in one leading manufacturer's business of automobile accessories. By establishing and maintaining effective standards, a business can standardize direct labor costs and control over-all costs.

TEXT QUESTIONS

1. In what different ways may time standards be determined?
2. How can valid time standards help in developing an ideal plant layout?
3. Explain the relationship between time standards and plant capacity.
4. In what way are time standards used for effective production control?
5. How do time standards allow the accurate determination of labor costs?
6. How does the development of time standards help maintain the quality of product?
7. In what way is customer service bettered through valid time standards?
8. What is the relationship between labor cost and efficiency?
9. If a daywork shop was paying an average rate of $1.65 per hour and had 250 direct labor employees working, what would be the true direct labor cost per hour if during a normal month 40,000 hours of work were produced?
10. How are management problems simplified through the application of time standards?
11. In what way did President Truman provide emphasis for the use of time standards in governmental operations?

GENERAL QUESTIONS

1. What other uses of time standards not mentioned in this chapter can be realized?
2. What is the relationship between accuracy of time standards and production control? Does the law of diminishing returns apply?
3. How does work measurement improve selection and placement of personnel?

CHAPTER **23**

Significant Wage Payment Plans

Experience has proven that workmen will not give extra or sustained effort unless some incentive, either direct or indirect, is in the offing. Incentives in one form or another have been used in industry for many years. Several of the incentive wage payment plans developed a generation or more ago are still in effect today with slight modifications. Before designing a wage payment plan for a specific plant, it is wise for the analyst to review the strength and weaknesses of past plans.

In the broad sense, all incentive plans that tend to increase the employee's production will fall under one of the following three classes: (1) direct financial plans, (2) indirect financial plans, and (3) plans other than financial.

Direct Financial Plans

Direct financial plans include all plans in which the workman's compensation is commensurate with his output. In this category is included both individual incentive plans and group plans. In the individual type of plan, each employee's compensation is governed by his own performance for the period in question. Group plans are applicable to two or more persons who are working as a team on operations that tend to be dependent on each other. In these plans, each employee's compensation within the group is based upon his base rate and the performance of the group for the period in question.

The incentive for high or prolonged individual effort is not nearly as great in group plans as in individual plans. Hence, there has been a tendency for industry to favor individual incentive methods. In addition to lower over-all productivity, group plans have other drawbacks:

(1) personnel problems brought about by nonuniformity of production coupled with uniformity of pay, and (2) difficulties in justifying base rate differentials for the various opportunities within the group.

Of course, group plans do offer some decided advantages over individual incentive, noteworthy of which are: (1) ease of installation brought about through ease of measuring group rather than individual output, and (2) reduction of cost in administration of the plan through reduced amount of paper work, less verification of inventory in process, and less in-process inspection.

In general, higher rates of production and lower unit cost of the product can be expected under individual incentive plans. If practical to install, the individual incentive plan should be given preference over group systems. On the other hand, the group approach has more application where it is difficult to measure individual output and where individual work is variable and frequently performed in co-operation with another employee on a team basis. For example, where four men are jointly working together in the operation of an extrusion press for extruding brass rods, it would be virtually impossible to install an individual incentive system, but a group plan would be applicable.

Indirect Financial Plans

Those company policies that tend to stimulate employee morale and result in increased productivity, yet have not been designed to bring about a direct relation between amount of compensation and amount of production, would fall in the indirect financial classification. Over-all company policies such as fair and relatively high base rates, equitable promotion policies, sound suggestion systems, guaranteed annual wage, and relatively high fringe benefits will lead to building healthy employee attitudes which stimulate and increase productivity. Thus, they are classified as indirect financial plans.

All indirect incentive methods have the weakness of allowing too broad a gap between employee benefits and production. After a period of time, the employee takes for granted the benefits bestowed upon him and fails to realize that the means for their continuance must be a result entirely of his productivity. The theories, philosophies, and techniques of indirect incentives are beyond the scope of this text; for added information in this area, the student is referred to books on personnel administration.

Plans Other than Financial

Nonfinancial incentives include any rewards that have no relation to pay, and yet improve the spirit of the employee to such an extent that added effort will be evidenced. Under this category would come such company policies as periodic shop conferences, frequent talks between the supervisor and the employee, proper employee placement, nonfinan-

cial suggestion plans, maintenance of ideal working conditions, posting
of individual production records, and many other techniques utilized
by effective supervisors and capable, conscientious managers.

Nonfinancial incentives represent an area that is thoroughly covered
in texts on industrial relations and will not be further discussed in this
book.

Classification of Direct Wage Financial Plans

Two classifications of direct wage financial plans may be made within
which the majority of individual plans may be placed. These two divisions with representative specific plans are outlined as follows:

        I. Employee participates in all the gain above standard
            A. Straight piecework
            B. Standard hour plan
            C. Taylor multiple piece rate
            D. Merrick multiple piece rate
            E. Measured daywork
       II. Employee shares the gains with his employer above standard
            A. Halsey plan
            B. Bedaux system
            C. Rowan plan
            D. Emerson plan
            E. Profit sharing

There are some plans where the relationship between output and
earnings has been established empirically, and at different levels of performance, the plan may either allow the employee all the gains, or a
share of the gains. For purposes of simplicity, plans with these characteristics have been included in the group of "gain sharing with the employer."

Straight Piecework

Straight piecework implies that all standards are expressed in terms of
money and the operator is rewarded in direct proportion to his output.
Under straight piecework, the day rate is not guaranteed. Prior to World
War II, straight piecework was used more extensively than any other incentive plan. The reasons for the popularity of straight piecework is that
it is easily understood by the worker, easily applied, and one of the oldest
types of wage incentive plans.

Since World War II, the popularity of straight piecework has rapidly
declined. There have been several reasons for this, first and foremost being that under straight piecework all standards are expressed in terms
of money. Thus every adjustment in base rates involves a monumental
amount of clerical work to change all standards to agree with the revised hourly base rates. From 1930 to 1940, base rates of pay remained
relatively stable, and standards expressed in terms of dollars and cents

were seldom changed. However, following World War II to the present writing, there has been practically an annual increase in base rates. Piece rates expressed in money have been exceedingly difficult to maintain, and for this reason many concerns have discontinued their use.

In piece rate plans, the worker is made aware of the close relationship between his earnings and the time study man. This situation makes it difficult for the time study analyst to convince the worker that the analyst's only interest is in establishing a fair rate of production,

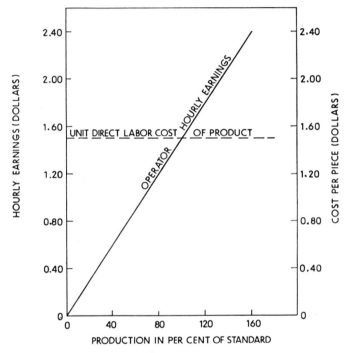

FIG. 23–1. Operator earnings and unit direct labor cost under straight piecework.

and that he is not concerned with restricting operator earnings. Then, too, the term "piece rate" was used extensively by the old "efficiency expert" who did so much to hinder the progress of the methods, standards, and wage payment function. Even today, the name "piece rate" leaves a sour taste with many of our older employees.

Figure 23–1 illustrates graphically the relationship between operator's earnings and unit direct labor costs under a straight piecework plan.

Standard Hour Plan

The fundamental difference between the standard hour plan and straight piecework plan is that under the former, standards are expressed in terms of time rather than money. The straight standard hour plan does not guarantee the base rate. The operator is rewarded throughout in direct proportion to his output.

Graphically, the relationship between operator earnings and unit direct labor cost, when plotted against production and money, would be identical to piecework.

For example, a standard may be expressed as 2.142 hours per 100 pieces. It is an easy operation to calculate either the money rate or the operator's earnings, once the base rate of the operator is known. If the operator had a base rate of $1.50, then the money rate of this job would be: $(1.50)(2.142) = \$3.21$ per hundred or $0.0321 per piece. Let us assume an operator produced 412 pieces in an 8-hour working day; his earnings for the day would be: $(\$1.50)(2.142)(4.12) = \$13.24$ and his hourly earnings would be: $13.24/8 or $1.655. The operator efficiency for the day, in this case, would then be: $(2.142)(4.12)/8$ or 110 per cent.

The standard hour plan offers all the advantages of straight piecework and eliminates the major disadvantages. However, it is somewhat more difficult for the workman to compute his earnings than if standards were expressed in terms of money. The principal advantage is, of course, that standards are not changed when base rates are altered. Thus, clerical work is reduced over a period of time when compared to the straight piecework plan. Moreover, the term "standard hour" is more palatable to the worker than "piecework," and with standards expressed in time, the amount of money earned by the workman is not quite so closely linked with time study practice. For these reasons there has been a marked growth in the popularity of standard hour plans.

Taylor Differential Piece Rate

The Taylor differential piece rate plan is not used in very many plants today. In this plan two piece rates were established and expressed in terms of money. The lower rate compensated in direct proportion to output until the operator's performance reached standard. Once standard performance was achieved or exceeded, the high piece rate went into effect. Thus the workman was encouraged not only to reach standard, but also, since he was paid in direct proportion to output beyond standard, he was encouraged to execute his maximum performance. Under the Taylor plan, standards were set "tight" enough so that only the proficient employees could exceed it. On so doing they were generously compensated. It is also to be noted that the poor worker was penalized.

Under this plan, for example, the piece rates for machining a part may be $0.20 each up to a standard of 7 pieces per hour. Daily production averaging 7 or more pieces per hour may be paid $0.25 each. Thus, if an operator turned out 56 pieces during a day, his earnings would be $14. However, if he produced only 55 pieces he would be paid at the lower piece rate and would have earned $11 for the day. Figure 23–2 illustrates the unit cost and earnings' relationship of this plan.

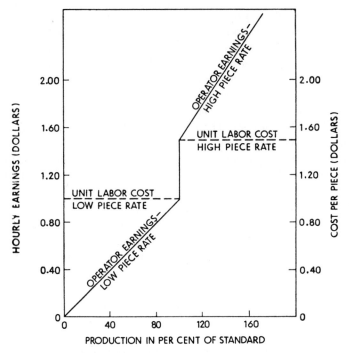

FIG. 23–2. Operator earnings and unit direct labor cost under the Taylor differential piece rate plan.

Merrick Multiple Piece Rate

Under the Merrick multiple piece rate plan, three graded piece rates were established rather than two as advocated by Taylor. There was a piece rate established for beginners, one for average employees, and one for the superior workmen. This plan endeavored to correct the low rate paid to operators performing below task and so overcome the defects of Taylor's plan, which had caused such severe criticism by employees. Merrick chose 83 per cent of task as the point for his first step, which involved a piece rate with a 10 per cent bonus. His high piece rate beginning at standard included an additional 10 per cent bonus.

Measured Daywork

During the early 1930's, shortly after the era of the "efficiency expert," there was an effort by organized labor to get away from time study practice and, in particular, piece rates. At this time, measured daywork was introduced as an incentive system that broadened the gap between the establishment of a standard and the worker's earnings. Many modifications of measured daywork installations are in operation today, and the majority of them follow a specific pattern. First, base rates are established by job evaluation for all opportunities falling under the plan. Then standards are determined for all operations by means of some form of work measurement. A progressive record of each employee's efficiency is maintained for a period of time, usually one to three months. This efficiency, multiplied by his base rate, forms the basis of his guaranteed base rate for the next period. For example, the base rate of a given operator may be $1.30 per hour. Let us assume that the governing performance period is one month or 173 working hours. If, during the month the operator earned 190 standard hours, his efficiency for the period would be 190/173 or 110 per cent. Then, in view of the performance, the operator would receive a base rate of (1.10)(1.30) or $1.43 for every hour worked during the next period regardless of his performance. However, his achievement during this period would govern his base rate for the succeeding period.

In most measured daywork plans, the base rate is guaranteed; thus an operator falling below standard (100 per cent) for any given period would receive his base rate for the following period.

The length of time used in determining performance usually runs three months so as to diminish the clerical work of calculating and installing new guaranteed base rates. Of course, the longer the period, the less incentive effort can be expected. When the spread between performance and realization is too great, the effect of incentive performance is diminished.

The principal advantage of measured daywork is that it takes the immediate pressure off the workman. He knows what his base rate is and realizes that, regardless of his performance, he will receive that amount for the period.

The limitations of measured daywork are apparent. First, because of the length of the performance period, the incentive feature is not particularly strong. Then, in order to be effective, it places a heavy responsibility on supervisors for the maintenance of production above standard. Otherwise, the employee's performance will drop, thus lowering his base rate for the following period and causing employee dissatisfaction. Clerical work is costly for the keeping of detailed rate records and the making of periodic adjustments in all base rates. In fact, as much clerical work is involved under measured daywork as under any straight incentive plan where the employee is rewarded according to his output.

Although we have classified measured daywork as a type of wage payment plan wherein the employee participates in all the gain above standard, it can be seen that this method of wage payment is really a hybrid of the other "one-for-one" plans. As the workman's seniority increases, his total earnings will approximate the amount he would have earned if he had been paid in direct proportion to his output. Therefore, the plan is, in effect, similar to other types discussed that fall under this category.

Halsey Plan

About 1890, Frederick Halsey developed a wage incentive plan that was one of the first to deviate from straight piecework. In Mr. Halsey's method, standards were established from past records, as time study had not yet come into use. The resulting standards, as could be expected, were low.

However, if the workman failed to meet the standard, he was paid his regular wages; thus this early proposal guaranteed the base rate, which is a requisite of an effective wage payment plan today. In Halsey's original plan, he compensated the operator for performance above standard so that the workman received one-third of the time saved. The amount of premium in subsequent installations varied with individual plants but tended to be set at 50 per cent. Using this percentage, it was easy to present the plan to the employees as an equitable arrangement in which both the employee and the company participated in one-half of the time saved.

Another characteristic of the Halsey method that has sound application today was that the standards were expressed in terms of time rather than money.

The Halsey plan was established as a curb to runaway piece rates that were characteristic of the time because scientific methods of work measurement had not as yet been developed and methods improvements were the prerogative of the employee. Since the employee was assured his base rate and was given up to half the share of the earnings above task, he was usually attracted to the plan. Figure 23–3 illustrates the

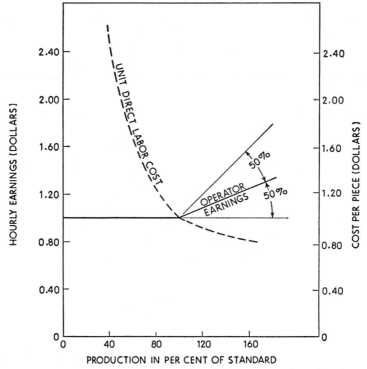

FIG. 23–3. Operator earnings and unit direct labor cost under the Halsey plan.

curves depicting operator's earnings and unit direct labor cost for a modified Halsey system. Inspection of these curves will show that a varying unit labor cost is provided. This is one distinct disadvantage of the Halsey plan and all plans where the employee shares the gain with his employer. With variable unit labor costs, it is difficult to establish true overall costs and budgets which are so necessary in the efficient operation of any business.

Since the Halsey plan does not reward the operator in direct proportion to his output, it is not readily accepted by labor today. Labor's attitude is that, if management is willing to pay a given amount per piece at the task point, it should be willing to pay the worker a like amount for production beyond task. Since total unit cost declines with increased productivity in view of being able to spread overhead over more pieces, management can afford to compensate the worker in direct proportion to his output.

Bedaux Point System

The Bedaux point system, as introduced in 1916 by Charles E. Bedaux, is similar in many respects to the Halsey plan just discussed. The hourly rate is guaranteed up to task or standard, and beyond this point constant sharing of time saved takes place. Bedaux expressed his standards in terms of "B's," which was defined as one minute "composed of relative proportions of work and rest as indicated by the whole job." A normal operator was expected to perform 60 B's every hour he worked. The number of B's comprising any job was determined by time study practice. Under the original Bedaux plan, the worker participated in 75 per cent of the B's earned above standard. The remaining 25 per cent of B's earned above standard was used to compensate indirect labor and supervision.

For example, if an operator earned 520 B's during the working day, his efficiency would be: 520/480 or 107.5 per cent.

Of the 40 B's above standard earned, the operator would be compensated for 75 per cent, or 30. Let us assume an hourly rate of $1.80. Then each B would have a value of $0.03 and the incentive earned on the above job would be $0.90. Graphically, the operator earnings curve and unit cost curves for the Bedaux point system would be identical to those for the Halsey plan except for the slopes above the task point. Since this plan does not reward the worker in direct proportion to output, it too is not well received by labor today.

Rowan Plan

In 1898, James Rowan proposed a sharing plan wherein the incentive was determined by the ratio of the time saved to the standard time.[1] The base rate was guaranteed, and the premium earning curve began at 62½

---

[1] "A Premium System of Remunerating Labor," *Proceedings, Mechanical Engineers* (British), 1901, p. 865.

per cent of standard. Since it is impossible to save all the standard time, it would be impossible for any operator to earn 200 per cent of his base wage. The fundamental purpose of Rowan's plan was to protect the employer from "runaway rates" that might be established from past performance records, and still provide sufficient incentive to the operator for high continuous effort. Although this system accomplished what was intended, the fact that large gains on the part of the operator were virtually impossible discouraged high production. The fact that the worker was compensated on an incentive basis at an early stage of the earnings curve made the plan more attractive to workmen than the Halsey plan if tight rates prevailed and high production performance was impossible.

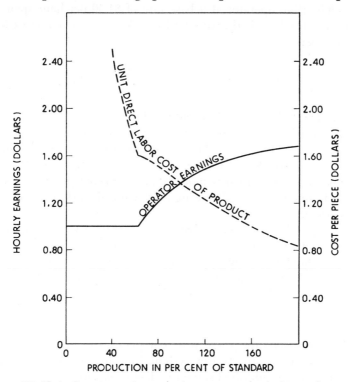

FIG. 23–4. Operator earnings and unit cost curve under the Rowan plan.

Per Cent of Standard	Time Taken, Hours	Time Saved, Hours	Ratio of Time Saved to Time Allowed	Premium Pay	Pay for Job	Hourly Rate
62.5	1.6	0	0	0	1.600	1.000
80	1.25	.350	.219	.274	1.524	1.220
100	1.00	.600	.375	.375	1.375	1.375
120	.833	.767	.480	.395	1.230	1.480
140	.714	.886	.554	.395	1.110	1.560
160	.625	.975	.610	.381	1.006	1.610
200	.500	1.100	.686	.343	.843	1.686

Operator earnings under this system can be expressed as follows:

$$E_a = R_a T + \frac{S_t R_a T}{T_a}$$

where

E_a = earnings
R_a = base rates
T = time spent on the work
S_t = time saved
T_a = allowed time .

For example, if an operator at a base rate of $1.50 per hour spent three hours on a job which had a standard of 3.5 hours, his earnings for the job would be:

$$E_a = (1.50)(3) + \frac{(.5)(1.50)(3)}{3.5} = \$5.14 .$$

His hourly rate for this assignment would amount to $1.71.

Figure 23–4 illustrates operator earnings and unit labor costs under the Rowan plan. This system has several disadvantages which limit its use in this country. First, it limits earnings and consequently restricts production. Then, this plan is more complex, making it difficult for the workman to understand and causing more clerical work in calculation of wages earned.

For example, let us assume a base rate of $1.00 per hour and a standard of one hour per piece for a given job. The task point taken at 62.5 per cent of standard would require 1.6 hours to do the job. As performance increased, the resulting pay, labor cost, and rates of production would be as shown in Figure 23–4 and accompanying table.

Emerson Plan

In many respects, the wage payment plan advocated by Harrington Emerson is not unlike the Halsey system. Emerson assured the employee his base rate and established standards based on careful study of all details entering into the production. However, the incentive portion of his plan differed somewhat from others. At 66⅔ per cent of a standard, he established a small incentive which increased as the performance increased until the task point was reached. Beyond this point, he established a straight-line earning curve which compensated the operator in direct proportion to his output plus 20 per cent. The premium paid from two thirds of task to task was empirically determined and is tabularized in Table XXIX.

Under Emerson's plan, the operator's earnings below two thirds of task may be computed from the expression:

$$E_a = R_a T$$

and between two thirds of task and task:

$$E_a = R_a T + F_t(R_a T)$$

and above task

$$E_a = R_a T + S_t R_a + .20 \, R_a T$$

where

F_t = factor taken from table
R_a = rate per hour
S_t = time hours saved
T = time taken in hours .

TABLE XXIX

Efficiency in Per Cent	Bonus in Per Cent of Base Wage	Efficiency in Per Cent	Bonus in Per Cent of Base Wage	Efficiency in Per Cent	Bonus in Per Cent in Base Wage
67	.0001	82	.0433	97	.1662
68	.0004	83	.0492	98	.1770
69	.0011	84	.0553	99	.1881
70	.0022	85	.0617	100	.2000
71	.0037	86	.0684		
72	.0055	87	.0756		
73	.0076	88	.0832		
74	.0102	89	.0911		
75	.0131	90	.0991		
76	.0164	91	.1074		
77	.0199	92	.1162		
78	.0238	93	.1256		
79	.0280	94	.1352		
80	.0327	95	.1453		
81	.0378	96	.1557		

In adopting his plan, Emerson advocated the calculation of efficiency for a pay period of either a week or a month, thus tending to equalize the very poor and the very high daily efficiencies. For example, if during a month involving 173 working hours an operator earned 180 hours for which he was paid a base rate of $1.50, his earnings for the period would be:

$$E_a = (1.50)(173) + (7)(1.50) + (.20)(1.50)(173) = \$321.90 .$$

Profit Sharing

The Council of Profit Sharing Industries has defined profit sharing as "any procedure under which an employer pays to all employees, in addition to good rates of regular pay, special current or deferred sums based not only upon individual or group performance, but on the prosperity of the business as a whole."[2]

---

[2] Council of Profit Sharing Industries, *Profit Sharing Manual* (First National Tower, Akron, Ohio, 1949), p. 3.

No one specific type of profit sharing has received general industrial acceptance. In fact, about every installation has certain "tailor-made" features which distinguish it from others. However, the majority of profit-sharing systems can be placed under one of the following broad categories: (1) cash plans, (2) deferred plans, and (3) combined plans.

As the name infers, the straight cash plan involves the periodic distribution of money from the profits of the business to the employees. The payment is not included with the regular pay envelope, but is made separately, so as to identify it as an extra reward, brought about by the individual and combined efforts of the entire operating force. The amount of the cash distribution is based upon the degree of financial success of the enterprise for the bonus period. The period varies in different companies. In some installations it is as short as one month, and in others the period is one year. There is general agreement, however, that the shorter the period, the closer will be the connection between effort and financial reward to the employees. Longer periods are selected because they will reflect more truly the status of the business over that particular length of time. For example, if a period of one month is used, the employees might give excellent performance for the entire period in anticipation of a sizable bonus. However, due to conditions beyond their control, such as high inventories or slow-moving products, the profit for the period may be nothing. With no additional reward, the employees would quickly lose confidence in the plan and appreciably drop their efforts.

Another factor of importance in the selection of the period for the distribution of the profits is the amount of cash that will be shared. If the period is too short, the amount may be of such an insignificant size that the plan itself may backfire. But, if a longer period such as six months or a year is used, the amount will be adequate to accomplish the purpose of the profit-sharing system.

Deferred profit-sharing plans are characterized by the periodic investment of portions of the profits of the business for the employees, so that upon retirement or separation from the company, they will have a source of income at a time when their needs may be more pronounced.

The deferred type of profit-sharing plan obviously does not provide the incentive stimulus to the degree that cash plans do.

However, deferred profit-sharing plans do offer the advantage of being easier to install and administer. Also, this type of plan offers more security than the cash reward plan. This makes it especially appealing to the stable workman.

Combined plans arrange that some of the profits are invested for retirement and similar benefits, and some are distributed in the form of cash rewards. This class of plans can realize the advantages of both the deferred plans and those employing the straight cash system. A representative installation might provide for sharing half the profits with the employees. Of this amount, one third may be distributed to the employees in the form of an extra bonus check, one third may be held in reserve to be given out when a less successful financial period develops, and the remaining one third may be placed with a trustee for deferred distribution.

Methods of Distribution under Profit Sharing

There are three methods in common use for determining the amount of money to be given individual employees from the company's profits. The first and the least used is the "share-and-share-alike" plan. Here each employee, regardless of his job class, participates in an equal amount of the profits, once he has attained the prescribed amount of company service. Proponents of this method believe that individual base rates have already taken care of the relative importance of the different workers to the company. The share-and-share-alike plan supplies a feeling of teamwork and importance to each employee, no matter what his position in the plant may be. Just as a complex mechanism is made inoperative by removal of an insignificant pin, so an enterprise is dependent upon each and every employee for its efficient operation.

The most commonly used method of distribution under profit sharing is on the basis of the regular compensation paid to the workers. The theory is that the employee who was paid the most during the period contributed to the greatest extent to the company's profits and consequently should share in them to a greater extent. For example, a toolmaker earning $3,000 in a six-month period would receive a greater share of the company's profits than a chip-hauler who was paid $1,200 for the same period.

Another popular means of profit distribution is through the allocation of points. Points are given for each year of seniority, and each $100 of pay. Some plans also endeavor to evaluate such factors as attendance, worker's co-operation, and standards of production. The number of points accumulated by each employee for the period then determines his share of the profits. This method endeavors to take into consideration the factors that influence the company's profits and then distribute the profits on a basis that gives each employee his just share. Perhaps the principal disadvantage of the point method is the difficulty of maintenance and administration brought about through complex and detailed records.

Criteria for Successful Profit-Sharing Plan

The Council for Profit Sharing Industries has summarized ten principles which it feels is fundamental if a plan is to succeed. These are:

1. There must be a compelling desire on the part of management to install the plan in order to enhance the team spirit of the organization. If there is a union, its co-operation is essential.
2. The plan should be generous enough to forestall any feeling on the part

of the employees that the lion's share of the results of extra effort will go to management and the stockholders.

3. The employees must understand that there is no benevolence involved, that they are merely receiving their fair share of the profits they have helped to create.

4. The emphasis should be placed on partnership, not on the amount of money involved. If financial return is emphasized, it will be more difficult to retain the employee's loyalty and interest in loss years.

5. The employees must be made to feel that it is their plan as well as management's and not something that is being done for them by management. The employees should be well represented on any committee set up to administer the plan.

6. Profit sharing is inconsistent with arbitrary management—it functions best in companies operating under a democratic system. This does not mean that management relinquishes its right, and in fact its obligation, to manage, but rather that management functions by leadership instead of arbitrary command.

7. Under no circumstances can profit sharing be used as an excuse for paying lower than prevailing wages.

8. Whatever its technical details, the plan must be adapted to the particular situation, and should be simple enough so that all can readily understand it.

9. The plan should be "dynamic," both as to its technical details and as to its administration. Both management and employees—and in profit-sharing companies it is often difficult to find the demarcation line—should give constant thought to ways of improving it.

10. Management should recognize the fact that profit sharing is no panacea. No policy or plan in the industrial relations field can succeed unless it is well adapted and unless it evidences the faith of management in the importance, dignity, and response of the human individual.

Attitude toward Profit Sharing

For the most part, union officials have not supported profit sharing. Their principal criticism is that the technique is a "hard-times, wage cutting method."[3] There can be no doubt that profit sharing, when practiced with perfect harmony between labor and management, minimizes the necessity of a union in the eyes of the employees. Therefore, union leaders can hardly be expected to uphold and propagate something that will diminish their own personal prestige, power, and income.

Where profit sharing has been practiced by a sincere, fair, and competent management team, individual workers are enthusiastic, and wholeheartedly support the plan. Attempts to unionize plants where profit sharing is flourishing, such as in the Lincoln Electric Company, have resulted in violent worker reaction against the organizers.

A successful profit-sharing program depends on the profits of the company, which frequently are not under the control of the direct labor force. In periods of low profits or losses, the plan may actually weaken rather than strengthen employee morale. Also, unless the team spirit is

---

[3] Charles E. Britton, *Incentives in Industry* (Esso Standard Oil Co., 1953), p. 30.

enthusiastically supported by *all* members of supervision, the plan does not provide the incentive to continuous effort characteristic of wage incentive installations. This is a result of the length of time between performance and reward; most companies wait twelve months and use the year's end for declaring the profits of the company. In large companies, it becomes virtually impossible to instill the team idea throughout the plant, and unless this is generally done, the plan will not completely succeed.

Perhaps the greatest objection to profit sharing that the writer has observed is the taking for granted that there will be an "extra" check received at the end of the year. The employee expects to receive it, and even makes substantial purchases on a time basis in anticipation of the added remuneration. If the company has experienced a lean year and the worker gets no extra remuneration, he does not see any relation between his productivity for the past year and the fact that no bonus was received. All he feels is that he has been cheated. Thus the whole profit-sharing plan fails to engender the spirit intended.

For these reasons, any employer should be very cautious before embarking on a profit-sharing program. On the other hand, many companies today are experiencing high worker efficiency, decreased costs, reduction of scrap, and better worker morale as a result of profit-sharing installations. James F. Lincoln, president of the Lincoln Electric Company, who has developed one of the most successful profit-sharing installations, offers the following suggestions to those companies which are contemplating the installation of some type of profit-sharing system:[4]

1. Determine that the system is going to be adopted and decide that whatever needs to be done to install it will be done.

2. Determine what plan and products the company will make that will carry out the philosophy of "more and more for less and less."

3. Get the complete acceptance of the board of directors and all management involved in the plan, together with their assurance that they will continue to take whatever steps are necessary for a successful application of it.

4. Arrange a means whereby management can talk to the men and the men can talk back. That means full discussion by all.

5. Make sure of co-operative action on the agreed plan of operation. This will include the plan for progressively better manufacturing by all people in the organization and the proper distribution of the savings that result from it.

6. Set your sights high enough. Do not try to get just a little better efficiency with the expectation that such gain will be to the good and expect to leave the matter there.

7. Remember, this plan for industry is a fundamental change in philosophy. From it new satisfactions will flow to all involved. There is not only more money for all concerned, there is also the much more important reward—the satisfaction of doing a better job in the world. There is that greatest of all satisfactions, the becoming a more useful man.

---

[4] James F. Lincoln, *Lincoln's Incentive System* (New York: McGraw-Hill Book Co., Inc.), pp. 171–72.

Conclusion

Of the several incentive plans discussed in this chapter, piecework and the standard hour plan with the guarantee of the day rate are certainly the most popular today.

Incentive principles have been applied in both job shops and production shops in the manufacture of hard goods and soft goods. The incentive system has application to direct and indirect production work and has been used for purposes other than increasing production. For example, incentive principles have been used for increasing safety, improving the quality of the product, reducing waste, and stimulating regularity of employees' attendance.

Soundly administered incentive systems possess important advantages, both for workers and management. The chief benefit to employees is that these plans make it possible for them to increase their total wages, not at some indefinite time in the future, but immediately—in their next pay checks. Management obtains a greater output and, assuming some profit is being made on each unit produced, therefore, a greater volume of profits. Normally, profits increase, not in proportion to production, but at a higher rate, for with greater output overhead costs per unit decreases.

The higher wages that result from incentive plans improve employee morale and tend to reduce labor turnover, absenteeism, and tardiness.

Since the proper functioning of incentive systems requires the performance of many prerequisites (such as good methods, standards, scheduling, and management practices) the installation of incentives normally results in important improvements in production and supervisory methods. The activities that bring about these improvements, however, should be performed even though incentives are not introduced; the improvements, therefore, are not necessarily attributable to the employment of the incentive plans.

In general, the harder the work is to measure, the more difficult will be the installation of a successful wage incentive plan. The United States Steel Company, in its *Labor Measurement and Incentive Manual*,[5] clearly expresses the criteria for determining the advisability of applying labor measurement and incentives. The points to be used as guides for making decisions are:

1. Application should not be made unless: the work on the job is subject to reasonably accurate measurement in terms of production or units related to production suitable for accounting record, report, and verification; administration of the application is subject to audit; and administrative cost to make and maintain the application is economically justifiable in relation to the direct benefits to be realized from the application.

2. Application should be made where: work available per hour to the em-

---

[5] Copyright, 1951, United States Steel Company.

ployee is unlimited; or the attainment of capacity operation of a significant machine or process requires the employee to perform work at a pace above normal.

3. Application may be made where performance of the available work can be increased from a lower level to an index of measured performance above 125 per cent on machine or process controlled operations which do not require the performance of work at a pace above normal pace.

Well planned and administered incentives will increase production and decrease total unit cost. Usually, it will more than compensate for the price paid in increased costs of industrial engineering, quality control, and timekeeping which may have resulted through its use.

TEXT QUESTIONS

1. Under what three general classes may the majority of wage incentive plans be classified?
2. Differentiate between individual wage payment plans and group type plans.
3. What is meant by the term "fringe benefits"?
4. What company policies are included under nonfinancial incentives?
5. What are the characteristics of straight piecework? Plot the unit cost curve and operator earnings curve for daywork and piecework on the same set of co-ordinates.
6. Why has straight piecework diminished in popularity since World War II?
7. How does the standard hour plan differ from straight piecework?
8. Why are there few installations of the Taylor differential piece rate plan today?
9. In what way is the Merrick plan similar to the Taylor differential piece rate system?
10. Why did measured daywork become popular in the 1930's?
11. Why are there many modified Halsey and Bedaux plans in existence today?
12. For what reason did James Rowan design a plan that restricted operator earnings?
13. An allowed time of .0125 hours/piece is established for machining a small component. A setup time of .32 hour is established also, as the operator performs the necessary setup work on "incentive." Compute:
    a) Total time allowed to complete an order of 860 pieces.
    b) Operator efficiency, if job is completed in an 8-hour day.
    c) Efficiency of the operator if he requires 12 hours to complete the job.
14. A "one-for-one" or 100 per cent time premium plan for incentive payment is in operation. The operator base rate for this class of work is $1.60. The base rate is guaranteed. Compute:
    a) Total earnings for the job at efficiency determined in problem 13 (b).
    b) Hourly earnings, from above.
    c) Total earnings for job at efficiency determined in problem 13 (c).
    d) Direct labor cost per piece from (a), excluding setup.
    e) Direct labor cost per piece from (c), excluding setup.

15. A forging operation is studied and a rate of .42 minute per piece is set. The operator works on the job for a full 8-hour day and produces 1,500 pieces.
    a) How many standard hours does the operator earn?
    b) What is his efficiency for the day?
    c) If his base rate is $1.45 per hour, compute his earnings for the day. (Use a 100 per cent time premium plan.)
    d) What is the direct labor cost per piece at this efficiency?
    e) What would be the proper piece rate (rate expressed in money) for this job, assuming that the above time standard is correct?

16. A 60–40 Gain Sharing plan is in operation in a plant. The established time value on a certain job is .75 minute, the base rate is $1.20. What is the direct labor cost per piece when the operator efficiency is:
    a) 50 per cent of standard?
    b) 80 per cent of standard?
    c) 100 per cent of standard?
    d) 120 per cent of standard?
    e) 160 per cent of standard?

17. Define profit sharing.

18. What specific type of profit-sharing plan has received general acceptance?

19. What three broad categories cover the majority of profit-sharing installations?

20. Upon what does the amount of money distributed depend under the cash plan?

21. What determines the length of period between bonus payments under the cash plan? Why is it poor practice to have the period too long? What disadvantages are there to the short period?

22. What are the characteristic features of the deferred profit-sharing plan?

23. Why is the "share-and-share-alike" method of distribution not particularly common? What is the basis of advocation of this technique by its proponents?

24. What ten principles summarized by the Council for Profit Sharing Industries are fundamental for a successful profit-sharing plan?

25. Why have many unions shown an antagonistic attitude toward profit sharing?

26. What suggestions has Mr. James Lincoln offered for those embarking on an incentive installation?

GENERAL QUESTIONS

1. A workman is employed in a plant where all the rates are set on a money basis (straight piece rates). He is regularly employed at a job where the guaranteed base rate is $1.08. His regular earnings are in excess of $10 per day. Due to the pressure of work, he is asked to help out on another job, classified so that it pays $1.20 per hour. He works 3 days on this job and earns $9.00 each day.
    a) How much should the operator be paid for each day's work on this new job? Why?
    b) Would it make any difference if he had worked on a new job where the base rate was $1.00 per hour and he had earned $8.50? Explain.

2. An incentive plan employing a "low-rate, high-rate" differential is in use. A certain class of work has the guaranteed "low-rate" of $1.50 per hour

and the "high-rate" for work on standard of $1.65 per hour. A job is studied and a rate of .036 hours per piece is set. What is the direct labor cost per piece at the following efficiencies:

a) 50 per cent?
b) 80 per cent?
c) 98 per cent?
d) 105 per cent?
e) 150 per cent?

3. A machining job is studied by a competent time study man. Since the job has been running on the approved standard method for a short time, the operator is rated low on skill. Since it is expected that the job will be a high-activity job, one that will run for a long time with several men doing the work, the time study man is especially anxious to set the standard right. (This is interpreted to mean that the efficiency will not exceed 135 per cent on the average if the job runs for a year or more.) The rate goes out into the shop and the 3 machine operators (one on each shift) object strongly to the "tight rate."

a) Outline the several possible courses of action the time study man may pursue.
b) Suggest the possible results from each course of action through the several steps likely to result.

CHAPTER 24

Characteristics of a Sound Wage Incentive System

THE SUBJECT OF WAGE INCEN-
tives has always been controversial to employees, unions, and management. Industries that have assured a good living wage and then applied incentive earnings that can easily be calculated for extra or prolonged effort will find that their employees will be receptive to wage incentives. In fact, where successful installations of this nature have been made, considerable labor unrest would result if any attempt was made to do away with the plan. On the other hand, in those industries where the workman finds it necessary to work at an incentive pace to earn the necessities of life, he can hardly be expected to be enthusiastic about any form of wage incentive payment.

The majority of union officials with whom the writer has been in contact oppose incentive wage payment. The principal objection by the union is fear of reduction in personnel brought about by high effort with only a fixed amount of production of goods and services available. Another reason cited for disapproval is the effect of "pitting worker against worker." Union officials state that when one workman makes high earnings and another low, a feeling of distrust and suspicion permeates the working group, which disrupts the partnership relations among workers. Actually, this criticism of incentives is rather weak and not very realistic. Perhaps the most important reason for organized labor's lack of interest in wage incentives is covered by the union statement, "A basic though rarely mentioned reason for organized labor's traditional antagonism to wage incentives is that the more directly the worker controls the amount of compensation he receives, the less need he is likely to feel for union assistance in securing higher wages, although when base rates are raised or lowered, his rates are equally affected."[1]

In the Grand Lodge constitution of the International Association of Machinists (Section 6 of Article J), the policy of this labor group toward incentives is clearly expressed in the statement that "any member guilty of advocating or encouraging any of these systems where they are not in existence is liable to expulsion." Carl Huhndorff, director of research of this labor group, states that the aforementioned clause has never been invoked against an individual member to the best of his knowledge; however, the Grand Lodge policy "has always opposed these (incentive) plans whenever possible as we do not feel that they work to the best interests of working men and women."

There are, of course, unions which approve of incentives. In fact, the late Philip Murray, past president of the C.I.O., was known to look with favor upon incentive wage payment and had expressed his belief that practically any sound system of wage payment can be made to work when a harmonious relationship prevails between labor and management.

The National Industrial Conference Board has made the following statement through its senior research specialist:

. . . wage incentive practices up to the 1939 period were used as one of the whipping boys by union organizers in shops which otherwise were free of unions. However, today the union's outlook is more favorable to wage incentive methods and related techniques of time and motion study. In fact, union officials from the local level up, advocate training in time study for shop stewards in order better to understand and explain to workers the pros and cons of wage incentive.

Most managers agree with the philosophies of incentive wage payment but realize that in view of the rapid growth of union activity, the installation within their own plants may not achieve the desired objectives.

A comparison of the relative percentage of manufacturing enterprises using incentives in the years 1948 through 1952, made by the National Metal Trades Association, reveals a slight annual decline since 1948. This decline of incentive plans' installations no doubt is due in part to the hostile attitude of certain labor unions. It is interesting to note that no definite pattern of attitude on the part of international unions seems to prevail. The same international union will have some locals that favor incentives and others that are bitterly opposed to them.

Prerequisites for a Sound Wage Incentive Plan

Certainly the majority of companies that have incentive installations favor their continuance and believe that their plans are:

[1] Charles E. Britton, *Incentives in Industry* (Esso Standard Oil Co., 1953), p. 55.

1. Increasing the rate of production.
2. Lowering over-all unit costs.
3. Reducing supervision costs.
4. Promoting increased earnings of their employees.

However, in a recent survey of 160 companies[2] where incentive wage payment was practiced, 84 replies from managers inferred that they felt that their plans were only fair, and additional improvement could be made. Five plant managers felt that their incentive systems were poor, and that some changes must be made to warrant continuance.

Before installing a wage incentive program, management should survey its plant to be sure that the plant is ready for an incentive plan. First, a policy of methods standardization must be introduced so that valid work measurement can be accomplished. If each operator follows his own pattern of performing his work, and the sequence of elements has not been standardized, then the organization is not yet ready for wage incentive installation.

Scheduling of work must be handled so that there is always a backlog of orders for each operator and chances of his running out of work are held to a minimum. Of course, this infers that adequate inventories of material are available, and machines and tools are properly maintained. Also, established base rates should be fair, and should provide for sufficient spread between job classes to recognize the positions that demand more skill, effort, and responsibility. Preferably, base rates should have been established through a sound job evaluation program.

Lastly, fair standards of performance must be developed before wage incentive installation can take place. In no case should these rates be set by judgment or past performance records. In order to be sure that they are correct, some form of work measurement based upon the time study or work sampling procedure should be used.

Once these prerequisites have been completed and management is fully sold on incentive wage payment, the company will be in a position to design the system.

Figure 24–1 illustrates the distribution of performance under daywork and incentive as experienced by one company. It will be noted that under the nonincentive plan, the average performance of the plant was 17 per cent below normal performance. It is also interesting to note that when the plan was introduced the entire force of personnel coming under the plan performed somewhere between 83 and 125 per cent efficiency. It had been expected that the dispersion of the plan would be from around 70 to 165 per cent.

Design for a Sound Wage Incentive Plan

To be successful, an incentive plan must be fair to both the company and the operators. The plan should give the operator the opportunity to

[2] National Metal Trades Association.

earn approximately 25 per cent above his base rate if he is normally skilled and executes high effort continuously. Management will benefit through the added productivity by being able to prorate fixed costs over a greater number of pieces, thus reducing total cost.

Perhaps next to fairness, the most important qualification of a good

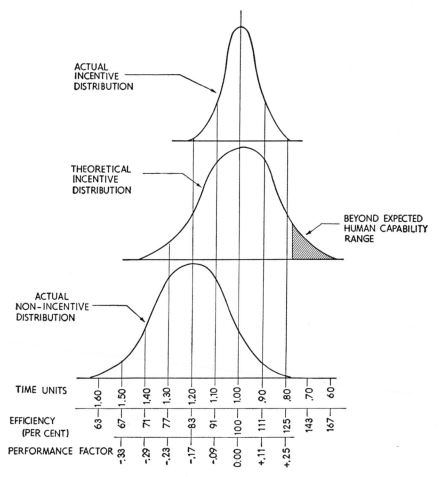

FIG. 24–1. Actual and theoretical distribution of performance under incentive and daywork as recorded by one company.

incentive plan is simplicity. In order to be successful, the plan must be completely sold to the employee, the union, and to management itself. The simpler it is, the easier it will be for all parties to understand; and with understanding the chances for approval are enhanced. Individual incentive plans are more easily understood and will work the best—if individual output can be measured.

The plan should guarantee the basic hourly rate set by job evaluation; the rate should be a good living wage comparable to the prevailing wage rate of the area for each job in question. Then, beyond standard, the operator should be compensated in direct proportion to his output, thus discouraging any restriction of production.

Due to "overrides" (flat across-the-board increases) many incentive installations in the 1946–1952 period did not compensate in direct proportion to output. The override figure reached as much as $0.70 per hour in some companies. For example, a company paying a base rate of $1.00 per hour in 1946 and establishing a standard of 10 pieces per hour on a given job, in effect had a piece rate of $0.10. Thus, if an operator averaged 12 pieces per hour during the course of the work week, he would receive an hourly rate of $1.20. As organized labor demanded greater compensation, increases were given on a flat hourly basis and were not put into the base rate structure nor were they incorporated into the piece rate. Over a period of several years, this "override" increase may have resulted in $0.70 per hour. For example, with the same piece rate of 10 units per hour, an operator working to standard performance would be earning $1.00 plus $0.70 or $1.70 per hour. An operator performing 20 per cent above standard, or averaging 12 pieces per hour, would be paid $1.20 plus $0.70 or $1.90 per hour. Obviously, in the latter instance, the operator is not being paid in direct proportion to his output. If he were so compensated, he would receive $1.70 plus 20 per cent of $1.70 or $2.04 per hour. Since 1952 up to the present time, overrides have been disappearing. New raises as well as old overrides are being negotiated into the piece rate structure.

In order for the employee to associate his effort with compensation, the pay check stub should clearly show both the regular and the incentive earnings. It is also advisable to indicate on a separate form, placed in the pay envelope, the efficiency of the operator for the past pay period. This is calculated as the ratio of standard hours produced during the period to the hours worked during the period.

Provision must be made in an efficient manner for unavoidable loss of time not included in the standard. Also, techniques must be established for insuring accurate piece counts of the required quality requirements. The plan should entail control of indirect labor through measuring productivity of those involved. Indirect labor should not be given a bonus equivalent to the direct workers' unless some yardstick has been determined to justify their incentive earnings. Once the plan has been installed, management must accept the responsibility of maintaining it. Administration of the plan calls for keen judgment in making decisions, and close analysis of all grievances submitted. Management must exercise its right to change the standards when the methods and equipment are changed. Employees must be guaranteed an opportunity to express their suggestions, but the advisability of their requests must be proved before any change is made. Compromising on standards must be avoided. A liberalizing of standards already based on facts will lead to complete failure of the plan. No incentive plan will continue to operate unless it is effectively maintained by a watchful, competent management team.

Reasons for Incentive Plan Failures

An incentive plan may be classified as a failure when it costs more for its maintenance than it actually saves and thus must be discontinued. Usually, it is not possible to put a finger on just what was the immediate cause of failure for a given incentive installation. If the facts were completely known, there would be numerous reasons found for the lack of success of the plan.

In one survey, the principal causes of failure were shown to be poor employee attitude, excessive cost, product insufficiently stable resulting in high cost of standards, and allowances too liberal, thus resulting in too costly a program.

Certainly all plans should be discontinued when their cost of maintenance exceeds the benefits derived through their use. The reasons given in the aforementioned survey are, for the most part, symptoms of a sick plan, of a plan doomed for failure; they are not really causes. Actual cause of the failure of any plan is incompetence in management; a management that permits installation with poor scheduling, unsatisfactory methods, lack of standardization or loose standards, and compromising of standards has no one to blame for failure but itself.

Of course all the requisites of a sound incentive system may be met and still the plan may be unsatisfactory because of failure to promote good industrial relations relative to the program. Employee, union, and supervision's complete co-operation must be won in order to get the team spirit which is so necessary to attain ultimate success from the incentive installation.

Recently, Bruce Payne, President of Bruce Payne & Associates, Inc., reported on 246 companies where incentive plans had either failed or developed weaknesses that necessitated revision. Three factors were enumerated as being responsible for the failures:[3]

	Per Cent
1. Fundamental deficiencies in the plan	41.5
2. Inept human relations	32.5
3. Poor technical administration	26.0

The reasons falling under each of these divisions and their relative importance were summarized as follows:

Fundamental deficiencies	*Per Cent*
a) Poor standards	11.0
b) Low incentive coverage of direct productive work	8.6
c) Ceiling on earnings	7.0
d) No indirect incentives	6.8
e) No supervisory incentives	6.1
f) Complicated pay formula	2.0

[3] Britton, *op. cit.*, p. 60.

Inept human relations
  a) Insufficient supervisor training................................... 6.9
  b) No guarantee of standards....................................... 5.7
  c) A fair day's work not required.................................. 5.0
  d) Standards negotiated with the union............................ 4.8
  e) Plan not understood.. 4.1
  f) Lack of top management support................................ 3.6
  g) Poorly trained operators.. 2.4

Poor technical administration
  a) Method changes not co-ordinated with standards.................... 7.8
  b) Faulty base rates.. 5.1
  c) Poor administration, i.e., poor grievance procedure.................. 4.9
  d) Poor production planning....................................... 3.2
  e) Large group on incentive....................................... 2.8
  f) Poor quality control... 2.2

Administration of the Wage Incentive System

As has been pointed out, in order to be successful, an incentive system must be adequately maintained; it cannot maintain itself. To maintain a plan effectively, management must keep all employees aware of how the plan works and of any changes that may be introduced into the plan. One technique frequently used is to distribute to all employees an "Operating Instruction" manual outlining in detail not only company policy relative to the plan, but also all its working details with sample examples. The basis of job classifications, piece rate prices, performance rating procedure, allowances, and grievance procedure should be thoroughly explained. The technique of handling any unusual situation should be described.

In the administration of the plan, a daily check should be made of low and excessively high performances in an effort to determine their causes. Low performance not only is costly to management in view of the guaranteed hourly rate, but it will lead to employee unrest and dissatisfaction. Unduly high performance is a symptom of loose standards, or the introduction of a method change for which no standard revision has been made. In any case, a loose rate will lead to dissatisfaction on the part of employees in the immediate vicinity of the operator who is working on the job carrying the low standard. A sufficient number of such poor standards can cause the whole incentive plan to fail. Frequently, the operator who has the loose rate will restrict his daily production in fear that management will adjust the standard. This restriction of output is costly to the operator, costly to the company, and results in dissatisfaction from neighboring workmen who see a fellow employee on a soft job.

There should be a continuing effort to include in the incentive plan a greater share of the employees. When only a portion of the plant is on standard, there will be a lack of harmony among operating personnel because of significant differentials in take-home pay.

Periodic reviews of old standards should be made to assure their validity. On standards that have been proved to be satisfactory, elemental values should be recapped for standard data purposes, so that even greater utilization may be made of the time values. Thus, greater coverage of the plant relative to the use of standards can be achieved.

Fundamental in the administration of any wage incentive plan that is keyed to production is the constant adjustment of standards to change in the work. No matter how insignificant the method change may be, it is well to review the standard for possible adjustment. Several minor method improvements, in aggregate, can amount to sufficient time differential to bring about a loose rate if the standard is not changed. When revising time standards due to method changes, it is necessary to study only those elements affected by the change.

So as to keep the incentive plan healthy, the company should arrange periodic meetings with operating supervisors to discuss fundamental weaknesses of the plan, and possible improvements in the installation. At these meetings, departmental performance should be compared, and specific standards that appear unsatisfactory should be brought to light and discussed.

Progress reports should be maintained, showing such pertinent information as departmental efficiency, over-all plant efficiency, number of workers not achieving standard performance, and highest individual performance. Frequently it is helpful to post on the company bulletin board departmental performances, as well as high individual performances, just as top major league batting averages are published in various sporting pages. This not only stimulates interest in the over-all program but also encourages those who are having difficulty in earning an attractive bonus. By seeing accomplishments of fellow employees, they realize the possibilities of greater earnings for themselves.

In the effective administration of the plan, it is essential that there be a continuing effort to minimize the nonproductive hours of direct labor. This nonproductive time for which allowance must be given to the operator represents lost time due to machine breakdowns, material shortages, tool difficulties, and long interruptions of any sort not covered in the allowances applied to the individual time standards. This time, frequently referred to as "blue ticket time" or "extra allowance time," must be carefully watched or it will destroy the purpose of the entire plan.

For example, let us assume that on a certain job a production rate of 10 pieces per hour is averaged and an hourly rate of $1.50 is in effect under a straight daywork operation. Thus, we would have a unit direct labor cost of $0.15. Now this shop changes over to incentive wage payment where the day rate of $1.50 per hour is guaranteed, and, above task, the operator is compensated in direct proportion to his output. Let us assume that the standard developed through time study is 12 pieces per hour, and that for the first 5 hours of the working day, a certain op-

erator averages 14 pieces per hour. His earnings for this period would
then be:

$$(\$1.50)(5)\left(\frac{14}{12}\right) = \$8.74 .$$

Now let us assume that for the remainder of the working day, due to a
material shortage, the operator could not be productively engaged in
work. He would then expect at least his base rate or:

$$(3)(\$1.50) = \$4.50$$

which would give him earnings for the day of

$$\$8.74 + \$4.50 = \$13.24 .$$

This would result in a unit direct labor cost of:

$$\frac{\$13.24}{70} = \$0.189 .$$

Under daywork, even with the low performance, the operator would
have produced the 70 pieces in less than the working day. Here his
earnings would have been: $8 \times \$1.50$ or $12.00 and the unit direct labor
cost would have been: $12.00/70 = \$0.171.$

Under incentive effort, production performance will be considerably
higher than under daywork operation, and with accompanying shorter
in-process time of materials, there will need to be very careful inventory control to prevent material shortages. Likewise, a program of preventative maintenance should be introduced, so as to assure continuous
operation of all machine tools. Equally important to material control is
the control of all nondurable tools, so that shortages with resulting operator delays do not develop.

An effective technique often employed to control the "extra allowance
time" is to key the supervisor's bonus to the amount of this nonproductive time credited to the operator. The more of this time turned in for
the pay period, the less would be the supervisor's compensation. Since
the foreman is in an ideal position to watch schedules and material inventories, and to maintain facilities, he can control nonproductive down
time better than anyone else in the plant.

In addition to controlling the "extra allowance" or daywork time, it is
essential that exact piece counts are recorded at each work station. The
piece count which determines the operator's earnings is usually done by
the operator himself. To prevent the operator from falsifying his production output, controls must be established.

Where the work is small (several pieces can be held in one hand),
the operator "weigh" counts his production at the end of the day or end
of the production run, whichever period is shorter. This "weigh" count is
verified by his immediate supervisor, who initials his production report.

On larger work, one technique that frequently is employed is to have a tray or box with built-in compartments to hold the work. The tote box will hold round numbers of the work such as 10, 20, or 50. Thus, at the end of the shift, it is a simple matter for the operator's supervisor to authenticate the production report by merely counting the number of boxes and multiplying by 10, 20, 50, or whatever number each box holds.

Conclusion

The following fifteen fundamental principles are recommended as a guide for sound practice in wage incentive installation and administration:

1. *Agreement of General Principles.* Management and labor should be in real agreement on the general principles involved in the relationship between work and wages.

2. *A Foundation of Job Evaluation.* There should be a sound wage rate structure, based upon an evaluation of the skill, responsibility, and working conditions inherent in the various jobs.

3. *Individual, Group, or Plant-Wide Incentives.* It is generally conceded that standards, applied to individuals or to small integrated groups, are most effective. Such standards need to be set with the utmost care, and undoubtedly tend toward the lowest unit cost. At times, due to difficulties in recording individual production, or due to the possibilities of teamwork, group standards may be advisable. The larger the group, the less the individual response. With plant-wide incentives, some of the jealousies and transfer difficulties often inherent in group plans are eliminated, but without an unusual degree of leadership and co-operation, the incentive effect is greatly diluted.

4. *The Production-Incentive Relationship.* When production standards are properly set, and based upon well-engineered conditions, good practice has demonstrated the desirability of adopting an incentive payment in which earnings above the established standard are in direct proportion to the increased production.

5. *Simplicity.* The plan should be as simple as possible, without causing inequities. Workers should be able to understand the effect of their own efforts on their earnings.

6. *Quality Control and Improvement.* The desirable and economical degree of quality should be determined and maintained, tied in with bonus payment where advisable.

7. *Improved Methods and Procedures.* To secure the lowest costs and to prevent uneven standards and inequitable earnings, which lead to poor labor relations, the establishment of production standards should be preceded by basic engineering improvements in design equipment, methods, scheduling, and material handling.

8. *Based on Detailed Time Studies.* Standards should be developed from detailed time studies. A permanent record of standard elemental times for each unit of an operation eliminates the occasion for many arguments. A table of basic standard times prepares the way for proper introduction of technological improvements.

9. *Based on Normal Operation under Normal Conditions.* In general, the production standard should be established by management setting up the amount of work performed per unit of time by a normal qualified operator under normal conditions.

10. *Changes in Standards.* The plan should provide for the changing of production standards whenever changes in methods, materials, equipment, or other controlling conditions are made in the operations represented by the standards. In order to avoid misunderstandings, the nature of such changes and the logic of making them should be made clear to labor or its representatives who should have the opportunity to appeal through the grievance machinery.

11. *Considerations in Changing Standards.* Except to correspond properly with changed conditions, production standards once established should not be altered unless by mutual agreement between management and labor representatives.

12. *Keep Temporary Standards at Minimum.* The practice of establishing temporary standards on new operations should be kept at a minimum. It should, in any event, be made clear to all that the standards are for a reasonably short period only.

13. *Guarantee of Hourly Rates.* Under ordinary circumstances, the employees' basic hourly rates should become guaranteed rates.

14. *Incentives for Indirect Workers.* Effective standards may be established for most indirect jobs in the same manner as for direct jobs. If the exigencies of a situation demand that some form of incentive payment be applied to indirect workers as a whole, or in groups, then the indirect man-hours should be correlated to some measurable unit, such as production or direct employee hours, so that indirect labor cost may be kept under control.

15. *Thorough Understanding of Human Relations Involved.* Finally, it should be emphasized that unless management is prepared to work on the problem with a thorough understanding of the human relations involved, it had better have no incentive plan. Whereas such a plan may be a progressively constructive force for increased production, it may also be a means of disrupting labor relations and of actually lowering production. While necessarily retaining its functions, management should take into account labor's point of view. It should impart to labor a complete understanding of the plan and patiently consider grievances, in whatever manner may be agreed upon.[4]

TEXT QUESTIONS

1. Why do many union officials prefer straight daywork as a form of wage payment?
2. What are the fundamental prerequisites of a successful wage incentive plan?
3. What are the requisites of a sound wage incentive system?
4. What is extra allowance or "blue ticket" time? How may it be controlled?
5. Why is it fundamental to keep time standards up to date if a wage incentive plan is to succeed?
6. What does unduly high performance indicate?
7. What are the responsibilities of the foreman, time study department, quality control department, production department, accounting department, and industrial relations department that are essential to effective administration of a sound wage incentive system?
8. What fifteen fundamental principles should be followed in order to assure a successful wage payment plan?

---

[4] From a talk by John W. Nickerson, "The Importance of Incentives," given at the Second Annual Time Study and Methods Conference, New York, N.Y.

9. What is meant by the term "overrides"? Why are "overrides" unpopular with labor?

GENERAL QUESTIONS

1. Why do many unions object to management posting incentive earnings?
2. Should indirect labor that is not on incentive carry a higher base rate than direct labor on incentive when both jobs carry the same evaluation? Why?
3. What is the major reason that causes many union officials to disfavor any form of incentive wage payment?
4. How can the piece count be controlled within the plant?
5. How can a yardstick of performance be established in the following jobs: tool crib attendant, tool grinder, floor sweeper, chip-hauler?

CHAPTER 25

Training for Methods, Time Study, and Wage Payment

From the time of the "efficiency expert" to the early World War II days, the time and motion study analyst made marked progress toward proving the necessity of analyzing work to determine the best method, to standardize on the improved method, and to establish time standards on the improved method.

Today, it is the opinion of many industrialists that World War II was won by the industrial engineer. The miracle of production was brought about primarily by the establishment of good manufacturing methods, fair time standards, and wage payment plans that provided the incentive for high and continuous effort. This area of work has become increasingly important in view of the return to normal business conditions characterized by a competitive market.

The demands upon American universities to supply engineers and technicians trained in this area of work have been unparalleled. Industrial America's demand for methods analysts and time study analysts continues to grow. In a survey conducted by Ralph E. Balyeat on subjects found in industrial engineering curriculums, the order of importance shown in Table XXX was given by industry and educators.

Motion and time study and operation analysis, in the opinion of both industrialists and educators, rank among the first five subjects that should be offered in an industrial engineering curriculum.

To meet the demand, and to reap more quickly the benefits of training in this field, many industries have embarked on education programs of their own, conducted in their own plants on company time.

452

TABLE XXX

SUBJECTS COMMONLY FOUND IN INDUSTRIAL ENGINEERING CURRICULUMS

ORDER OF IMPORTANCE AS REPORTED BY EDUCATORS		ORDER OF IMPORTANCE AS REPORTED BY COMPANIES EMPLOYING INDUSTRIAL ENGINEERS	
Rank	Subject	Rank	Subject
1	Motion and Time Study	1	Mathematics
2	Accounting	2	Plant Layout
3	Mathematics	3	Operation Analysis
4	Operation Analysis	4	Plant Operation
5	Industrial Organization and Management	5	Motion and Time Study
6	Labor Relations, Personnel	6	Production Engineering
7	Mechanics	7	Factory Planning
8	Physics	8	Wages, Job Evaluation
9	Plant Layout	9	Production Planning
10	Factory Planning	10	Mechanics
11	Production Planning	11	Production Control
12	Mechanical Drawing	12	Mechanical Drawing
13	Technical Writing	13	Labor Relations, Personnel
14	Strength of Materials	14	Industrial Organization and Management
15	Engineering Materials	15	Human Engineering
16	Production Control	16	Industrial Reports
17	Engineering Economy	17	Quality Control
18	Statistics	18	Surveys and Reports
19	Technical English	19	Engineering Economy
20	Economics	20	Industrial Economics
21	Production Engineering	21	Physics
22	Electrical Engineering	22	Statistics
23	Plant Operation	23	Safety Engineering
24	Wages, Job Evaluation	24	Technical Writing
25	Quality Control	25	Technical English
26	Industrial Economics	26	Accounting
27	Tool Engineering	27	Mechanisms
28	Business Law	28	Machine Design
29	Thermodynamics	29	Economics
30	Machine Design	30	Tool Engineering
31	Human Engineering	31	Engineering Materials
32	Safety Engineering	32	Electrical Engineering
33	Mechanisms	33	Strength of Materials
34	Chemistry	34	Chemistry
35	Metallurgy	35	Finance
36	Surveys and Reports	36	Metallurgy
37	Fluid Mechanics	37	Fluid Mechanics
38	Industrial Reports	38	Business Law
39	Finance	39	Thermodynamics
40	Government and Political Science	40	Government and Political Science
41	Surveying	41	Surveying

Source: "Concepts and Practices in Industrial Engineering," *Journal of Industrial Engineering*, Vol. V, No. 3 (May, 1954), p. 20.

Individual Plant Method Training Programs

Any methods training program when properly undertaken will prove to be self-supporting. In the experience of the writer, several concerns that have introduced and gone ahead with training in the area of methods have almost immediately realized substantial savings in all areas of their plants. One manufacturer of farm machinery gave a 64-hour course in methods analysis over a period of 21 weeks. In attendance were 42 foremen, assistant foremen, time study analysts, and other key operating personnel. At the termination of the course, 28 methods projects were turned in, representing methods improvement solutions that could be introduced in the plant. These ideas included machine coupling, redesign of tools and product, paper-work simplification, improved layout, better means of material handling, improved dies, jigs, and fixtures, elimination of operations, adjusting of tolerances and specifications, and many other usable improvements resulting in the saving of thousands of dollars annually.

In addition to the immediate gains mentioned, the training in operation analysis and work simplification developed an analytical approach on the part of the operating personnel so that in the future they will be continually on the alert to find a "better way." They developed an appreciation of cost of manufacture, and, at the completion of the course, were more cognizant of the relationship between output and selling price.

This company, by providing the means for employee "on-the-job" training in the field of methods and related areas, has gone a long way toward assuring its place in an extremely competitive market.

Training in Motion and Time Study

The lack of success of some time and motion study programs is in part due to a lack of understanding of the techniques by both management and the operating personnel. One of the easiest ways to assure the success of any practical innovation is to inform all affected parties as to how and why it operates. When the theories, techniques, and economic necessity of work measurement are understood by all parties, little difficulty will be encountered in its application. In unionized shops, it is especially important that the officers of the union at the local level understand the need and the steps involved in establishing standards of performance. Training in the areas of performance rating, application of allowances, standard data methods, and job evaluation are especially important. In the experience of the writer, the companies that have provided training in the elements of time study for union officials and stewards, as well as representatives of management, have had harmonious relationships in the field of standards and wage payment.

In addition to the informative training to acquaint the various operating and supervisory members of the plant with the philosophies and techniques of time and motion study, it is wise for industry to provide training for its personnel who plan on making this field of endeavor their life's work. Not only is it necessary to train the neophyte, but the experienced analyst should be continually checked to make certain that his conception of normal is not deviating from standard. As new developments, which are constantly being made, are recognized, the information

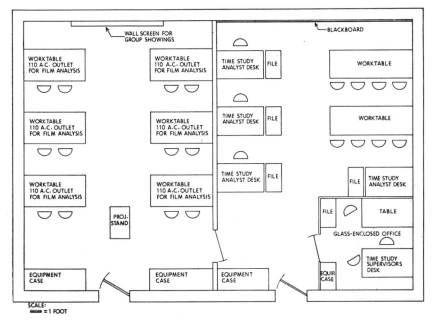

FIG. 25–1. Motion and time study office and laboratory adapted for periodic training programs. Scale ¼ inch = 1 foot.

FIG. 25–2. Group of time study analysts studying a horizontal milling operation in order to check individual end points and performance rating factors.

should be circulated throughout the personnel of the methods, time study, and wage payment sections. This should be done through the medium of formalized training. Figure 25–1 illustrates a typical motion and time study lecture room and laboratory that provide a suitable place for film analysis and the establishment of synthetic standards, as well as office space for the time study department which can be readily converted into a lecture room for formalized training.

It is recommended that any company that has, or plans to have, a program of work simplification or methods analysis, time study, or work

FIG. 25–3. Time study analysts and their instructor reviewing a film for the determination of basic motions.

measurement, and incentive wage payment, include as part of its installation a continuing training program. The devotion of a two-hour period once a week for training foremen, union stewards, direct labor, and management, will be well worth the time and money spent. The periodic verification of the rating ability of the staff of the time study department is fundamental. Figure 25–2 illustrates a group of analysts studying a horizontal milling operation. After the study has been completed, the number and length of elements will be compared, the performance factors will be considered, and the resulting standards established by the different observers will be evaluated. Frequent checks like this assure a uniformity of rating of the various time study analysts employed, and keep all members of the time study group alert and free from slovenly habits in the taking of the study.

Figure 25–3 shows two time study analysts and their instructor reviewing a film and separating it into its basic divisions for the purpose of establishing a standard. Supervised training such as this facilitates consistency of the group in establishing therblig end points, classes of motion, distances moved, and other variables which affect the normal time required to perform an operation.

Developing Creativity

Creative work is not confined to a particular field or to a few individuals, but is carried on in varying degrees by people in many occupations: the artist sketches, the newspaper writer promotes an idea, the teacher encourages student development, the scientist experiments with a theory, the method and time study analyst develops improved methods of doing work.

Creativeness implies newness, but it is as often concerned with the improvement of old products as it is with the creation of new ones. A "how-to-produce-something-better" attitude, tempered with good judgment, is an important characteristic of the effective methods and time study analyst.

To develop creativity in the practicing methods and time study analyst is a continuing problem. Knowledge of the fundamental principles of physics, chemistry, mathematics, and engineering subjects is a good foundation for creative thinking. If the practicing analyst does not have this basic background, he should acquire it either by educational programs or else through study alone. Of course, knowledge is only a basis for creative thinking and does not necessarily stimulate it.

The inherent personal characteristics of curiosity, intuition, perception, ingenuity, initiative, and persistence produce an effective creative thinker. Of these, curiosity seems to stimulate more ideas than does any other personal characteristic. One aid to development or restoration of curiosity is to train oneself to be observant. The methods and time study analyst should get in the habit of asking himself how a particular object is made, of what materials it is constructed, why it was designed of a particular size and shape, why and how it was finished as it was, and how much it cost. If he isn't able to answer these questions, he should find the answer either through analysis or by referring to source materials and consulting others. These observations lead the creative thinker to see ways in which the product or process can be improved through cost reduction, quality improvement, ease of maintenance, or improved aesthetic appeal.

One significant creative idea usually opens up fields of activities that lead to many new ideas. Frequently one idea that has application on a given product or process will have equal application on other products and similar processes.

Decision-Making Methods and Processes

The methods and time study analyst should become trained in the various decision-making processes. Judgment alone will not always provide the best answer. The analyst is continually confronted with such questions as, "Would it be economically wise to go ahead with this process," "Should this tool be redesigned with the probability of .50 that production requirements will be increased by between 500 and 1,000 pieces," "Will it be necessary to take 5,000 work sampling observations if we are seeking an element that occurs approximately 12 per cent of the time and tolerance limits are so much." These are typical questions that must be answered, and analytical means provide a much better method than mere judgment.

In order to be able to handle problems similar to these, the analyst should have a working knowledge of engineering economy, statistical analysis, and the theory of probability. More and more, the practicing method and time study analyst is realizing the necessity of a background in these fields of study so that he can make the most effective decisions for his company.

TEXT QUESTIONS

1. Is methods training when conducted within a plant self-supporting?
2. Why is plant-wide training in the areas of methods and time study a healthy management step?
3. Why should training in time study be looked upon as a continuing project?
4. Why is American industry more receptive to the time study analyst today than prior to World War II?
5. What order of importance does diversified industry place upon time study in the development of an industrial engineering curriculum?
6. What intangible benefits can be achieved through a methods training program on the foreman level?
7. Why should the experienced analyst be continually checked relative to his ability to performance rate?
8. How can a person develop creative ability?

GENERAL QUESTIONS

1. Who should handle the training in methods, time study, and wage payment when conducted within a plant?
2. Is it advisable to provide training in the area of methods, time study, and wage payment down to the operator level? Why?
3. To what opportunities within an industry can the experienced analyst in methods and time study expect to be promoted?
4. What is the relation between work measurement and Operations Research?
5. Will "automation" diminish the need for the method and time study analyst?

Glossary of Terms Used in Methods, Time Study, and Wage Payment

Abnormal time. Elemental time values taken during the course of a time study that are either considerably higher or lower than the mean of the majority of observations—synonym for "Wild values."

Actual time. The average elemental time actually taken by the operator during the course of a time study.

Allowance. An amount of time added to the normal time so as to provide for personal delays, unavoidable delays, and fatigue.

Allowed time. The time utilized by the normal operator to perform an operation while working at a standard rate of performance with due allowance for personal and unavoidable delays and fatigue.

Assemble. The act of bringing two mating parts together.

Automation. Increased mechanization to produce goods and services.

Average elemental time. The mean elemental time taken by the operator to perform the task during the course of a time study.

Average hourly earnings. The mean dollar and cent monies paid to an operator on an hourly basis. It is determined by dividing the hours worked per period into the total wages paid for the period.

Avoidable delay. A cessation of productive work which is entirely due to the operator and which would not occur in the regular work cycle.

Balancing delay. The cessation of productive work by one body member as a result of orienting another body member in the process of useful work.

Base time. The time required to perform a task by a normal operator working at a standard pace with no allowance provided for personal delays, unavoidable delays, or fatigue.

Base wage rate. The hourly money rate paid for a given work assignment performed at a standard pace by a normal operator.

Bedaux plan. A constant sharing wage incentive plan with a high task and with the provision that the bonus for incentive effort be distributed between the employee and management.

Bonus earnings. Those monies paid in addition to the regular wage or salary.

Change direction. A basic division of accomplishment characterized by a slight hesitation when the hand alters its directional course while reaching or moving.

Chronocyclegraph. Photographic record of body motion that may be used to determine both speed and direction of body motion patterns.

Chronograph. A time-recording device which operates by marking a tape that is driven at a constant speed. Time is determined by measuring the distance between successive markings on the tape.

Constant element. An element that does not vary significantly in the amount of time required to perform it when changes in the process or dimensional changes in the product occur.

Continuous timing method. A method of studying an operation in which the stop watch is kept running continuously during the course of the study and is not snapped back at elemental termination.

Controlled time. Elapsed elemental time that is dependent entirely on the facility or process.

Curve. A graphic representation of the relation between two factors, one of which is usually time.

Cycle. A series of elements that occur in regular order and make possible an operation. These elements repeat themselves as the operation is repeated.

Cyclegraph. A photographic record of body motion.

Daywork. Any work for which the operator is compensated on the basis of time rather than output.

Decimal-hour stop watch. A stop watch used for work measurement, the dial of which is graduated in .0001 of an hour.

Decimal-minute stop watch. A stop watch used for work measurement, the dial of which is graduated in .01 of a minute.

Delays. Any cessation in the work routine that does not occur in the typical work cycle.

Differential piecework. Compensation of labor in which the money rate per piece is based on the total pieces produced during the period (usually one day).

Direct labor. Labor performed on each piece that advances the piece toward its ultimate specifications.

Disassemble. The basic division of accomplishment that takes place when two mating parts are separated.

Drop delivery. The disposal of a part by dropping it on a conveyor or gravity chute, thus minimizing move and position therbligs.

Efficiency. The ratio of actual output to standard output.

Effort. The will to perform productive work either mental or manual.

Effort time. That portion of the cycle time that is dependent upon the skill and effort of the operator.

Elapsed time. The actual time that has transpired during the course of a study or an operation.

Element. A division of work that can be measured with stop-watch equipment and that has readily identified terminal points.

External time. The time required to perform elements of work when the machine or process is not in operation.

Fair day's work. The amount of work that is performed by an operator or group of operators that is fair to both the company and the operator, considering wages paid. It is the "amount of work that can be produced by a qualified employee when working at a normal pace and effectively utilizing his time where work is not restricted by process limitations."

Fatigue. A lessening in the capacity for the will to work.

Fatigue allowance. An amount of time that is added to the normal time to compensate for fatigue.

Feed. The speed at which the cutting tool is moved into the work, as in drilling and turning, or the rate that the work is moved past the cutting tool.

First piece time. The time allowed to produce the first piece of an order. This time has been adjusted so as to make allowance for the operators' unfamiliarity with the method and to accommodate for minor delays resulting from the newness of the work. It does not include time for setting up the work station.

Flow diagram. Pictorial presentation of the layout of a process showing location of all activities appearing on the flow process chart and the paths of travel of the work.

Flow process chart. Graphic representation of all operations, transportations, inspections, delays, and storages occurring during a process or procedure. The chart includes information considered desirable for analysis, such as time required and distance moved.

Foreign element. An interruption in the regular work cycle.

Frame. The space occupied by a single picture on a moving-picture film.

Frame counter. A device that automatically tabulates the number of frames that have passed the lens of the projector.

Fringe benefits. That portion of tangible compensation given by the employer to employees which is not paid in the form of wages, salaries, or bonuses, such as insurance, retirement funds, and other employee services. These exclude benefits paid for by employees by pay deductions, such as their participating portions of insurance premiums and retirement funds.

Gain sharing. Any method of wage payment where the worker participates in all or a portion of the added earnings resulting from his production above standard.

Gantt chart. A series of graphs consisting of horizontal lines or bars in positions and lengths which show schedules or quotas and progress plotted on a common time scale.

Get. The act of picking up and gaining control of an object. It will consist of the therbligs reach and grasp, and move; also sometimes includes search and select.

Grasp. The elemental hand motion of closing the fingers around a part in an operation.

Job analysis. A procedure for making a careful appraisal of each job and then recording the details of the work so that it can be equitably evaluated.

Job evaluation. A procedure for determining the relative worth of various work assignments.

Leveling. A term used synonymously with performance rating. It is the assignment of a percentage to the operator's average observed time to adjust his time to the observer's conception of normal.

Loose rate. An established allowed time that permits the normal operator to achieve standard performance with poorer than average effort.

Machine attention time. That time during the work cycle in which the operator must devote his attention to the machine or process.

Machine cycle time. The time required for the machine in process to complete one cycle.

Machine down time. That time when the machine or process is inoperative because of some breakdown or because of material shortage.

Machine idle time. That time when the machine or process is inoperative.

Man-hour. The standard amount of work performed by one man in one hour.

Marsto-chron. A time study instrument that records elapsed time on a tape driven by a synchronous motor. Elapsed time is determined by measuring the distance on the tape between parallel markings that are recorded at element terminal points.

Maximum performance. That performance which will result in the highest obtainable production.

Measured daywork. An incentive system in which hourly rates are periodically adjusted on the basis of operator performance during the previous period.

Memomotion study. The division of a work assignment into elements by analyzing motion pictures taken at speeds of 50, 60, or 100 frames per minute, and then improving the operation.

Merit rating. A method of evaluating an employee's worth to a company in terms of such factors as quantity of work, quality of work, dependability, and general contribution to the company.

Merrick differential piece rate. An incentive wage payment plan having three different piece rates established on the basis of operator performance.

Method. A term used to signify the technique employed for performing an operation.

Methods study. Analysis of an operation so as to increase the production per unit of time and consequently reduce the unit cost.

Microchronometer. A specially designed clock devised by Frank B. Gilbreth that is capable of measuring elapsed time in "winks" (.0005 minute).

Micromotion study. The division of a work assignment into therbligs by analyzing motion pictures frame by frame and then improving the operation by eliminating unnecessary movements and simplifying the necessary movements.

Minimum time. The least amount of time taken by the operator to perform a given element during the course of a time study.

Modal time. The elapsed elemental time value that occurs most frequently during the course of a time study. Occasionally used in preference to the average elemental time.

Motion study. The analysis and study of the motions comprising an operation so as to improve the motion pattern by eliminating ineffective motions and shortening the effective motions.

Move. The term to signify a hand movement with a load.

M.T.M. A procedure which analyzes any manual operation or method into the basic motions required to perform it, and assigns to each motion a predetermined time standard which is determined by the nature of the motion and the conditions under which it is made.

Normal operator. An operator who can achieve the established standard of performance when following the prescribed method and working at an average pace.

Normal performance. The performance that is expected from the average trained operator when he is following the prescribed method and working at an average pace.

Normal time. The time required for the standard operator to perform the operation when working at a standard pace without delay for personal reasons or unavoidable circumstances.

Normal working area. That space at the work area which can be reached by either the left hand or the right hand when both elbows are pivoted on the edge of the work station.

Observation. The gathering and recording of time to perform an element, or one watch reading.

Observation board. A convenient board used to support the stop watch and hold the observation form during the course of a time study.

Observation form. A form designed to accommodate the elements of a given time study with space for recording their duration.

Observer. The analyst who is taking a time study of a given operation.

Occupational physiology. Scientific study of the worker and his environment.

Occurrence. An incident or event happening during the course of a time study.

Operation. The intentional changing of a part toward its ultimate desired shape, size, form, and characteristics.

Operation analysis. Investigative process dealing with an operation in factory or office work. Usually the process leading to operation standardization, including motion and time study.

Operation card. A form that outlines the sequence of operations, the time allowed, and the special tools required in the manufacture of a part.

Output. The total production of a machine, process, or workman for a specified unit of time.

Over-all study. The recording of cycle time as a verification of a developed time study standard.

Performance. The ratio of the actual production produced by an operator to the standard production.

Performance rating. The assignment of a percentage to the operator's average observed time which is based on the actual performance of the operator compared to the observer's conception of normal.

Personal allowance. A percentage added to the normal time to accommodate the personal needs of the operator.

Piece rate. A standard of performance expressed in terms of money per unit of production.

Plan. A basic division of accomplishment involving the mental process of determining the next action.

Point. A unit of output identified as the production of one standard man in one minute. Used as a basis for establishing standards under the Bedaux system.

Point system. A method of job evaluation in which the relative worth of different jobs is determined by totaling the number of points assigned to the various factors applicable to the different jobs.

Position. An element of work consisting of locating an object in such a way that it will be properly oriented in a specific location.

Preposition. An element of work which consists of positioning an object in a predetermined place in such a way that it may be grasped in the position in which it is to be held when it is needed.

Process. A series of operations that advances the product towards its ultimate size, shape, and specifications.

Process chart. A graphic representation of a manufacturing process.

Productive time. Any time that is spent on advancing the progress of a piece of production toward its ultimate specification.

Profit sharing. Any procedure by which an employer pays to all employees, in addition to good rates of regular pay, special current or deferred sums, based not only upon individual or group performance but also on the prosperity of the business as a whole.

Rate. A standard expressed in dollars and cents.

Rate setting. The act of establishing money rates or time values on any operation.

Ratio-delay study. Making a study using the work sampling procedure where a large number of obervations are taken at random intervals.

Synthetic basic motion times. A collection of time standards assigned to fundamental motions and groups of motions.

Unavoidable delay. An interruption in the continuity of an operation beyond the control of an operator.

Use. An objective therblig that occurs when either or both hands have control of an object during that part of the cycle when productive work is being performed.

Variable element. An element the time of which is affected by one or more characteristics such as size, shape, hardness, or tolerance, so that as these conditions change, the time required to perform the element changes.

Wage incentive. The provision of a financial inducement for effort above normal.

Wage rate. The money rate expressed in dollars and cents paid to the employee per hour.

Waiting time. That time when the operator is unable to do useful work because of the nature of the process or because of immediate lack of material.

Wild value. Elemental time values taken during the course of a time study that are either considerably higher or lower than the mean of the majority of observations. Synonym for "abnormal time."

Wink. One division on the microchronometer equal to $1/2,000$ (.0005) minute.

Wink counter. A timing device either mechanically or electrically driven that records elapsed time in winks.

Work-factor. Index of additional time required over and above the basic time as established by the Work-Factor system of synthetic basic motion times.

Work sampling. Method of analyzing work by taking a large number of observations at random intervals, for the purpose of establishing standards and improving methods.

Work station. That area where the workman performs the elements of work involved in a specific operation.

Collection of Helpful Formulas

(1) *Quadratic*

$$Ax^2 + Bx + C = 0$$

$$x = \frac{-B \pm \sqrt{B^2 - 4AC}}{2A}$$

(2) *Logarithms*

$$\log ab = \log a + \log b$$
$$\log \frac{a}{b} = \log a - \log b$$
$$\log a^n = n \log a$$
$$\log \sqrt[n]{a} = \frac{1}{n} \log a$$
$$\log 1 = 0$$
$$\log{}_a a = 1$$

(3) *Binomial theorem*

$$(a + b)^n = a^n + na^{n-1}b + \frac{n(n-1)}{2} a^{n-2}b^2 + \frac{n(n-1)(n-2)}{3} a^{n-3}b^3 + \cdots$$

(4) *Circle*

$$\text{Circumference} = 2\pi r$$
$$\text{Area} = \pi r^2$$

(5) *Prism*

$$\text{Volume} = Ba$$

(6) *Pyramid*

$$\text{Volume} = \tfrac{1}{3}Ba$$

(7) *Right circular cylinder*

$$\text{Volume} = \pi r^2 a$$
$$\text{Lateral surface} = 2\pi r a$$
$$\text{Total surface} = 2\pi r(r + a)$$

(8) *Right circular cone*

$$\text{Volume} = \tfrac{1}{3}\pi r^2 a$$
$$\text{Lateral surface} = \pi r s$$
$$\text{Total surface} = \pi r(r + s)$$

(9) *Sphere*

$$\text{Volume} = \tfrac{4}{3}\pi r^3$$
$$\text{Surface} = 4\pi r^2$$

(10) *Frustrum of a right circular cone*

$$\text{Volume} = \tfrac{1}{3}\pi a(R^2 + r^2 + Rr)$$
$$\text{Lateral surface} = \pi s(R + r)$$

(11) *Measurement of angles*

$$1 \text{ degree} = \frac{\pi}{180} = .0174 \text{ radians}$$
$$1 \text{ radian} = 57.29 \text{ degrees}$$

(12) *Trigonometrical functions*

Right triangles:

The sine of the angle A is the quotient of the opposite side divided by the hypotenuse. Sin $A = \dfrac{a}{c}$.

The tangent of the angle A is the quotient of the opposite side divided by the adjacent side. Tan $A = \dfrac{a}{b}$.

The secant of the angle A is the quotient of the hypotenuse divided by the adjacent side. Sec $A = \dfrac{c}{b}$.

The cosine, cotangent, and cosecant of an angle are respectively the sine, tangent, and secant of the complement of that angle.

Law of sines

$$\frac{\iota}{\sin A} = \frac{b}{\sin B} = \frac{c}{\sin C}$$

Law of cosines

$$a^2 = b^2 + c^2 - 2bc \cos A$$

(13) *Equation of straight lines*

Slope—intercept form

$$y = mx + b$$

intercept form

$$\frac{x}{a} + \frac{y}{b} = 1$$

Special Tables

TABLE XXXI

NATURAL SINES AND TANGENTS

Angle	Sin	Tan	Cot	Cos	
0	0.0000	0.0000	∞	1.0000	90
1	0.0175	0.0175	57.2900	0.9998	89
2	0.0349	0.0349	28.6363	0.9994	88
3	0.0523	0.0524	19.0811	0.9986	87
4	0.0698	0.0699	14.3007	0.9976	86
5	0.0872	0.0875	11.4301	0.9962	85
6	0.1045	0.1051	9.5144	0.9945	84
7	0.1219	0.1228	8.1443	0.9925	83
8	0.1392	0.1405	7.1154	0.9903	82
9	0.1564	0.1584	6.3138	0.9877	81
10	0.1736	0.1763	5.6713	0.9848	80
11	0.1908	0.1944	5.1446	0.9816	79
12	0.2079	0.2126	4.7046	0.9781	78
13	0.2250	0.2309	4.3315	0.9744	77
14	0.2419	0.2493	4.0108	0.9703	76
15	0.2588	0.2679	3.7321	0.9659	75
16	0.2756	0.2867	3.4874	0.9613	74
17	0.2924	0.3057	3.2709	0.9563	73
18	0.3090	0.3249	3.0777	0.9511	72
19	0.3256	0.3443	2.9042	0.9455	71
20	0.3420	0.3640	2.7475	0.9397	70
21	0.3584	0.3839	2.6051	0.9336	69
22	0.3746	0.4040	2.4751	0.9272	68
23	0.3907	0.4245	2.3559	0.9205	67
24	0.4067	0.4452	2.2460	0.9135	66
25	0.4226	0.4663	2.1445	0.9063	65
26	0.4384	0.4877	2.0503	0.8988	64
27	0.4540	0.5095	1.9626	0.8910	63
28	0.4695	0.5317	1.8807	0.8829	62
29	0.4848	0.5543	1.8040	0.8746	61
30	0.5000	0.5774	1.7321	0.8660	60
31	0.5150	0.6009	1.6643	0.8572	59
32	0.5299	0.6249	1.6003	0.8480	58
33	0.5446	0.6494	1.5399	0.8387	57
34	0.5592	0.6745	1.4826	0.8290	56
35	0.5736	0.7002	1.4281	0.8192	55
36	0.5878	0.7265	1.3764	0.8090	54
37	0.6018	0.7536	1.3270	0.7986	53
38	0.6157	0.7813	1.2799	0.7880	52
39	0.6293	0.8098	1.2349	0.7771	51
40	0.6428	0.8391	1.1918	0.7660	50
41	0.6561	0.8693	1.1504	0.7547	49
42	0.6691	0.9004	1.1106	0.7431	48
43	0.6820	0.9325	1 0724	0.7314	47
44	0.6947	0.9657	1.0355	0.7193	46
45	0.7071	1.0000	1.0000	0.7071	45
	Cos	Cot	Tan	Sin	Angle

TABLE XXXII

Useful Information

To find the circumference of a circle, multiply the diameter by 3.1416.

To find the diameter of a circle, multiply the circumference by .31831.

To find the area of a circle, multiply the square of the diameter by .7854.

The radius of a circle $\times$ 6.283185 = the circumference.

The square of the circumference of a circle $\times$ .07958 = the area.

Half the circumference of a circle $\times$ half its diameter = the area.

The circumference of a circle $\times$ .159155 = the radius.

The square root of the area of a circle $\times$ .56419 = the radius.

The square root of the area of a circle $\times$ 1.12838 = the diameter.

To find the diameter of a circle equal in area to a given square, multiply a side of the square by 1.12838.

To find the side of a square equal in area to a given circle, multiply the diameter by .8862.

To find the side of a square inscribed in a circle, multiply the diameter by .7071.

To find the side of a hexagon inscribed in a circle, multiply the diameter of the circle by .500.

To find the diameter of a circle inscribed in a hexagon, multiply a side of the hexagon by 1.7321.

To find the side of an equilateral triangle inscribed in a circle, multiply the diameter of the circle by .866.

To find the diameter of a circle inscribed in an equilateral triangle, multiply a side of the triangle by .57735.

To find the area of the surface of a ball (sphere), multiply the square of the diameter by 3.1416.

To find the volume of a ball (sphere), multiply the cube of the diameter by .5236.

Doubling the diameter of a pipe increases its capacity four times.

To find the pressure in pounds per square inch at the base of a column of water, multiply the height of the column in feet by .433.

A gallon of water (U. S. Standard) weighs 8.336 pounds and contains 231 cubic inches. A cubic foot of water contains $7\frac{1}{2}$ gallons, 1728 cubic inches, and weighs 62.425 pounds at a temperature of about 39° F.

These weights change slightly above and below this temperature.

TABLE XXXIII

AREAS OF THE NORMAL CURVE

z	Area	z	Area
−3.0	.0013	0.1	.5398
−2.9	.0019	0.2	.5793
−2.8	.0026	0.3	.6179
−2.7	.0035	0.4	.6554
−2.6	.0047	0.5	.6915
−2.5	.0062	0.6	.7257
−2.4	.0082	0.7	.7580
−2.3	.0107	0.8	.7881
−2.2	.0139	0.9	.8159
−2.1	.0179	1.0	.8413
−2.0	.0228	1.1	.8643
−1.9	.0287	1.2	.8849
−1.8	.0359	1.3	.9032
−1.7	.0446	1.4	.9192
−1.6	.0548	1.5	.9332
−1.5	.0668	1.6	.9452
−1.4	.0808	1.7	.9554
−1.3	.0968	1.8	.9641
−1.2	.1151	1.9	.9713
−1.1	.1357	2.0	.9772
−1.0	.1587	2.1	.9821
−0.9	.1841	2.2	.9861
−0.8	.2119	2.3	.9893
−0.7	.2420	2.4	.9918
−0.6	.2741	2.5	.9938
−0.5	.3085	2.6	.9953
−0.4	.3446	2.7	.9965
−0.3	.3821	2.8	.9974
−0.2	.4207	2.9	.9981
−0.1	.4602	3.0	.9987
0.0	.5000		

Above table tabularizes $P(z)$ where

$$P(z) = \int_{-\infty}^{z} \frac{1}{\sqrt{2\pi}} e^{-\frac{z^2}{2}} dz$$

$$\text{and } z = \frac{x - u}{\sigma}$$

TABLE XXXIV

Decimal and Millimeter Equivalents of Fractional Parts of an Inch

Inches		Inches	mm	Inches		Inches	mm
	1-64	.01563	.397		33-64	.51563	13.097
1-32		.03125	.794	17-32		.53125	13.494
	3-64	.04688	1.191		35-64	.54688	13.890
1-16		.0625	1.587	9-16		.5625	14.287
	5-64	.07813	1.984		37-64	.57813	14.684
3-32		.09375	2.381	19-32		.59375	15.081
	7-64	.10938	2.778		39-64	.60938	15.478
1-8		.125	3.175	5-8		.625	15.875
	9-64	.14063	3.572		41-64	.64063	16.272
5-32		.15625	3.969	21-32		.65625	16.669
	11-64	.17188	4.366		43-64	.67188	17.065
3-16		.1875	4.762	11-16		.6875	17.462
	13-64	.20313	5.159		45-64	.70313	17.859
7-32		.21875	5.556	23-32		.71875	18.256
	15-64	.23438	5.953		47-64	.73438	18.653
1-4		.25	6.350	3-4		.75	19.050
	17-64	.26563	6.747		49-64	.76563	19.447
9-32		.28125	7.144	25-32		.78125	19.844
	19-64	.29688	7.541		51-64	.79688	20.240
5-16		.3125	7.937	13-16		.8125	20.637
	21-64	.32813	8.334		53-64	.82813	21.034
11-32		.34375	8.731	27-32		.84375	21.431
	23-64	.35938	9.128		55-64	.85938	21.828
3-8		.375	9.525	7-8		.875	22.225
	25-64	.39063	9.922		57-64	.89063	22.622
13-32		.40625	10.319	29-32		.90625	23.019
	27-64	.42188	10.716		59-64	.92188	23.415
7-16		.4375	11.113	15-16		.9375	23.812
	29-64	.45313	11.509		61-64	.95313	24.209
15-32		.46875	11.906	31-32		.96875	24.606
	31-64	.48438	12.303		63-64	.98438	25.003
1-2		.5	12.700	1		1.00000	25.400

TABLE XXXV

HOURLY PRODUCTION TABLE

Showing 60% to 80% Efficiency

Sec per Piece	Gross Prod. Per Hr	60%	65%	70%	75%	80%
1/2	7200	4320	4680	5040	5400	5760
5/8	5760	3456	3744	4032	4320	4608
3/4	4800	2880	3120	3360	3600	3840
7/8	4114	2468	2674	2880	3086	3291
1	3600	2160	2340	2520	2700	2880
1 1/4	2880	1728	1872	2016	2160	2304
1 1/2	2400	1440	1560	1680	1800	1920
1 3/4	2057	1234	1337	1440	1543	1646
2	1800	1080	1170	1260	1350	1440
2 1/4	1600	960	1040	1120	1200	1280
2 1/2	1440	864	936	1008	1080	1152
2 3/4	1309	785	851	916	982	1047
3	1200	720	780	840	900	960
3 1/4	1107	664	720	775	830	886
3 1/2	1028	617	668	720	771	822
3 3/4	960	576	624	672	720	768
4	900	540	585	630	675	720
4 1/4	847	508	551	593	635	678
4 1/2	800	480	520	560	600	640

Sec per Piece	Gross Prod. Per Hr	60%	65%	70%	75%	80%
12 1/2	288	173	187	202	216	230
13	276	166	179	193	207	221
13 1/2	267	160	174	187	200	214
14	257	154	167	180	193	206
14 1/2	248	149	161	174	186	198
15	240	144	156	168	180	192
15 1/2	232	139	151	162	174	186
16	225	135	146	158	169	180
16 1/2	218	131	142	153	164	174
17	212	127	138	148	159	170
17 1/2	206	124	134	144	155	165
18	200	120	130	140	150	160
18 1/2	195	117	127	137	146	156
19	189	113	123	132	142	151
19 1/2	185	111	120	130	139	148
20	180	108	117	126	135	144
21	171	103	111	120	128	137
22	164	98	107	115	123	131
23	156	94	101	109	117	125

Sec per Piece	Gross Prod. Per Hr	60%	65%	70%	75%	80%
50	72	43	47	50	54	58
52	69	41	45	48	52	55
54	67	40	44	47	50	54
56	64	38	42	45	48	51
58	62	37	40	43	47	50
60	60	36	39	42	45	48
62	58	35	38	41	44	46
64	56	34	36	39	42	45
66	54	32	35	38	41	43
68	53	32	34	37	40	42
70	51	31	33	36	38	41
72	50	30	33	35	38	40
74	49	29	32	34	37	39
76	47	28	31	33	35	38
78	46	28	30	32	35	37
80	45	27	29	32	34	36
82	44	26	29	31	33	35
84	43	26	28	30	32	34
86	42	25	27	29	32	34

Size																				
4 3/4	757	454	492	530	568	606	24	150	90	98	105	113	120	88	41	25	27	29	31	33
5	720	432	468	504	540	576	25	144	86	94	101	108	115	90	40	24	26	28	30	32
5 1/4	686	412	446	480	515	549	26	138	83	90	97	104	110	92	39	23	25	27	29	31
5 1/2	654	392	425	458	491	523	27	133	80	86	93	100	106	94	38	23	25	27	28	30
5 3/4	626	376	407	438	470	501	28	128	77	83	90	96	102	96	37	22	24	26	28	30
6	600	360	390	420	450	480	29	124	74	81	87	93	99	98	36	22	24	26	27	30
6 1/4	576	346	374	403	432	461	30	120	72	78	84	90	96	100	34	20	23	25	26	29
6 1/2	553	332	359	387	415	442	31	116	70	75	81	87	93	105	33	20	22	24	25	27
6 3/4	533	320	346	373	400	426	32	112	67	73	78	84	90	110	31	19	21	23	23	27
7	514	308	334	360	386	411	33	109	65	71	76	82	87	115	30	18	20	22	23	26
7 1/4	497	298	323	348	373	398	34	106	64	69	74	80	85	120	29	17	20	21	22	25
7 1/2	480	288	312	336	360	384	35	103	62	67	72	77	82	125	28	17	19	20	21	24
7 3/4	465	279	302	326	349	372	36	100	60	65	70	75	80	130	27	16	18	20	20	23
8	450	270	293	315	338	360	37	97	58	63	68	73	78	135	26	16	18	19	19	22
8 1/4	436	262	283	305	327	349	38	95	57	62	67	71	76	140	25	15	17	18	18	22
8 1/2	423	254	275	296	317	338	39	92	55	60	64	69	74	145	24	14	16	18	17	21
8 3/4	411	247	267	288	308	329	40	90	54	59	65	68	72	150	23	14	16	17	17	20
9	400	240	260	280	300	320	41	88	53	57	62	66	70	155	22	13	15	16	16	19
9 1/4	389	233	253	272	292	311	42	86	52	56	60	65	69	160	22	13	14	15	16	18
9 1/2	379	227	246	265	284	303	43	84	50	55	59	63	67	165	21	12	14	15	15	18
9 3/4	369	221	240	258	277	295	44	82	49	53	57	62	66	170	21	12	14	15	15	17
10	360	216	234	252	270	288	45	80	48	52	56	60	64	175	20	12	13	15	14	17
10 1/2	342	205	222	239	257	274	46	78	47	51	55	59	62	180	20	11	13	14	14	16
11	327	196	213	229	245	262	47	77	46	50	54	58	60	185	19	11	12	14	13	16
11 1/2	313	188	205	219	235	250	48	75	45	49	53	56	58	190	18	11	12	13	13	15
12	300	180	195	210	225	240	49	73	44	47	51	55	56	195						14

Source: National Twist Drill & Tool Co.

TABLE XXXVI

SPEED AND FEED CALCULATIONS

FOR MILLING CUTTERS AND OTHER ROTATING TOOLS

TO FIND	HAVING	FORMULA
Surface (or Periphery) Speed in Feet per Minute = S.F.M.	Diameter of Tool in Inches = D and Revolutions per Minute = R.P.M.	$S.F.M. = \dfrac{D \times 3.1416 \times R.P.M.}{12}$
Revolutions per Minute = R.P.M.	Surface Speed In Feet per Minute = S.F.M. and Diameter of Tool in Inches = D	$R.P.M. = \dfrac{S.F.M. \times 12}{D \times 3.1416}$
Feed per Revolution in Inches = F.R.	Feed in Inches per Minute = F.M. and Revolutions per Minute = R.P.M.	$F.R. = \dfrac{F.M.}{R.P.M.}$
Feed in Inches per Minute = F.M.	Feed per Revolution in Inches = F.R. and Revolutions per Minute = R.P.M.	$F.M. = F.R. \times R.P.M.$
Number of Cutting Teeth per Minute = T.M.	Number of Teeth in Tool = T and Revolutions per Minute = R.P.M.	$T.M. = T \times R.P.M.$
Feed per Tooth = F.T.	Number of Teeth in Tool = T and Feed per Revolution in Inches = F.R.	$F.T. = \dfrac{F.R.}{T}$
Feed per Tooth = F.T.	Number of Teeth in Tool = T Feed in Inches per Minute = F.M. and Speed in Revolutions per Minute = R.P.M.	$F.T. = \dfrac{F.M.}{T \times R.P.M.}$

Source: National Twist Drill & Tool Co.

TABLE XXXVII

TABLE OF CUTTING SPEEDS

FOR FRACTIONAL SIZES

Ft. per Min.	30	40	50	60	70	80	90	100	110	120	130	140	150
Diam. In.						Revolutions per Minute							
1/16	1833	2445	3056	3667	4278	4889	....	....	....	....	....	....	....
1/8	917	1222	1528	1833	2139	2445	2750	3056	3361	3667	3973	4278	4584
3/16	611	815	1019	1222	1426	1630	1833	2037	2241	2445	2648	2852	3056
1/4	458	611	764	917	1070	1222	1375	1528	1681	1833	1986	2139	2292
5/16	367	489	611	733	856	978	1100	1222	1345	1467	1589	1711	1833
3/8	306	407	509	611	713	815	917	1019	1120	1222	1324	1426	1528
7/16	262	349	437	524	611	698	786	873	960	1048	1135	1222	1310
1/2	229	306	382	458	535	611	688	764	840	917	993	1070	1146
5/8	183	244	306	367	428	489	550	611	672	733	794	856	917
3/4	153	204	255	306	357	407	458	509	560	611	662	713	764
7/8	131	175	218	262	306	349	393	437	480	524	568	611	655
1	115	153	191	229	267	306	344	382	420	458	497	535	573
1 1/8	102	136	170	204	238	272	306	340	373	407	441	475	509
1 1/4	91.7	122	153	183	214	244	275	306	336	367	397	428	458
1 3/8	83.3	111	139	167	194	222	250	278	306	333	361	389	417
1 1/2	76.4	102	127	153	178	204	229	255	280	306	331	357	382
1 5/8	70.5	94.0	118	141	165	188	212	235	259	282	306	329	353
1 3/4	65.5	87.3	109	131	153	175	196	218	240	262	284	306	327
1 7/8	61.1	81.5	102	122	143	163	183	204	224	244	265	285	306
2	57.3	76.4	95.5	115	134	153	172	191	210	229	248	267	287
2 1/4	50.9	67.9	84.9	102	119	136	153	170	187	204	221	238	255
2 1/2	45.8	61.1	76.4	91.7	107	122	138	153	168	183	199	214	229
2 3/4	41.7	55.6	69.5	83.3	97.2	111	125	139	153	167	181	194	208
3	38.2	50.9	63.7	76.4	89.1	102	115	127	140	153	166	178	191
3 1/4	35.3	47.0	58.8	70.5	82.3	94.0	106	118	129	141	153	165	176
3 1/2	32.7	43.7	54.6	65.5	76.4	87.3	98.2	109	120	131	142	153	164
3 3/4	30.6	40.7	50.9	61.1	71.3	81.5	91.7	102	112	122	132	143	153
4	28.7	38.2	47.7	57.3	66.8	76.4	85.9	95.5	105	115	124	134	143
4 1/2	25.5	34.0	42.4	50.9	59.4	67.9	76.4	84.9	93.4	102	110	119	127
5	22.9	30.6	38.2	45.8	53.5	61.1	68.8	76.4	84.0	91.7	99.3	107	115
5 1/2	20.8	27.8	34.7	41.7	48.6	55.6	62.5	69.5	76.4	83.3	90.3	97.2	104
6	19.1	25.5	31.8	38.2	44.6	50.9	57.3	63.7	70.0	76.4	82.8	89.1	95.5
6 1/2	17.6	23.5	29.4	35.3	41.1	47.0	52.9	58.8	64.6	70.5	76.4	82.3	88.2
7	16.4	21.8	27.3	32.7	38.2	43.7	49.1	54.6	60.0	65.5	70.9	76.4	81.9
7 1/2	15.3	20.4	25.5	30.6	35.7	40.7	45.8	50.9	56.0	61.1	66.2	71.3	76.4
8	14.3	19.1	23.9	28.7	33.4	38.2	43.0	47.7	52.5	57.3	62.1	66.8	71.6
8 1/2	13.5	18.0	22.5	27.0	31.5	36.0	40.4	44.9	49.4	53.9	58.4	62.9	67.4
9	12.7	17.0	21.2	25.5	29.7	34.0	38.2	42.4	46.7	50.9	55.2	59.4	63.6
9 1/2	12.1	16.1	20.1	24.1	28.2	32.2	36.2	40.2	44.2	48.3	52.3	56.3	60.3
10	11.5	15.3	19.1	22.9	26.7	30.6	34.4	38.2	42.0	45.8	49.7	53.5	57.3
11	10.4	13.9	17.4	20:8	24.3	27.8	31.3	34.7	38.2	41.7	45.1	48.6	52.1
12	9.5	12.7	15.9	19.1	22.3	25.5	28.6	31.8	35.0	38.2	41.4	44.6	47.8
Ft. per Min.	30	40	50	60	70	80	90	100	110	120	130	140	150

Source: National Twist Drill & Tool Co.

TABLE XXXVIII

Comparative Weights of Steel and Brass Bars

Steel—Weights cover hot worked steel about .50% carbon. One cubic inch weighs .2833 lbs. High speed steel 10% heavier.
Brass—One cubic inch weighs .3074 lbs.
Actual weight of stock may be expected to vary somewhat from these figures because of variations in manufacturing processes.

| Size, Inches | Weight of Bar One Foot Long, Lbs. | | | | | |
| | Steel | | | Brass | | |
	○	□	⬡	○	□	⬡
$\frac{1}{16}$	.0104	.013	.0115	.0113	.0144	.0125
$\frac{1}{8}$	.042	.05	.046	.045	.058	.050
$\frac{3}{16}$	.09	.12	.10	.102	.130	.112
$\frac{1}{4}$	.17	.21	.19	.18	.23	.20
$\frac{5}{16}$	.26	.33	.29	.28	.36	.31
$\frac{3}{8}$	.38	.48	.42	.41	.52	.45
$\frac{7}{16}$	.51	.65	.56	.55	.71	.61
$\frac{1}{2}$	.67	.85	.74	.72	.92	.80
$\frac{9}{16}$	.85	1.08	.94	.92	1.17	1.01
$\frac{5}{8}$	1.04	1.33	1.15	1.13	1.44	1.25
$\frac{11}{16}$	1.27	1.61	1.40	1.37	1.74	1.51
$\frac{3}{4}$	1.50	1.92	1.66	1.63	2.07	1.80
$\frac{13}{16}$	1.76	2.24	1.94	1.91	2.43	2.11
$\frac{7}{8}$	2.04	2.60	2.25	2.22	2.82	2.45
$\frac{15}{16}$	2.35	2.99	2.59	2.55	3.24	2.81
1	2.67	3.40	2.94	2.90	3.69	3.19
$1\frac{1}{16}$	3.01	3.84	3.32	3.27	4.16	3.61
$1\frac{1}{8}$	3.38	4.30	3.73	3.67	4.67	4.04
$1\frac{3}{16}$	3.77	4.80	4.16	4.08	5.20	4.51
$1\frac{1}{4}$	4.17	5.31	4.60	4.53	5.76	4.99
$1\frac{5}{16}$	4.60	5.86	5.07	4.99	6.35	5.50
$1\frac{3}{8}$	5.04	6.43	5.56	5.48	6.97	6.04
$1\frac{7}{16}$	5.52	7.03	6.08	5.99	7.62	6.60
$1\frac{1}{2}$	6.01	7.65	6.63	6.52	8.30	7.19
$1\frac{9}{16}$	6.52	8.30	7.19	7.07	9.01	7.80
$1\frac{5}{8}$	7.05	8.98	7.77	7.65	9.74	8.44
$1\frac{11}{16}$	7.60	9.68	8.38	8.25	10.51	9.10
$1\frac{3}{4}$	8.18	10.41	9.02	8.87	11.30	9.78
$1\frac{13}{16}$	8.77	11.17	9.67	9.52	12.12	10.49
$1\frac{7}{8}$	9.39	11.95	10.35	10.19	12.97	11.24
$1\frac{15}{16}$	10.02	12.76	11.05	10.88	13.85	12.00
2	10.68	13.60	11.78	11.59	14.76	12.78
$2\frac{1}{16}$	11.36	14.46	12.53	12.33	15.69	13.60
$2\frac{1}{8}$	12.06	15.35	13.30	13.08	16.66	14.42
$2\frac{3}{16}$	12.78	16.27	14.09	13.87	17.65	15.29
$2\frac{1}{4}$	13.52	17.22	14.91	14.67	18.68	16.17
$2\frac{5}{16}$	14.28	18.19	15.75	15.50	19.73	17.09
$2\frac{3}{8}$	15.06	19.18	16.62	16.34	20.81	18.02

Source: Brown & Sharpe Manufacturing Co.

TABLE XXXIX

S. A. E. Standard Specifications for Steels

S. A. E. STEEL NUMBERING SYSTEM

A numerical index system is used to identify compositions of S. A. E. steels, which makes it possible to use numerals that are partially descriptive of the composition of materials covered by such numbers. The first digit indicates the type to which the steel belongs. The second digit, in the case of the simple alloy steels, generally indicates the approximate percentage of the predominant alloying element and the last two or three digits indicate the average carbon content in points, or hundredths of 1 per cent. Thus, 2340 indicates a nickel steel of approximately 3 per cent nickel (3.25 to 3.75) and 0.40 per cent carbon (0.35 to 0.45).

In some instances, it is necessary to use the second and third digits of the number to identify the approximate alloy composition of a steel. An instance of such departure is the steel numbers selected for several of the High Speed Steels and corrosion and heat resisting alloys. Thus, 71360 indicates a Tungsten Steel of about 13 per cent Tungsten (12 to 15) and 0.60 per cent carbon (0.50 to 0.70).

The basic numerals for the various types of S. A. E. steel are listed below:

Type of Steel	Numerals (and Digits)
Carbon Steels	1xxx
Plain Carbon	10xx
Free Cutting, (Screw Stock)	11xx
Free Cutting, Manganese	X13xx
High Manganese	T13xx
Nickel Steels	2xxx
0.50 Per Cent Nickel	20xx
1.50 Per Cent Nickel	21xx
3.50 Per Cent Nickel	23xx
5.00 Per Cent Nickel	25xx
Nickel Chromium Steels	3xxx
1.25 Per Cent Nickel, 0.60 Per Cent Chromium	31xx
1.75 Per Cent Nickel, 1.00 Per Cent Chromium	32xx
3.50 Per Cent Nickel, 1.50 Per Cent Chromium	33xx
3.00 Per Cent Nickel, 0.80 Per Cent Chromium	34xx
Corrosion and Heat Resisting Steels	30xxx
Molybdenum Steels	4xxx
Chromium	41xx
Chromium Nickel	43xx
Nickel	46xx and 48xx
Chromium Steels	5xxx
Low Chromium	51xx
Medium Chromium	52xxx
Corrosion and Heat Resisting	51xxx
Chromium Vanadium Steels	6xxx
Tungsten Steels	7xxx and 7xxxx
Silicon Manganese Steels	9xxx

Source: *Brown & Sharpe Mfg. Co.*

TABLE XL

HORSEPOWER REQUIREMENTS

FOR TURNING

When metal is cut in a lathe there is a downward pressure on the tool. This pressure, called chip pressure, depends on the material cut, shape and sharpness of the tool, and the size and shape of the chip.

For average conditions, a simple formula which will give sufficiently accurate results for power estimating purposes is as follows:

$P = CA$, where

A = cross sectional area of the chip in square inches, which is the product of depth of cut and feed per revolution of the work.

C = a constant depending on material being cut.

P = chip pressure on the tool in pounds.

Values of C

MATERIAL CUT	CONSTANT C
Low alloy steel	270,000
High alloy steel	350,000
High carbon steel	340,000
Medium carbon steel	300,000
Mild Steel	270,000
Cast iron—soft	132,000
Wrought iron	198,000
Malleable iron	170,000
Brass and bronze	110,000

Horsepower may be figured by using the following formula:

$H. P. = \dfrac{P \times S}{33,000}$ where

Example 2: Assuming that SAE 4140 is heat treated so that its strength is 100,000 pounds per square inch, the horsepower necessary to cut it, when other conditions remain the same as in Example 1, is:

$$H. P. = 3.25 \times 100,000 \times \dfrac{3.14 \times 4}{12} \times \dfrac{200}{33,000} = 7.8 \text{ as before.}$$

Multiplying the result by 1.25, we get 10 horsepower.

FOR MILLING

Generally accepted approximate values of power for steel cutting is one horsepower per ¾ cubic inches of material removed per minute, although 1 cubic inch can be used for rapid estimating purposes. The horsepower is figured using the following formula:

$H. P. = KdfNnw$, in which

d = depth of cut taken in inches

f = feed per tooth in inches

$H. P.$ = horsepower necessary to cut

K = a constant depending on material cut

n = number of teeth in the cutter

N = number of revolutions per minute the cutter makes

w = the width of cut in inches

For estimating the horsepower, approximate values of constant K are given below:

MATERIAL CUT	CONSTANT K
Bakelite	0.2
Brass	0.4
Cast Iron, soft	0.5
Cast Iron, medium hard	0.7
Cast Iron, hard	1.0
Steel: 120 Brinell	1.2
150 Brinell	1.4

H. P. = the horsepower necessary to revolve the work against the cutting pressure.

P = pressure on the tool in pounds.

S = cutting speed in feet per minute, and is equal to $\frac{3.14 \times D}{12}$

in which D is the diameter of the work.

Example 1: Determine the horsepower necessary to take a cut ¼ inch deep, with feed of 1/64 inch per revolution, on SAE 4140 steel bar 4 inches in diameter turning 200 times per minute.

Solution: Using C = 325,000

$$P = 325,000 \times \tfrac{1}{4} \times \tfrac{1}{64} = 1220 \text{ pounds}$$

$$\text{The H. P.} = 1220 \times \frac{3.14 \times 4}{12} \times \frac{200}{33,000} = 7.8$$

This should be multiplied by 1.25 to allow for the efficiency of the machine, thus:

H. P. = 7.8 x 1.25 = 9.7 or 10.

When the tensile strength of the material cut is known, the following formula may be used for computing the horsepower necessary to cut the material:

$$\text{H. P.} = \frac{3.25\,ATS}{33,000} \quad \text{where}$$

A = the cross section area of the chip in square inches, and is equal to the product of depth of cut and feed per revolution.

H. P. = the horsepower necessary to cut the metal.

S = the cutting speed in f.p.m.

T = the ultimate strength of the material cut.

Source: *Vascoloy-Ramet Corp.*

175 Brinell	1.5
250 Brinell	1.7
300 Brinell	1.9
400 Brinell	-2.0
500 Brinell	2.3
600 Brinell	2.5

It is to be noted that for a given material cut, fixed width of cut, and fixed number of teeth, the horsepower will vary with the depth of cut, the feed per tooth and the r.p.m.

Example: Assuming a width of cut 2 inches, the depth ⅛ inch, the feed 0.004" per tooth, what horsepower will be required to mill with a 3-inch 6-tooth cutter running at 600 r.p.m. and cutting steel 250 Brinell hardness.

Solution: K = 1.7 from Table; d = ⅛" or 0.125"; f = 0.004"; n = 6; N = 600, and w = 2".

Substituting these values in the formula, we get:

H. P. = 1.7 x 0.125 x 0.004 x 6 x 600 x 2 = 6.14

If the machine was powered with a 5 horsepower motor, we could reduce the r.p.m. and come within the capacity of the machine, using formula: $N = \frac{\text{H. P.}}{Kdfnw}$ in which the symbols have the same meaning as before.

Substituting the known values in this formula, we get:

$$N = \frac{5}{1.7 \times 0.125 \times 0.004 \times 6 \times 2} = 490 \text{ (approx.)}$$

The speed of the machine should not be allowed to drop more than 50 per cent from that recommended on page 25, since this would impair the performance of the cutter. 490 r.p.m. for a 3-inch cutter will give us a cutting speed

$$S = \frac{3.14 \times 3 \times 490}{12} = 385 \text{ f.p.m. (approx.)}$$

TABLE XLI
Random Numbers III*

```
22 17 68 65 84   68 95 23 92 35   87 02 22 57 51   61 09 43 95 06   58 24 82 03 47
19 36 27 59 46   13 79 93 37 55   39 77 32 77 09   85 52 05 30 62   47 83 51 62 74
16 77 23 02 77   09 61 87 25 21   28 06 24 25 93   16 71 13 59 78   23 05 47 47 25
78 43 76 71 61   20 44 90 32 64   97 67 63 99 61   46 38 03 93 22   69 81 21 99 21
03 28 28 26 08   73 37 32 04 05   69 30 16 09 05   88 69 58 28 99   35 07 44 75 47

93 22 53 64 39   07 10 63 76 35   87 03 04 79 88   08 13 13 85 51   55 34 57 72 69
78 76 58 54 74   92 38 70 96 92   52 06 79 79 45   82 63 18 27 44   69 66 92 19 09
23 68 35 26 00   99 53 93 61 28   52 70 05 48 34   56 65 05 61 86   90 92 10 70 80
15 39 25 70 99   93 86 52 77 65   15 33 59 05 28   22 87 26 07 47   86 96 98 29 06
58 71 96 30 24   18 46 23 34 27   85 13 99 24 44   49 18 09 79 49   74 16 32 23 02

57 35 27 33 72   24 53 63 94 09   41 10 76 47 91   44 04 95 49 66   39 60 04 59 81
48 50 86 54 48   22 06 34 72 52   82 21 15 65 20   33 29 94 71 11   15 91 29 12 03
61 96 48 95 03   07 16 39 33 66   98 56 10 56 79   77 21 30 27 12   90 49 22 23 62
36 93 89 41 26   29 70 83 63 51   99 74 20 52 36   87 09 41 15 09   98 60 16 03 03
18 87 00 42 31   57 90 12 02 07   23 47 37 17 31   54 08 01 88 63   39 41 88 92 10

88 56 53 27 59   33 35 72 67 47   77 34 55 45 70   08 18 27 38 90   16 95 86 70 75
09 72 95 84 29   49 41 31 06 70   42 38 06 45 18   64 84 73 31 65   52 53 37 97 15
12 96 88 17 31   65 19 69 02 83   60 75 86 90 68   24 64 19 35 51   56 61 87 39 12
85 94 57 24 16   92 09 84 38 76   22 00 27 69 85   29 81 94 78 70   21 94 47 90 12
38 64 43 59 98   98 77 87 68 07   91 51 67 62 44   40 98 05 93 78   23 32 65 41 18

53 44 09 42 72   00 41 86 79 79   68 47 22 00 20   35 55 31 51 51   00 83 63 22 55
40 76 66 26 84   57 99 99 90 37   36 63 32 08 58   37 40 13 68 97   87 64 81 07 83
02 17 79 18 05   12 59 52 57 02   22 07 90 47 03   28 14 11 30 79   20 69 22 40 98
95 17 82 06 53   31 51 10 96 46   92 06 88 07 77   56 11 50 81 69   40 23 72 51 39
35 76 22 42 92   96 11 83 44 80   34 68 35 48 77   33 42 40 90 60   73 96 53 97 86

26 29 13 56 41   85 47 04 66 08   34 72 57 59 13   82 43 80 46 15   38 26 61 70 04
77 80 20 75 82   72 82 32 99 90   63 95 73 76 63   89 73 44 99 05   48 67 26 43 18
46 40 66 44 52   91 36 74 43 53   30 82 13 54 00   78 45 63 98 35   55 03 36 67 68
37 56 08 18 09   77 53 84 46 47   31 91 18 95 58   24 16 74 11 53   44 10 13 85 57
61 65 61 68 66   37 27 47 39 19   84 83 70 07 48   53 21 40 06 71   95 06 79 88 54

93 43 69 64 07   34 18 04 52 35   56 27 09 24 86   61 85 53 83 45   19 90 70 99 00
21 96 60 12 99   11 20 99 45 18   48 13 93 55 34   18 37 79 49 90   65 97 38 20 46
95 20 47 97 97   27 37 83 28 71   00 06 41 41 74   45 89 09 39 84   51 67 11 52 49
97 86 21 78 73   10 65 81 92 59   58 76 17 14 97   04 76 62 16 17   17 95 70 45 80
69 92 06 34 13   59 71 74 17 32   27 55 10 24 19   23 71 82 13 74   63 52 52 01 41

04 31 17 21 56   33 73 99 19 87   26 72 39 27 67   53 77 57 68 93   60 61 97 22 61
61 06 98 03 91   87 14 77 43 96   43 00 65 98 50   45 60 33 01 07   98 99 46 50 47
85 93 85 86 88   72 87 08 62 40   16 06 10 89 20   23 21 34 74 97   76 38 03 29 63
21 74 32 47 45   73 96 07 94 52   09 65 90 77 47   25 76 16 19 33   53 05 70 53 30
15 69 53 82 80   79 96 23 53 10   65 39 07 16 29   45 33 02 43 70   02 87 40 41 45

02 89 08 04 49   20 21 14 68 86   87 63 93 95 17   11 29 01 95 80   35 14 97 35 33
87 18 15 89 79   85 43 01 72 73   08 61 74 51 69   89 74 39 82 15   94 51 33 41 67
98 83 71 94 22   59 97 50 99 52   08 52 85 08 40   87 80 61 65 31   91 51 80 32 44
10 08 58 21 66   72 68 49 29 31   89 85 84 46 06   59 73 19 85 23   65 09 29 75 63
47 90 56 10 08   88 02 84 27 83   42 29 72 23 19   66 56 45 65 79   20 71 53 20 25

22 85 61 68 90   49 64 92 85 44   16 40 12 89 88   50 14 49 81 06   01 82 77 45 12
67 80 43 79 33   12 83 11 41 16   25 58 19 68 70   77 02 54 00 52   53 43 37 15 26
27 62 50 96 72   79 44 61 40 15   14 53 40 65 39   27 31 58 50 28   11 39 03 34 25
33 78 80 87 15   38 30 06 38 21   14 47 47 07 26   54 96 87 53 32   40 36 40 96 76
13 13 92 66 99   47 24 49 57 74   32 25 43 62 17   10 97 11 69 84   99 63 22 32 98
```

* Table XLI is reprinted with permission from Random Numbers III and IV of Table XXXIII of R. A. Fisher and F. Yates, *Statistical Tables for Biological, Agricultural and Medical Research* (Edinburgh: Oliver & Boyd, Ltd.).

TABLE XLI (*Continued*)

Random Numbers IV*

10 27 53 96 23	71 50 54 36 23	54 31 04 82 98	04 14 12 15 09	26 78 25 47 47
28 41 50 61 88	64 85 27 20 18	83 36 36 05 56	39 71 65 09 62	94 76 62 11 89
34 21 42 57 02	59 19 18 97 48	80 30 03 30 98	05 24 67 70 07	84 97 50 87 46
61 81 77 23 23	82 82 11 54 08	53 28 70 58 96	44 07 39 55 43	42 34 43 39 28
61 15 18 13 54	16 86 20 26 88	90 74 80 55 09	14 53 90 51 17	52 01 63 01 59
91 76 21 64 64	44 91 13 32 97	75 31 62 66 54	84 80 32 75 77	56 08 25 70 29
00 97 79 08 06	37 30 28 59 85	53 56 68 53 40	01 74 39 59 73	30 19 99 85 48
36 46 18 34 94	75 20 80 27 77	78 91 69 16 00	08 43 18 73 68	67 69 61 34 25
88 98 99 60 50	65 95 79 42 94	93 62 40 89 96	43 56 47 71 66	46 76 29 67 02
04 37 59 87 21	05 02 03 24 17	47 97 81 56 51	92 34 86 01 82	55 51 33 12 91
63 62 06 34 41	94 21 78 55 09	72 76 45 16 94	29 95 81 83 83	79 88 01 97 30
78 47 23 53 90	34 41 92 45 71	09 23 70 70 07	12 38 92 79 43	14 85 11 47 23
87 68 62 15 43	53 14 36 59 25	54 47 33 70 15	59 24 48 40 35	50 03 42 99 36
47 60 92 10 77	88 59 53 11 52	66 25 69 07 04	48 68 64 71 06	61 65 70 22 12
56 88 87 59 41	65 28 04 67 53	95 79 88 37 31	50 41 06 94 76	81 83 17 16 33
02 57 45 86 67	73 43 07 34 48	44 26 87 93 29	77 09 61 67 84	06 69 44 77 75
31 54 14 13 17	48 62 11 90 60	68 12 93 64 28	46 24 79 16 76	14 60 25 51 01
28 50 16 43 36	28 97 85 58 99	67 22 52 76 23	24 70 36 54 54	59 28 61 71 96
63 29 62 66 50	02 63 45 52 38	67 63 47 54 75	83 24 78 43 20	92 63 13 47 48
45 65 58 26 51	76 96 59 38 72	86 57 45 71 46	44 67 76 14 55	44 88 01 62 12
39 65 36 63 70	77 45 85 50 51	74 13 39 35 22	30 53 36 02 95	49 34 88 73 61
73 71 98 16 04	29 18 94 51 23	76 51 94 84 86	79 93 96 38 63	08 58 25 58 94
72 20 56 20 11	72 65 71 08 86	79 57 95 13 91	97 48 72 66 48	09 71 17 24 89
75 17 26 99 76	89 37 20 70 01	77 31 61 95 46	26 97 05 73 51	53 33 18 72 87
37 48 60 82 29	81 30 15 39 14	48 38 75 93 29	06 87 37 78 48	45 56 00 84 47
68 08 02 80 72	83 71 46 30 49	89 17 95 88 29	02 39 56 03 46	97 74 06 56 17
14 23 98 61 67	70 52 85 01 50	01 84 02 78 43	10 62 98 19 41	18 83 99 47 99
49 08 96 21 44	25 27 99 41 28	07 41 08 34 66	19 42 74 39 91	41 96 53 78 72
78 37 06 08 43	63 61 62 42 29	39 68 95 10 96	09 24 23 00 62	56 12 80 73 16
37 21 34 17 68	68 96 83 23 56	32 84 60 15 31	44 73 67 34 77	91 15 79 74 58
14 29 09 34 04	87 83 07 55 07	76 58 30 83 64	87 29 25 58 84	86 50 60 00 25
58 43 28 06 36	49 52 83 51 14	47 56 91 29 34	05 87 31 06 95	12 45 57 09 09
10 43 67 29 70	80 62 80 03 42	10 80 21 38 84	90 56 35 03 09	43 12 74 49 14
44 38 88 39 54	86 97 37 44 22	00 95 01 31 76	17 16 29 56 63	38 78 94 49 81
90 69 59 19 51	85 39 52 85 13	07 28 37 07 61	11 16 36 27 03	78 86 72 04 95
41 47 10 25 62	97 05 31 03 61	20 26 36 31 62	68 69 86 95 44	84 95 48 46 45
91 94 14 63 19	75 89 11 47 11	31 56 34 19 09	79 57 92 36 59	14 93 87 81 40
80 06 54 18 66	09 18 94 06 19	98 40 07 17 81	22 45 44 84 11	24 62 20 42 31
67 72 77 63 48	84 08 31 55 58	24 33 45 77 58	80 45 67 93 82	75 70 16 08 24
59 40 24 13 27	79 26 88 86 30	01 31 60 10 39	53 58 47 70 93	85 81 56 39 38
05 90 35 89 95	01 61 16 96 94	50 78 13 69 36	37 68 53 37 31	71 26 35 03 71
44 43 80 69 98	46 68 05 14 82	90 78 50 05 62	77 79 13 57 44	59 60 10 39 66
61 81 31 96 82	00 57 25 60 59	46 72 60 18 77	55 66 12 62 11	08 99 55 64 57
42 88 07 10 05	24 98 65 63 21	47 21 61 88 32	27 80 30 21 60	10 92 35 36 12
77 94 30 05 39	28 10 99 00 27	12 73 73 99 12	49 99 57 94 82	96 88 57 17 91
78 83 19 76 16	94 11 68 84 26	23 54 20 86 85	23 86 66 99 07	36 37 34 92 09
87 76 59 61 81	43 63 64 61 61	65 76 36 95 90	18 48 27 45 68	27 23 65 30 72
91 43 05 96 47	55 78 99 95 24	37 55 85 78 78	01 48 41 19 10	35 19 54 07 73
84 97 77 72 73	09 62 06 65 72	87 12 49 03 60	41 15 20 76 27	50 47 02 29 16
87 41 60 76 83	44 88 96 07 80	83 05 83 38 96	73 70 66 81 90	30 56 10 48 59

Bibliography

BOOKS

ALFORD, L. P., and BANGS, JOHN R. *Production Handbook.* New York: Ronald Press Co., 1944.

AMERICAN SOCIETY OF TOOL ENGINEERS. *Tool Engineers Handbook.* New York: McGraw-Hill Book Co., Inc., 1949.

BARNES, R. M. *Motion and Time Study.* 3rd ed.; New York: John Wiley & Sons, Inc., 1948.

————. *Work Sampling.* New York: John Wiley & Sons, Inc., 1957.

BRITTON, C. E. *Incentives in Industry.* Esso Standard Oil Co., 1953.

CARROLL, PHIL. JR. *Time Study for Cost Control.* 3rd ed.; New York: McGraw-Hill Book Co., Inc., 1953.

COLVIN, F. H., and HAAS, L. L. *Jigs and Fixtures.* 4th ed.; New York: McGraw-Hill Book Co., Inc., 1943.

COLVIN, F. H., and STANLEY, F. A. *Drilling and Surfacing Practice.* New York: McGraw-Hill Book Co., Inc., 1936.

EASTMAN KODAK CO. *How to Make Good Movies.* 1948.

ENRICK, N. L. *Quality Control.* Industrial Press.

HOLMES, W. G. *Applied Time and Motion Study.* New York: Ronald Press Co., 1938.

IMMER, JOHN R. *Layout Planning Techniques.* New York: McGraw-Hill Book Co., Inc., 1950.

IRESON, GRANT W., and GRANT, EUGENE L. *Handbook of Industrial Engineering and Management.* Englewood Cliffs, N.J.: Prentice-Hall, Inc., 1955.

INDUSTRIAL MANAGEMENT SOCIETY. *Proceedings of the Time and Motion Study Clinic.* Chicago, 1938–54.

KIMBALL, D. S., and KIMBALL, D. S. JR. *Principles of Industrial Organization.* 6th ed.; New York: McGraw-Hill Book Co., Inc., 1947.

LEHRER, R. N. *Work Simplification.* Englewood Cliffs, N.J.: Prentice-Hall, Inc., 1957.

LINCOLN, JAMES F. *Lincoln's Incentive System.* New York: McGraw-Hill Book Co., Inc., 1946.

LOUDEN, J. K. *Wage Incentives.* New York: John Wiley & Sons, Inc., 1944.

LOWRY, S. M., MAYNARD, H. B., and STEGEMERTEN, G. J. *Time and Motion Study.* 3rd ed.; New York: McGraw-Hill Book Co., Inc., 1940.

LYTLE, C. W. *Wage Incentive Methods.* New York: Ronald Press Co., 1938.

MALLICK and GAUDREAU. *Plant Layout: Planning and Practice.* New York: John Wiley & Sons, Inc.

MAYNARD, H. B., STEGEMERTEN, G. J., and SCHWAB, J. L. *Methods-Time-Measurement.* New York: McGraw-Hill Book Co., Inc., 1948.

————. *Industrial Engineering Handbook.* New York: McGraw-Hill Book Co., Inc., 1956.

MOGENSEN, A. H. *Common Sense Applied to Motion and Time Study.* New York: McGraw-Hill Book Co., Inc., 1932.

MORROW, R. L. *Time Study and Motion Economy.* New York: Ronald Press Co., 1946.

MUNDEL, M. E. *Motion and Time Study.* Englewood Cliffs, N.J.: Prentice-Hall, Inc., 1950.

NADLER, GERALD. *Motion and Time Study.* New York: McGraw-Hill Book Co., Inc., 1955.

PRESGRAVE, R. *Dynamics of Time Study.* New York: McGraw-Hill Book Co., Inc., 1945.

SCHUTT, W. H. *Time Study Engineering.* New York: McGraw-Hill Book Co., Inc., 1943.

STEGEMERTEN, G. J., and MAYNARD, H. B. *Operation Analysis.* New York: McGraw-Hill Book Co., Inc., 1939.

STOCKER, H. E. *Materials Handlings.* 2nd ed.; Englewood Cliffs, N.J.: Prentice-Hall, Inc., 1951.

BULLETINS AND ARTICLES

ABRUZZI, ADAM. "The Snap-Back and Continuous Methods of Taking Time Study Readings," *Advanced Management,* April, 1951, pp. 11, 12.

AMERICAN SOCIETY OF MECHANICAL ENGINEERS (A.S.M.E.) "Standards Operation and Flow Process Charts," and "Standards Plant Layout Templates and Models," New York.

ANDERSON, C. A. and THUERING, G. L. "Mirrors Extend the Scope of Camera," *Advanced Management,* April, 1951, pp. 19–20.

BALYEAT, R. E. "Concepts and Practices in Industrial Engineering," *Journal of Industrial Engineering,* May 1954, pp. 19–21.

BRISLEY, C. L. "The How and Why of Ratio Delay Study," *IMS Clinic Proceedings,* pp. 100–105.

CARROLL, PHIL. "Notes on Standard Elemental Data," *Modern Machine Shop,* April, 1950, pp. 154–76.

COUNCIL OF PROFIT SHARING INDUSTRIES. "Proceedings of Fourth Annual Conference," Akron, 1951.

DAVIS, LOUIS E. "Human Factors in Design of Manual Machine Controls," *Mechanical Engineering,* October, 1949, pp. 811–16.

DUTTON, HENRY P. "A History of Scientific Management in the United States of America," *Advanced Management,* October, 1953, pp. 9–12.

EDITORS' DATA SHEET. "Materials & Methods Cost, Design and Production Comparisons," *Materials and Methods,* May, 1952, pp. 76–77.

EITEL, WALTER F. "Movement Analysis In Planning," *National Time and Motion Study Clinic Proceedings,* November, 1947.

EMERZIAN, JOSEPH. "Graphical Analysis In Objective Ratings," *Advanced Management,* April, 1954, pp. 10–14.

GARDNER, A. R. "Short Cuts to Productivity," *Dun's Review and Modern Industry,* May 12, 1950, pp. 41–47.

GAYLORD, L. E., and GILLESPIE, C. R. "Incentive Standards Without Time Studies," *Flow,* February, 1954, pp. 78–81.

GENERAL ELECTRIC. "Wage Rate Procedures—Stopwatch Time Study," April, 1952.

GENERAL ELECTRIC COMPANY. "Pointers For Lower-Cost Designs," *American Machinist Reference Sheets,* 12th ed., p. 18.

HUMMEL, J. O. P. "Are You Ready for an Incentive Plan?" *Industrial Relations.* Chicago: The Dartnell Corporation, September, 1947.

INTERNATIONAL ASSOCIATION OF MACHINISTS. Grand Lodge Constitution, Washington, D.C.

JONES, DALE. "A New Time Study Tool," *Advanced Management,* April, 1953, pp. 10–14.

KENT, R. F. "Establishing and Using Allowance Factors," *Industrial Management Society IMS Clinic Proceedings.* Industrial Management Society (1948), pp. 100–105.

MATERIAL HANDLING INSTITUTE, INC. *Materials Handling Booklet No. 1,* Pittsburgh.

McALLISTER, ERIC. "Random Ratio Delay," *The Journal of Industrial Engineering,* August, 1953, pp. 15–17.

NATIONAL ELECTRICAL MANUFACTURERS ASSOCIATION. "NEMA Job Rating Plan for Hourly Rated Jobs," New York.

NATIONAL METAL TRADES ASSOCIATION. "Wage Incentive Practices," A Survey Report No. 4 (February, 1953).

NATIONAL SAFETY COUNCIL. *Safe Practices Pamphlet No. 32* and *Safe Practices Pamphlet No. 50.*

NATIONAL TWIST DRILL & TOOL COMPANY. Catalog 16 (Rochester, Michigan).

NIEBEL, B. W., and THUERING, G. L. "Let's Have More Accurate Time Standards for Basic Motions," *Factory Management and Maintenance,* September, 1951, p. 101.

NISSLEY, HAROLD R. "How to Make Your Time Study Standards More Accurate . . . More Salable," *Machine and Tool Blue Book,* March, 1954, pp. 200–208.

PAYNE, BRUCE. "Incentives That Work," *Society for Advancement of Management Proceedings,* New York, November 2, 1951.

PRESGRAVE, RALPH. "Application of Allowances," *Fifth Annual Time Study and Methods Conference,* April, 1950.

PRODUCT ENGINEERING. Sixth Series Design Work Sheets, *Product Engineering,* New York.

SOCIETY FOR ADVANCEMENT OF MANAGEMENT. "The Glossary of Terms Used in Methods, Time Study and Wage Incentives," The Management Research —Development Division, New York.

THUERING, G. L. "How to Get Faster, Better, Less Expensive Plant Layout Drawings Without Drafting," *Factory Management and Maintenance,* October, 1952, pp. 86–89.

UNITED STATES STEEL CORPORATION. "Labor Measurement and Incentive Manual," Pittsburgh, Pa.

VASCOBY-RAMET CORPORATION. "Calculation of Horsepower Requirements," Catalogue UR-441.

WADDELL, HENRY LEE. "Work Sampling," *Factory Management and Maintenance,* Vol. X (November 7, 1952), pp. 83–89.

WAITE, JACK M. "A Look at the Efficiency Department," AC Spark Plug Division, Flint, Michigan.

WESTINGHOUSE ELECTRIC CORPORATION. *Manual of Time Study Procedure,* March, 1949.

WOLLAM, G. Z. "Responsibility for Incentive Administration," *Factory Management and Maintenance,* October, 1947.

WORK-FACTOR COMPANY. *Work-Factor Bulletin 104,* Haddon Heights, New Jersey.

Index

This book has been set on the linotype in 10 point Caledonia leaded 2 points and 9 point Caledonia leaded 1 point. Chapter numbers are in 14 point Spartan Medium with a 24 point Spartan Medium numeral. Chapter titles are in 24 point Spartan Medium. The size of the type page is 27 by 47 picas.